The Fellowship of Women

Two hundred surgical lives

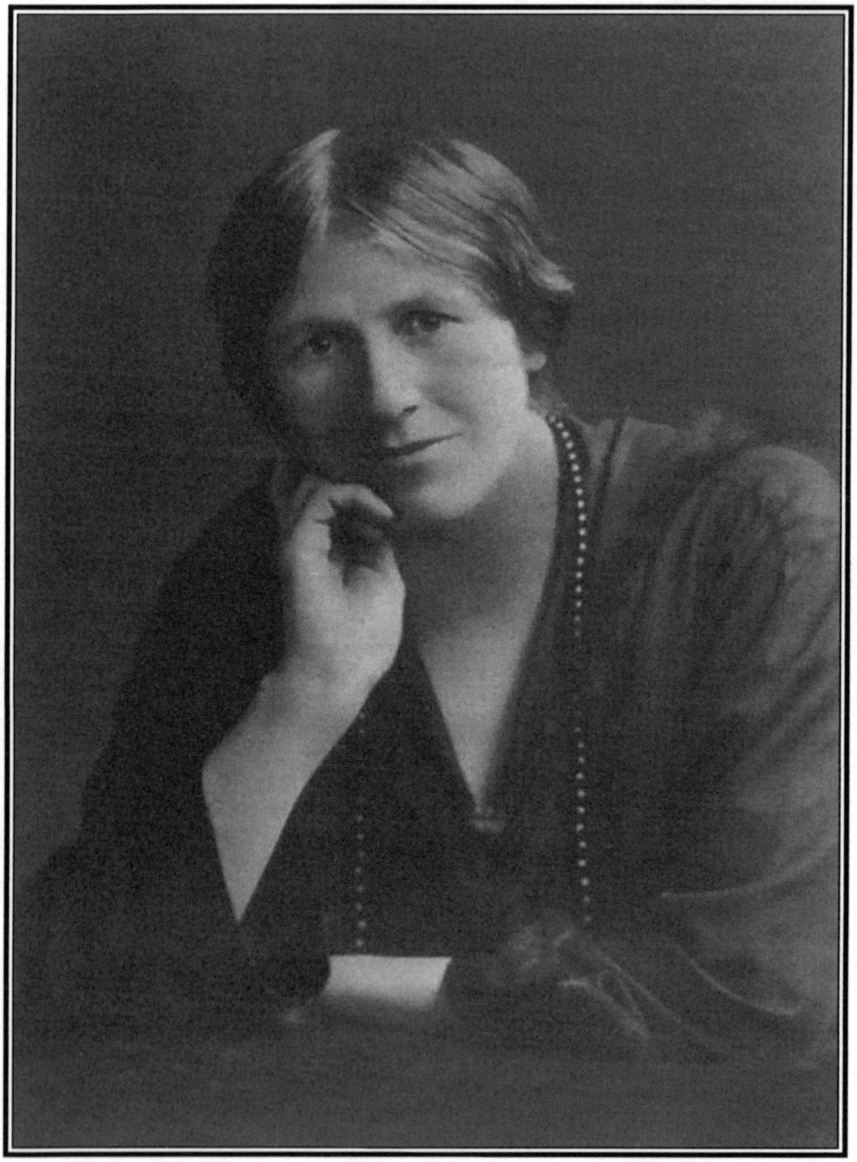

Eleanor Davies-Colley

This portrait is reproduced from an original photograph kindly given to the author by Michael and Ann Forbes

The Fellowship of Women

Two hundred surgical lives

Margaret Ghilchik

SMITH-GORDON

Published by Smith-Gordon
In cooperation with Nishimura

In North America contact Linda P. Jones, Enfield Publishing and Distribution Co Inc,
PO Box 699, Enfield, NH 03748, USA
Tel: +1 603 632 7377, Fax: 603 632 5611

Sales enquiries except for the countries listed below may be directed to:
mlevens@smith-gordon.com
Postal address: Smith-Gordon, Media House, Burrel Road, St Ives,
Cambs, PE27 3LE, United Kingdom
For special editions contact publisher@smithgordon.com

In Japan contact Nishimura Company Limited, 1-754-39 Asihimashi-dori,
Niigata-shi 950 Japan
Tel: +81 03-3239-7671 Tokyo and +81 025-223-2388 Niigata
Email: info@nishimurashoten.co.jp www.nishimurashoten.co.jp

In South East Asia contact Alkem Company Pte Ltd. 1 Penjuru Close,
Singapore 608617, Singapore
Tel: +65 6265 6666; Fax: + 65 6261 7875
Email: chubong@alkem.com.sg

First published in Great Britain 2011
Smith-Gordon, Media House, Burrel Road, St Ives, Cambs, PE27 3LE, United Kingdom

British Library Cataloguing in Publication Data
A catalogue record of this book is available from the British Library
ISBN 978-1-85463-246-3
Typeset and printed by Mimeo, St Ives, Cambridgeshire, UK

Contents

Foreword by Professor Harold Ellis CBE, FRCS

IN 1967, I appointed Miss Margaret Childe, as she then was, as registrar to the Surgical Unit at Westminster Medical School. She came to us from Bart's, where she had qualified and had recently obtained her FRCS. She rapidly proved her worth as a sound clinician and efficient young surgeon. I was particularly impressed with her management, late one night, of a young man from Pimlico, who had had a fracas with his lady wife. She ran into the kitchen, picked up the carving knife and thrust it into the back of his left chest. He was not well! Margaret released his pneumothorax with an intercostal drain, then took out his ruptured spleen at a rapid laparotomy. I cannot recall whether or not Margaret also saved the marriage.

The following year, Margaret was promoted to lecturer at St. Mary's and gained her surgical consultant's appointment in 1971. From her early days in her career, she has been an inspiration to women medical students, and I invited her back to Westminster to talk to our own girls in how to further their careers.

Things have changed. When I retired from Surgery in 1989, I proudly claimed to have helped to train 10% of all the women consultant general surgeons in England; HER name was Margaret Ghilchik, (as she had now become). Yes, there were but a handful of women surgeons in those days in the NHS. The last twenty years have seen a remarkable change, of course, with increasing numbers of women being found at every level in every specialty and in ever increasing numbers.

I was honoured when Margaret asked me to write a Foreword to this book, which I have read in manuscript with the very greatest of interest. She provides a fascinating account of women's struggle to train and to practice as surgeons and to be allowed to sit for, and to obtain, the FRCS – a hurdle first achieved by Eleanor Davies-Colley, who joined her two brothers and her father in obtaining this diploma in 1911. Today, she is commemorated by having a large and very beautiful lecture theatre named after her at the College.

The book then goes on to relate the lives and careers of the first two hundred female Fellows of the College, up to 1970. There were the handful of early pioneers, there were the women who served as surgeons in the two World Wars, and those who established themselves in every branch of surgery in many parts of the world. My personal heroine is Ruth Watson, a Birmingham graduate, who I met at her hospital in Pokhrah, Nepal, during my British Council visit. I was filled with admiration by her work, in every field of Surgery and Midwifery, perhaps especially in the treatment of advanced leprosy. I was among others who recommended her for an honorary FRCS, which she was delighted to receive at the College in 1976, at the age of fifty, although at that time she was already severely ill with an inoperable brain tumour.

I can recommend this book to all surgeons, but, of course, it will be of especial interest, and indeed inspiration, to women medical students and surgical trainees, who hope, one day, to receive the accolade of Fellowship of the Royal College of Surgeons of England.

Author's acknowledgements

I am grateful to all those women surgeons and their families who took time to talk to me about their careers and lives over the years. Any errors and omissions are mine for which I am responsible and invite further comments. Piers Plowright and my son Peter Ghilchik gave helpful advice on structure and writing; my husband Tony Ghilchik and son Tim were invaluable guides on the computer; I gleaned more on Eyes from Michael Roper-Hall and on Gynaecology from Richard Beard. The Libraries and Archives in the Wellcome Institute, the Royal Society of Medicine, the Royal College of Surgeons and the British Library were all welcoming.

Particular thanks are owed to the expertise of my editor and publisher Eldred Smith-Gordon who was never daunted by the task and never wearied as the dead-lines for the centenary conference drew near.

PREFACE

THIS BOOK tells the story of the long and determined struggle for women doctors to be accepted into the Fellowship of the Royal College of Surgeons of England.

It begins with Eleanor Davies-Colley who stood before the examiners in 1911 and so joined her two younger brothers and her late father as a Fellow of the Royal College of Surgeons, FRCS, the first woman surgical Fellow. The narrative proceeds through the lives of the Fellows who followed, celebrating some extraordinary achievements, dealing with the commonplace incidents of everyday life, and inevitably the disappointment of ambitions that had to be surrendered.

There is a back-story of course of our Royal College, inheriting as it does the tradition of centuries of conflict, displaying intransigence to change, but in the end inevitably welcoming the determined lady doctors with a fairly good grace.

As I donned the academic gown with long crimson facings and crimson cord and buttons on the sleeve and stood to receive the Fellowship, the FRCS, in 1967, I was aware how few women were standing alongside, though I did not have any precise feeling of the numbers. It was said that members of Council or Court of Examiners who were from your own teaching hospital might break rank to seek you out, shake your hand, welcome you in, but this was a fantasy that never occurred.

Was I aware of the four hundred years of tradition that stretched back to the Barber-surgeons of Henry VIII, of the history of great men across the centuries practising their surgical craft, of the disputatious wrangles, of the letters from Elizabeth Garrett in the 1860s requesting inclusion, of the passing of half a century before success came? I was certainly unaware of Eleanor Davies-Colley, the first woman to become a Fellow of the College in 1911, unaware that no more joined her until after the Great War, and that the numbers subsequently were so few.

When I became a consultant surgeon in a DGH, district general hospital, in 1971, ten years after qualifying, I joined six other women consultant general surgeons currently working in the whole of the United Kingdom. We did not meet.

Ten years passed. In my DGH I was on emergency call ' a 1 in 2' and covered the whole panoply of general surgery, had been chairman of our medical staff committee, had great colleagues, all men, ten registrars had passed through my firm each leaving as competent surgeons with the FRCS, and I had four children, two dogs, a husband who thought it was wonderful that I could go out at night to 'save a life', and a nanny. I was a senior lecturer at the local medical school, had sporadic surgical firms allotted to me for teaching, and had been roped in to man the breast clinic. In a commitment to women, I had added the Elizabeth Garrett Anderson Hospital, a women-for-women's service, to my work, doing particularly breast there but also general surgery and female urology. I had been a surgical tutor at the College and was for three years Penrose May Tutor running the FRCS course. I became committed to an interest in how few were the numbers of women coming through as surgeons to take the FRCS. With this in mind, Wilfred Webber an administrator at the College furnished me with a list of the women Fellows who were currently on the College lists and I wrote to them, sending a small questionnaire and received a good response, the results incorporated in the book and included at the end as an appendix.

The lives of the first women surgeons command our attention because this year November 2011 is the centenary of the date when our first woman doctor became FRCS, a Fellow of the Royal College of Surgeons of England. This book celebrates the achievement of Eleanor Davies-Colley. It was another eight years, the years including the First World War, before other women began to join her and then in desultory numbers, one or two a year. In the twenty years from 1911 to 1930, only twenty-four women doctors, intent on a surgical career, attained the Fellowship.

From the first woman FRCS in 1911 to the two hundredth in 1970 there were profound changes in social history in what may be termed the cognitive map. There were obstacles in their path of course. Only a small nucleus managed to stay in general surgery. Many found it easier or were directed or persuaded to exercise their surgical talents and advance in the specialties, in the delicate practice of eye surgery, or in ENT (ear, nose and throat), some went into the field of radiotherapy, or of thoracic, plastic, orthopaedic, paediatric surgery, or neurosurgery, or research, and many of course were attracted to obstetrics and gynaecology where a special welcome awaited them from female patients.

Without doubt two world wars had a profoundly beneficial effect on opening up the possibilities of advance in a career in surgery for women. The exodus of men from hospital posts to serve in the armed forces made space for women to achieve clinical appointments that would have been unlikely otherwise. By the end of the First War, more than half of all male doctors had been called-up. In the medical schools of the great London teaching hospitals the shortage of men to fill student places drove them to accept a number of women, only to retract the offer in peace-time.

Society in general changed, granting women a more equal place in the world of work.

The blossoming of secondary education for girls from Miss Beale and Miss Buss in 1850 onwards had dispelled some of the disparity of opportunities for girls compared with their brothers and the schools that the women surgeons attended read like a litany of privilege in public (private) schools and in the excellent city grammar and high schools, but even in the best the teaching of science was not always adequate to matriculate and the sixth forms of adjacent boys' grammar schools and evening classes at polytechnics, Birkbeck College or Queen's College Harley Street were needed.

On home life, marriage, children and the domestic scene, more than half of the women surgeons married and many had children. Some, who were single, adopted children. Some set-up house with other women and shared the household. The easy acceptance in society in the early part of the twentieth century of the friendship and cooperation between women should be celebrated.

Nor did marriage and children form a barrier to their continuing their life's work as surgeons, particularly in the early part of the century. The lives of those who pioneered the way, from Elizabeth Garrett Anderson, married with three children, onwards, made it clear that the surgical life and family life were not incompatible. Her surgical colleague, Dame Mary Scharlieb, married with two sons and a daughter, wrote in her Reminiscences as she passed on the torch to future doctors 'I also wished to supply an answer to those who ask whether professional life is compatible with wifely and motherly duties. I know that it is.'

An analysis of the difficulties encountered by a few amongst some of the later women surgeons, post World War II, in the second half of the twentieth century, in combining the surgical life with home life, is a discourse of seminal importance. Social class, the support of family money, the disappearance of domestic help, attitudes of society, disapproval from colleagues, feminism, the husband as a new man, these are subjects that should be able to be confronted and discussed.

The proliferation of the foundation of hospitals founded and staffed exclusively by women, undoubtedly provided hospital appointments where women surgeons could be employed and find work, and it sometimes reads as though the posts were passed around amongst them. The fact that the majority had trained in the same medical school, the London (Royal Free Hospital) School of Medicine for Women provided a pool of friends and colleagues. Although the Elizabeth Garrett Anderson Hospital in Euston and the South London Hospital for Women and Children in Clapham are well known, the New Hospital for Women in Brighton in Sussex should be equally feted, the hospitals in Edinburgh and the children's hospital in Harrow Road and a multitude of others, now all closed. Similarly in Melbourne, Australia and in Sydney, women doctors set up hospitals staffed by women, giving clinical care to women and children and providing valuable practical experience.

Work abroad was a common part of the working life of many women surgeons, sometimes presenting as the only outlet for surgical practice, sometimes with missionary zeal. To India obviously with a two-way transit between India and England, English women surgeons with the Fellowship travelling abroad to offer their services, particularly to women, in the empire; Indian women coming to England for further training and to achieve the coveted FRCS before returning home to practice in India. Numbers of women Fellows were professors in India in surgery, in anatomy, and in obstetrics and gynaecology. They attained rewarding operative expertise and experience, returning home to England, sometimes to regain health, usually in retirement.

But also the women Fellows went to Africa and among the first women Fellows to become professors of surgery were Anne Christine Bayley, FRCS 1966, the professor who was among the first to recognize and report the emergence of virulent HIV, one of the founders of the East African Association of Surgeons, who was professor of surgery in Zambia, and Jocelyn Moore, FRCS 1933, who became professor of obstetrics and gynaecology in 1971 in Ahmundu Bello University in Nigeria. At home Dame Hilda Lloyd must be the first woman Fellow to be a professor and

Dame Ida Mann, the Eye Surgeon, has the special distinction of being the first woman to be a professor in any subject at Oxford University. A substantial number of women, reaching retirement age and still desirous of working, took themselves off to Africa or India or the Far East where their expertise was needed and their experience valued.

As Professor Anne Christine Bayley stood in St Paul's Cathedral to be ordained a woman priest in the Church of England, a second career she was entering on retiring from the surgical chair in Zambia, and aware that women priests were not being given an unequivocal welcome in the Anglican canon, she told me that the thought crossed her mind – where have I been like this before – and then she remembered that it was as she stood to receive the Fellowship in 1966, one year before I stood there, wearing the gown with the long crimson facings and cord and buttons on the sleeve at the Royal College of Surgeons.

The lives of the first women surgical Fellows are recorded here, those who became FRCS from 1911 to 1970, the contribution made in differing fields of practice, working in Great Britain and abroad, experiencing two World Wars, and *The Fellowship of Women* recounts the way they lived, the difficulties they faced, the choices they had to make. The narrative affirms the freedom they had to claim to work as independent professional women in society, celebrates their friendships and cooperation with each other and makes observations on the differing ways in which they dealt with obstacles in their pathway.

Number of Women Fellows qualifying each year

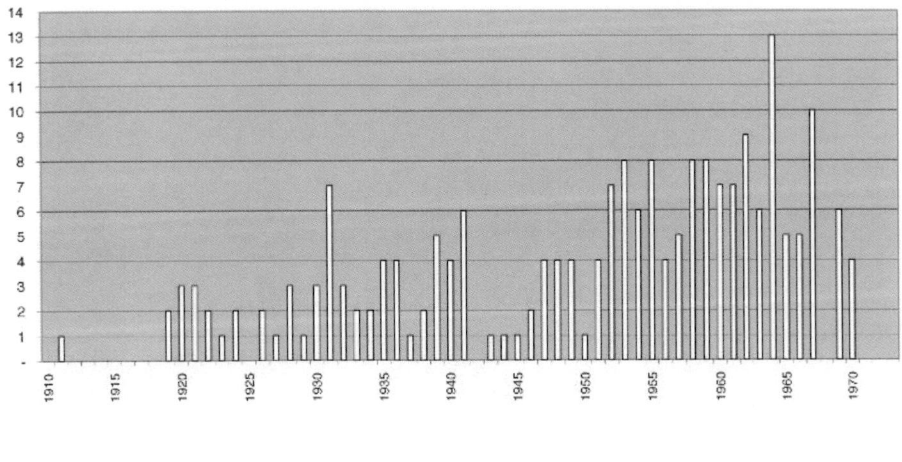

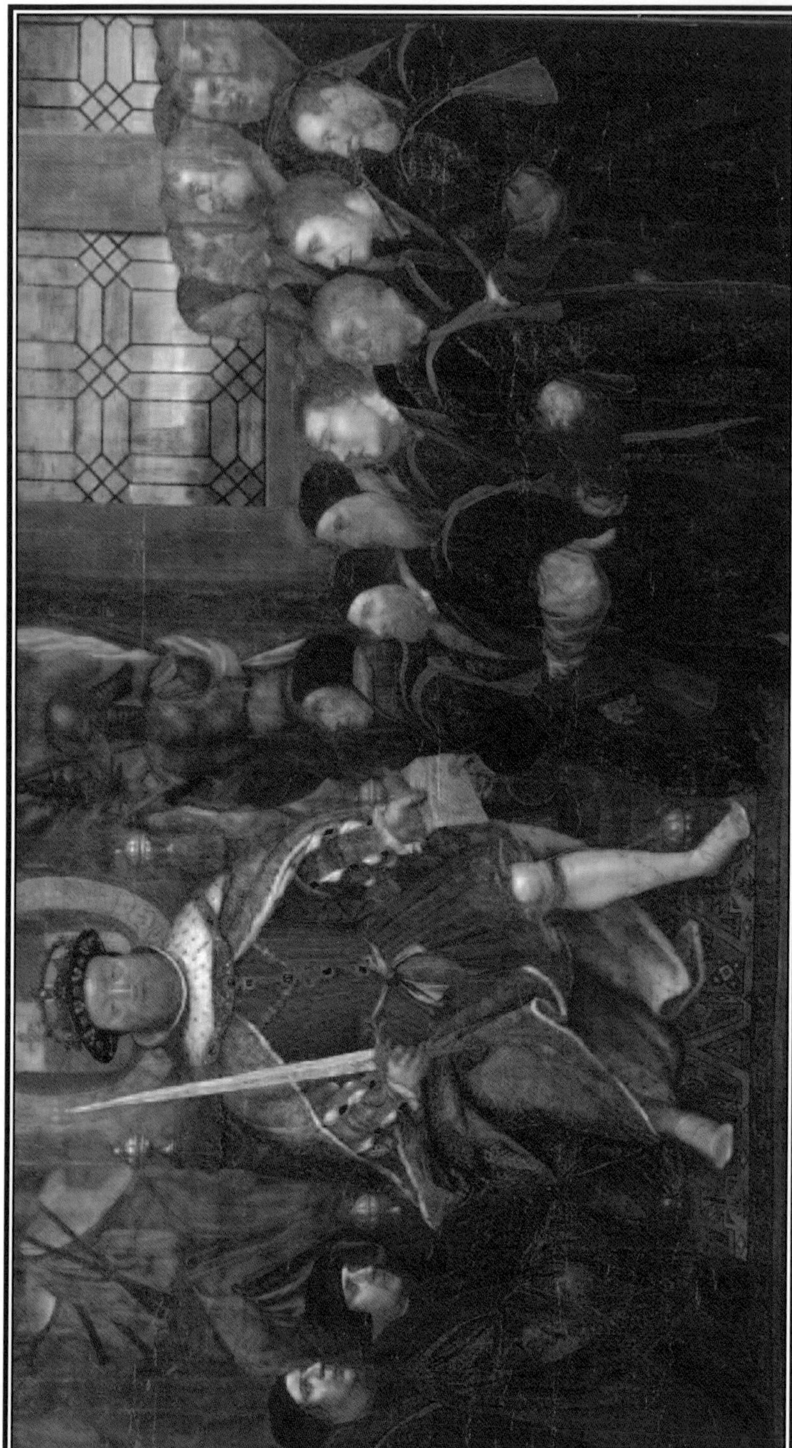

Henry VIII and the Barber Surgeons by Hans Holbein the Younger (Royal College of Surgeons of England, London).

CHAPTER 1

Breaking Down the Doors: The Royal College of Surgeons Capitulates

WHEN in 1911 Eleanor Davies-Colley made surgical history as she became the first woman Fellow of the Royal College of Surgeons she joined her two younger brothers Hugh and Robert. Her father had been an eminent Guy's surgeon, well-regarded and respected, but had died unexpectedly early two years before Eleanor enrolled as a medical student in 1902. Brother Hugh had then been in his final year at Guy's, and brother Robert was still up at Cambridge, so the three were undergoing their medical training simultaneously. The boys both became Fellows (FRCS) at the time that the College embarked on a postal poll in 1908 of all its Fellows and Members, asking them to reply with a straightforward Yes or No to whether women should be allowed to become Members and Fellows (for discussion of Members and Fellows see page 17). Time was given for the postcard replies, with a halfpenny stamp with King Edward the Seventh's bearded head on it, to be received back from the farthest outposts of the Empire. It is to be hoped that both brothers voted Yes. In fact the Fellows proved to be largely in favour, the more numerous Members, mostly general practitioners, marginally against, but the Council deliberating, not for the first time, at last acceded and women were granted entry.

It is said that surgeons habitually display a special vigour in the fray of personal and political battles, possibly necessary attributes summoned up for their courageous operative work. Certainly, the Royal College of Surgeons had put up a spirited defence against the admission of women to the College in a battle that lasted fifty years. The amazing history of the College is however studded with colourful disputes of which the attempts by the pioneer women doctors to storm the citadel are but one fray.

The great oil paintings by Holbein hang, one in the Royal College of Surgeons, the other – possibly the more authentic – in the Barber-Surgeons' Hall. The King, Henry VIII, in glorious coloured clothes straddles his throne on a dais as he hands out the charter in 1540 to form the Company of Barber-Surgeons amalgamating the Guild of Surgeons with the Company of Barbers. The men stand monk-like on either side. Ten great men rule the Company, four surgeons, four barbers, and two 'foreigners', members of neither company. Overall, although the barbers outnumbered the surgeons by twenty to one, the Masters were drawn equally, two from each body, and the Court of Assistants also equally balanced, fifteen from each. There were Barber-Surgeon Companies also in Newcastle, Bristol, Norwich, Chester and York, as well as in London. Were there any women? Women midwives were licensed at Chirurgeon's Hall after examination and later at Doctors' Commons and there were sporadic accounts of noblewomen practising medicine and surgery but generally without training or affiliation.

It has to be said that over the years the surgeons were a disputatious body. In 1745 the Company of Surgeons broke away precipitately from the Barber-Surgeons, turning their back on being a livery company, severing allegiance to the City of London, with the various attendant advantages, foregoing their barge on the River Thames. The library of books they had no use for and sold for £13. They moved to Surgeons' Hall, adjacent to Newgate Prison, from where the bodies for teaching dissection could be obtained after a hanging, and established a constitution of a Master and two Wardens amongst a Court of Assistants of twenty-one surgeons and also a separate Court of Examiners of ten men.

Throughout the eighteenth and nineteenth century, the College continued on a combative and dysfunctional path. The teaching of anatomy by dissection had been carried out in the past by a number of individuals, Cheselden, William Hunter, and others, outside the Surgeons' Hall, the popularity of their courses and the manuals they had written for students being resented by the Courts of Assistants and Examiners because it reduced the number of students enrolling in the Company. The Court attempted to put a stop to the outside courses by fining the teachers. They instituted penalties also for those who didn't confine their activities to surgery but practised pharmacy, for those who charged a fee for a medical consultation, for those who performed eye surgery and those who practised bone-setting and orthopaedics, shunned branches of surgery, and extracted penalty payments if surgeons wished to resign from the Court of Assistants or Court of Examiners, which had been set up to be a life-tenure. Control proved to be hard to achieve. Even William

Hunter, brother of John, was fined and paid up, although the money was later refunded.

In 1790, a new Master, John Gunning, presented a broadside to the Court in what became known as Gunning's Philippic: Here we have, he said, a lecture theatre without lectures, a library without books, allowed to become an office for the clerk, a committee room used as the clerk's eating parlour, a museum without specimens, and the finances of the college not audited and paid late. In other words, altogether a dysfunctional college. They took heed and began to institute changes.

In 1796, by an extraordinary action, the Court of Examiners set about selling the building of the Surgeons' Hall, acting alone, without informing the Court of Assistants, buying a new home at 41 Lincoln's Inn Fields, and moving the Company there. In an attempt to regularise the legality of the move, it was decided to write a new constitution and the Court wrote to Edinburgh and Dublin for advice but were rebuffed by the College of Physicians who declined to share their arrangements. A Bill presented to the House of Commons in 1797, was at once opposed in the Lords by two members, one of whom a member of the Company of Surgeons happened to live in Lincoln's Inn and did not want the students and their dissections as neighbours. In fact as the law stood, the bodies obtained from the prison had to be dissected within four hundred yards of Newgate and the move to Lincoln's Inn was well outside the area. The Company had to hire a warehouse for dissection and eventually had to compromise with the popularity of the outside anatomy schools.

There were rules on the number of years of apprenticeship and examinations before becoming members of the College and controls to authorise men as surgeons for the Army and the Navy. During the exigencies of war, the length of time that had to be served before certification was sometimes shortened and standards reduced. One such Army surgeon was James Miranda Barry, a deft and diminutive surgeon who had honed his operative skills in Edinburgh and at Guy's and St Thomas's and was passed to be a regimental surgeon by the Royal College of Surgeons in 1813 and was renowned for his skills in a life-time of service in the Army. He was quite a dandy, slim and immaculate in his red coat, private and proper in his habits, smooth complexioned, speaking in a soft high voice, always accompanied by his little pet dog. It was only after his death when he was being laid out for burial that the discovery was made that the body was in fact that of a woman or possibly intersex, and his identity later questioned. It was possible that he was born Margaret Ann Bulkley in Ireland and he took the name of his mother's brother, James Barry, a celebrated Irish artist and a professor of painting at the Royal Academy, acknowledging General Francisco de Miranda as a sponsor, and re-invented himself as a young man at the time he entered Edinburgh University to study for a medical degree. Whatever the actual truth of his gender, he served with great distinction as an Army surgeon, quite possibly at Waterloo, and certainly in India, in South Africa, where he carried out a caesarean section – before the days of anaesthetics – with both mother and baby, a boy who was named after him, surviving, and went on to serve in Mauritius, Trinidad and Tobago, St Helena, Malta, Corfu, on the hospital ships in the Crimea, in Jamaica and Canada. He was much respected for his concern for improvements to the water supply and sanitation for the troops and better medical care for soldiers and their families and compassion for the wellbeing of prisoners and lepers. Lesley Hall, Curator of Medical History at the Wellcome, makes the point that it is possible that other women followed the same route, qualified in medicine in male disguise and, undetected, practised as doctors. Nothing is known of them. Both Elizabeth Blackwell, the first woman doctor, MD 1849, and her sister Emily were advised to wear male attire if they wished to be accepted, Elizabeth being already a doctor when she sought further surgical and midwifery training in hospitals in Paris, and Emily in America seeking a medical school that would accept her.

As the College settled into their new building in Lincoln's Inn Fields in 1800, the new constitution was deemed necessary to legalise the position on the move. The wrangles and arguments on the new arrangements were many and varied over the years, Company becoming College, then Royal College, Master giving way to President, and the balancing act between Council and Examiners continuing. Particular difficulties were encountered in persuading senior members to give up their life-tenure on their august positions. The concept of a self-electing Council was vigorously challenged by Thomas Wakley, the Editor of *The Lancet*, himself a member of the College; it was his preference that all the members should have a vote. He was not a man to be careful with his words or his actions. He referred to the Apothecaries as Rhubarb Hall. According to David Innes Williams,

Wakley's co-agitator, the surgeon George James Guthrie, later to be President in his turn, was a gadfly on every committee he attended. Wakley went on from an initial meeting held in the Freemasons' Tavern to organise mass meetings of the members on the occasions of Hunterian lectures in the College and on the second occasion of this disruption there was uproar, the President and members of Council having to vacate the lecture room leaving Bow Street Officers to forcibly eject Wakley who was struck by a truncheon. Reform had to happen. Lectures and meetings were temporarily suspended. As usual, committees were formed, reports written and submitted, and time allowed to pass. The library and the museum were improved, petty rules done away with that had required members to go to the rear of the College via Portugal Street and not enter between the marble pillars, and restrictions of the days and hours when museum and library could be used were lifted. An unfortunate embargo against the naval surgeons attending the King's levee was reversed. More importantly, the recognition of twenty provincial hospitals and nine provincial medical schools including Birmingham, Liverpool and Bristol was accepted as necessary, and with it the abandonment of having to reside within five miles of the General Post Office in the City of London. The institution of the examination to be a teacher was at first an extraordinary ill-thought out affair where the entire Council was summoned repeatedly to examine one candidate with questions plucked at random from a balloting-glass, but eventually an examination which was the forerunner of the Fellowship became an organised event.

The formation of a body of Surgical Fellows proposed in 1842 eventually took place, the first three hundred being selected by the Council, and there followed much dispute and lobbying to include further surgeons from the provincial medical schools, the Army, the Navy, colonials, and the East India Company, and much unhappiness from the vast numbers of members who were not included in the franchise. The numbers were temporarily swelled by some who paid to join, the ten-guinea surgeons. Joseph Lister was amongst a group who wished all the Fellows to have a vote for the President, partly to obviate the election of older surgeons such as Sir William Savory who were slow to accept the discipline of asepsis and antiseptic surgery, but it was not to be and the Fellows voted for the Council and then the Council voted amongst themselves for the President. The members did not have a vote.

The Government, as represented by Sir James Graham, the Secretary of State for Home Affairs in Sir Robert Peel's ministry, was keen to bring order into the medical profession and in spite of a series of proposed Bills all in turn opposed by the College, eventually agreement was reached. Mid-century, 1858, registration of all medical practitioners came into being with the formation of the Medical Register of Great Britain. One woman doctor had been put on the Register. Born in England, Elizabeth Blackwell had her MD from Geneva College, New York State, and had returned to England to lecture and visit hospitals but because she had conducted a practice in London before the register was set up, she was entitled to have her name included on the Register.

It is fitting that the earliest of the landmarks for women was made in the New World, America being relatively free from the oppressive confinement of women that prevailed in Victorian England. Elizabeth Blackwell, English-born, was able to travel independently in America, determinedly seeking out practical experience and finding the Geneva medical school in upstate New York that agreed to admit her and allow her to qualify as MD 1849.

The Blackwell family had crossed the Atlantic in 1832 in the sailing ship Cosmo (the Atlantic crossing took seven and a half weeks) when Elizabeth was eleven, emigrating from Bristol where England was experiencing civil unrest, high taxes, low wages, unemployment due to the Industrial Revolution, a riot when the Reform Bill was defeated, schools refusing to educate the sons of dissenters, a cholera outbreak, then a fire at their sugar-refining factory – that was the last straw. They were a large family group, eight children, four aunts and a governess as well as the parents. Samuel Blackwell, in spite of the links of his refinery factory with the sugar plantations and therefore slavery, was an abolitionist and a dissenter. Life was hard on the East coast of America for him to establish himself again in the sugar trade, and after a move to Cincinnati, his health failed and he died leaving a family of nine children, a widow and debts. The determined way in which Elizabeth Blackwell sought practical medical and clinical experience, as well as supporting herself by teaching in school, was impressive but what was as striking was the calming effect that her presence had on the unruly crowd of medical students in the rural college where teaching and learning was transformed by her presence and by her refusal to be provoked by their pranks and teasing. 'I guess my quiet manner will stop any nonsense' she wrote home. She earned universal support as she processed up the church in 1849, the last of the student year to receive her diploma and have the President of the College doff his mortar-board to her now Elizabeth Blackwell MD.

Dr Elizabeth Blackwell travelled back to England, the home country, visited relatives, was received graciously by Sir James Paget as a visitor to the wards of St Bartholomew's Hospital - save only the obstetric wards- had obtained further experience with Sir James Simpson in Edinburgh, and worked in Paris at La Maternité, and conducted a medical practice in London. She gave lectures and gathered a small committee together to encourage English women to enter the profession of medicine.

At one such meeting, Elizabeth Garrett heard her speak and was fired with the desire to become a doctor. It was at this time,1861, that the Royal College of Surgeons received their first request from a woman that she be allowed to register with them and, after studying and apprenticeship, take their examinations. Elizabeth Garrett was the first to knock on the door of the Royal College of Surgeons of England.

Elizabeth Garrett in 1861 had found what she was looking for: a future that would involve her with meaningful work, a life that would incorporate a commitment to service, particularly to helping other women, a position that would make her an independent woman, and one that was consistent with retaining the feminine decorum that was necessary to her self-respect and upbringing. She would become a lady doctor.

She had been fortunate in her family. Four brothers and five sisters had provided the friendship and cohesion of family life that had given her confidence of her place in the world. Her father was energetic, strong-minded, reasonably prosperous in business. Without much education himself, he valued it highly for his daughters as for his sons, sending the girls away to Miss Browning's school in Blackheath where they took all the extras, including a hot bath once a week and hence got known as the Bathing Garretts. But he was no over-bearing Victorian pater familias at home. His wife involved herself in the accounts of his business, wrote his letters, held her important place in the household. With the servants usual to their position in life, Elizabeth was free to study with her brothers' tutors and with the Aldeburgh schoolmaster Mr Tate, applying herself to

Latin and Greek, mathematics and French. Staying with friends from the Blackheath school, Jane and Annie Crow, she and her sister Louisa met Emily Davies, a rector's daughter. Visiting her elder sister Louisa now married and living in London, she again met Emily Davies, six years her senior and already active in the cause of access to the higher education of women (she was later to be the founder of Girton College Cambridge), and through her friendship with her, she heard Dr Elizabeth Blackwell speak. Dr Elizabeth Blackwell, English born, educated in America, qualified in Geneva medical school in New York State, was the first woman on the newly formed British medical register. Elizabeth Garrett resolved to be the second.

The Garretts, father and daughter, traipsed the length of Harley Street, seeking advice as to how Elizabeth might access a medical education. The universal rejection brought out a stubborn streak in her strong-minded father, Newson Garrett, and he agreed to give his daughter his support. Elizabeth had her father's spirit: when one of the specialists asked why she did not settle for becoming a nurse, she told him tartly that she preferred to earn a thousand rather than twenty pounds a year. At her sister Louie's home, Elizabeth was introduced to Mrs Russell Gurney, the president of the committee that Dr Blackwell had formed to progress the cause of women doctors in England and through her was given a note of introduction to Mr Hawes, a governor of the Middlesex Hospital and so began her informal attendance at the hospital in October 1860, on the wards, doing surgical dressings, and gradually working her way into attending ward rounds, outpatients, the operating theatre and finally allowed into lectures and the dissecting rooms. She took lessons each afternoon from the hospital apothecary, Dr Joshua Plaskitt, not without initial heart-searching whether decorum allowed her to be alone with him, a mild unthreatening man, and to attend evening tutorials three times a week from Dr Willis the house physician, paying him a guinea a week. Two physicians, Dr Thompson, the lecturer in materia medica and who was an examiner at the Royal College, and Dr A P Stewart, who demonstrated to her how to distinguish typhoid and typhus, accepted her on their teaching ward rounds. She had found her métier. Eventually Mr Campbell de Morgan, the treasurer, who had initially refused to register her as a formal student, accepted her fees for the chemistry lectures and allowed her to sign the students' book stating that she would not smoke on the premises and would conduct herself as a gentleman. She was admitted to the chemistry course, lectures and practicals with Drs V R Heisch and Redwood Taylor, and the dissecting rooms with the Dean himself, Mr Nunn. She was allowed to enter for the end of course examinations in May 1861 and did splendidly well. Too well. Jealous of her success in the examinations, a group amongst the male students petitioned against her and, in spite of other students rallying to her support, and her father offering to endow a medical scholarship with two thousand pounds for a woman student, the Medical School Committee decided against her. Five of the Committee abstained, presumably amongst them her 'friends', the Dean – Mr Nunn, Dr Heisch, Dr Thompson, Dr Stewart, Mr de Morgan, Dr Redwood Taylor, and seven voted against. Only one had the courage to vote in favour. The decision was that she could no longer attend once the present lecture series were over. Dreadfully disappointed, she held her head high, and none-the-less continued to attend the remainder of the lectures and take the examinations that she had paid for, and in due course, and after delay, collected her certificates of honour in chemistry and materia medica. With generosity of spirit, she left the Middlesex Hospital on civilized and friendly terms with all.

She wrote around then to try to register. The Royal College of Surgeons was amongst those she wrote to. Her letter dated 5 August 1861, which was read out to a meeting of Council at their meeting, asked if they would register her attendance at the lectures so that at the end of her four years of apprenticeship she might take the special examination in midwifery. Mr Newson Garrett, her father, also wrote in a letter dated 27 July 1861, asking that, should they refuse to register her now, would they agree to examine her for the special diploma in midwifery if she produced a certificate that she had studied all the necessary branches of the profession under well-known public teachers?

Council consulted their solicitor Mr Wilde. His wily answer to the Council was that although, admittedly, there was nothing in the College's charter relating to the examination for the certificate of qualification in midwifery showing an intention that such certificates should be confined to male persons, yet on the whole his impression was that there was quite sufficient doubt as to women having any right to claim to be examined, to justify the College refusing to depart from the practice which had hitherto prevailed of admitting men only to examination for the certificate in midwifery, and he suggested that an answer to that effect be sent to the letters from Miss Garrett and her father. This long-winded piece of special pleading was followed by the answer No, they would not register her.

Alone amongst those she wrote to, the Society of Apothecaries stated that they accepted all persons after five years of apprenticeship and certificates of attendance at six courses of lectures and six months attendance at a public hospital with study under recognized teachers of the medical schools and universities. They also had taken advice from Mr Hannen QC, and it was his opinion that the Apothecaries' original charter had been granted for the purpose of selling drugs and medicines and they had no legal reason to refuse to allow a woman to be admitted to their examinations for their licence.

The Garretts therefore took out an indenture back-dated to when she had started her weekly tutorials and paid for a formal apprenticeship with the apothecary Dr Plaskitt and, depositing it with the Society of Apothecaries, received from them a list of the topics she must cover before presenting herself to qualify.

Elizabeth Garrett enrolled on a course on botany at the Pharmaceutical Society with demonstrations at the Physic Garden in Chelsea, attended a course in physics at the Royal Institution given by the Professor of Natural Philosophy, John Tyndall, and sat under T H Huxley in the Natural History Museum. When she entered, a solitary woman in a lecture hall full of men, to hear the first lecture, the subject was the physiological differences between the sexes. Thomas Huxley subsequently brought his daughter to sit with her and keep her company, gallantly starting his lectures with 'Ladies and Gentlemen', a courtesy not invariably followed, even in recent times, at the Royal College of Surgeons, a century later, when it has been commonplace for a President to start his address 'Gentlemen' and the floor to respond 'Mr President, Gentlemen'. By the end of 1861 she was able to tick off chemistry and practical chemistry, materia medica & therapeutics, and a prolonged exposure to clinical medical practice throughout 1860 and 1861, all achieved at the Middlesex Hospital, and she had made a good start on the lecture series.

Elizabeth went up to Scotland to St Andrews in 1862, where they gave her a ticket as a member of the University for a fee of £1, which permitted her to take classes in chemistry and anatomy and allowed her to attend for matriculation. But then they tried to take it back and she became a cause celebre, but excluded. She spent that winter in a private course of anatomy and physiology and some dissecting sea-beasts with Professor George Day, then on to Edinburgh where she obtained invaluable midwifery training under Alexander Keiller, colleague of the renowned Professor James Simpson, and achieved the necessary number of obstetric deliveries by July 1863. And the all-important certificate. To her relief she managed to obtain admittance to the anatomy dissecting rooms at the London Hospital with L S Little, young orthopaedic surgeon son of the great W J Little for a session in all three years 1863, 1864 and 1865 and attended the anatomical lectures in 1863 of John Adams FRCS, a member of the Council of the Royal College of Surgeons. She yet needed some further clinical experience and, after being rejected as a student, and after trying to get some exposure to practical work amongst appalling conditions in the London Dispensary in Spitalfields, she applied and was accepted as a nursing assistant at the London Hospital, living in a flat in nearby Philpot Street between Whitechapel High Street and the Commercial Road. The young resident accoucheur, Nathaniel Heckford, five years younger than Elizabeth and a gold medallist in medicine and surgery, took her under his wing to show her cases and teach her, but there was soon dissension and the physicians were told that they must not accompany her on the ward rounds. Undaunted, Elizabeth found the source of the hostility and called at the home of a Dr Parker in Finsbury Square, at first giving him a piece of her mind, then bargaining with him, and finally charming him and getting agreement to her obtaining the necessary clinical experience. She even went back to the Middlesex Hospital for the last six months, until once again they decreed that her visits must cease but wrote to her in friendly terms. A series of lectures in toxicology and forensic medicine given by the Professor of Medical Jurisprudence, George Harley, completed her studies. She had eventually gathered piecemeal the necessary evidence of her attendance at courses and lectures of recognised teachers and was eligible at last to take the examination of the Society of the Apothecaries. She must have been the most thoroughly educated and well-read medical student in the country.

The Apothecaries did demur at first but capitulated when threatened with legal action by Newson Garrett. Elizabeth presented herself at the

Apothecaries Hall at five o'clock in the afternoon for the qualifying examination with Mr Wheeler. Over the next two and a half hours they discussed medicine, midwifery and medical pathology. It was conducted as an entirely oral examination, a viva voce; there were no written papers and no clinical practical observation. Elizabeth passed with flying colours, the conferring examiners agreeing that she was the outstanding candidate of the three who were granted the certificate, LSA, that day, 22 September, 1865. Her name went down as the second woman on the Medical Register.

The brass name-plate on the door of 20 Upper Berkeley Street, between Portman Square and the Edgware Road, read Elizabeth Garrett LSA and she shared the house with her friend from schooldays Jane Crow who was running the Society for Promoting the Employment of Women. Within a year she had opened the St Mary's Dispensary for Women and Children at 69 Seymour Place and was forging good professional relationships. The dispensary was opened by the Professor of Medicine at the London Hospital, Dr Billings FRS, and many of her former teachers, L S Little and John Adams and Nathaniel Heckford were supportive.

The Society of Apothecaries to their shame however then changed their charter to state that only persons who had been students at a recognised *medical school*, rather than having been taught by recognised *teachers*, would be examined and as no medical school in Britain accepted women students, the door was effectively shut for any further women doctors.

Three women would-be doctors, Louisa Atkins, Frances Morgan and Eliza Walker Dunbar had been studying and gaining clinical experience with Elizabeth Garrett with a view to taking the Apothecaries examination. Now that door was shut. But on the continent of Europe the acceptance of university education for women was gaining ground. The three took themselves to Zurich. They became part of the Zurich Seven. These were seven women doctors, the first intake of women allowed to study for a medical degree in Zurich: their names indicate their country of origin: Suslova and Bokova (Russian), Susan J Dimock from the USA, Louisa Atkins, Frances Morgan and Eliza Walker Dunbar from England, and Vogtilin (Swiss).

Louisa Atkins, as a young woman, had gone out to India for a social season and married an Army officer much her senior. When she was left a widow, she had decided to embark on medicine as a career. In Zurich, the Seven experienced some harassment during their studies but nothing like as unpleasant as the Edinburgh Seven who included Sophia Jex-Blake, studying as extramural students, taking the examinations but not being allowed to qualify, being subject to vilification, physically jostled as they entered the lecture rooms, even pelted with mud and horse manure.

The destinies of the Zurich Seven were varied. Susan Dimock became known for her surgical skills and founded the first graded nursing school in America; she lost her life when the steamship SS Schiller ran aground in fog off the Isles of Scilly south of the English coast. One of the Russian women surgeons too was imprisoned and sentenced to death in the Russian uprisings. Louisa Atkins, was appointed to the staff of the Birmingham Hospital as resident medical officer in 1872 and was much valued there and Eliza Walker Dunbar was house surgeon in 1873 to the Hospital for Sick Children in Bristol. They worked unregistered as the General Medical Council was refusing to acknowledge any further degrees from abroad in spite of having put Elizabeth Blackwell's name on the register with her MD from Geneva medical college in New York State, USA, allowed because she had briefly practised in England before the register was instituted. No medical school in Britain accepted women as students so no further women could qualify. Only the names of Elizabeth Blackwell and Elizabeth Garrett stood on the register.

There were however to be two further rejections, the Obstetrical Society and the British Medical Association. Dr Elizabeth Garrett applied to the Obstetrical Society to become a member and received a refusal stating baldly that obstetrics was an unsuitable practice for a woman. (As described previously it was the obstetric unit at St Bartholomew's Hospital that was the only department in Barts that did not receive Dr Elizabeth Blackwell MD as a visitor from America and disallowed her entry to the wards).

Elizabeth Garrett had joined the British Medical Association once she qualified as LSA. The British Medical Association had not been quite aware that it was a woman who was the new member until she turned up to give a paper at their meeting. They made strenuous attempts to block her, moved her speaking slot to late Friday afternoon, asked her to resign, passed a resolution that no further women would be allowed to join. She responded by refusing to resign, assiduously attending all meetings of the

BMA as the sole woman member for nineteen years, as was her right, enduring a sleepless night before each meeting, speaking in the discussions, attending the receptions in the face of icy hostility, disregarding their snubs, always acting with civility. No-one who has not had to determinedly turn up and attend where they know they are not wanted can know what this cost her emotionally.

And in fact, the stable door was shut after the horse had bolted. Dr Elizabeth Garrett conducted herself with such decorum, with professionalism, without rancour, forging professional friendships, ignoring opposition, opening first her dispensary, then enlarging it into a little hospital, the New Hospital for Women and Children in Marylebone, caring for patients rich and poor in an exemplary manner, that she disarmed some of the criticism. She stood for election for the new school boards and swept to success, harvesting an enormous number of votes, the first woman – the first women, she and Emily Davies – to sit on the school board. She was appointed visiting consultant to the East London Children's Hospital that had been set up in Hackney by Nathaniel Heckford who had shared his patients with her and taught her in the London Hospital, Whitechapel. She married James Skelton Anderson, the Vice Chairman of the Governors of that Children's Hospital, becoming Dr Elizabeth Garrett Anderson, but told her husband that she would keep her professional fees and income separate from him, as was her right under the Married Woman's Property Act, although he protested that he would never have touched her earnings; she gave birth to children, and continued working in her clinic and hospital. She studied for and took the MD Paris and was applauded on her thesis.

And what of the Royal College of Surgeons? When Elizabeth Garrett had qualified LSA and was on the General Medical Register, she had written again to the College, 6 April 1865, asking whether 'a Licentiate of the Society of Apothecaries, being a lady, could enter for the Membership of the College.' The reply was again that she could not do so.

The ideal and most usual qualification for a doctor in the middle of the nineteenth century was to possess both the LSA and the MRCS, the Apothecaries' diploma giving medical and dispensing approval, the membership of the Royal College of Surgeons giving a limited surgical authority. Some doctors of course took a university degree, none of which were open to women.

Mr Wilde, the College's solicitor, in a new piece of special pleading, admitted again that the admission to the examination of membership of the College was not couched in terms of male persons, that it did not specify men, but felt there was sufficient doubt as to women having any right to claim to be examined, to justify the College refusing to depart from their usual practice. Council wrote to her that she could not enter for the membership of the College. Elizabeth Garrett left it at that and when, three years later, in 1868, Paris opened its doors to women, she studied and took herself off to take the MD Paris which she sat, of course, in French, and was generously feted when she passed and received her degree.

Just over ten years after the Council had rejected Dr Garrett's application to enter the membership of the College, public opinion was slowly coming round to the idea of medicine as a career for women, and Russell Gurney's Enabling Act was being presented to Parliament. Three women, Miss Sophia Jex-Blake, Miss Edith Pechey and Mrs Isobel Thorne, three of the Edinburgh Seven, applied to the College, 1875, to be admitted for their examination in midwifery. They had attended the appropriate lectures and taken the examinations in Edinburgh as extra-mural students, where they were not of course being allowed to qualify as doctors. Again, the College took legal opinion.

Confusingly, Counsel deemed that:

1. The Council have the power
2. They can be compelled to admit women to the examination.
3. A woman could be registered and could practice.
4. Women are not entitled to claim to be admitted to the examination for the membership or the fellowship of the College since 'the person' has always been a man.

The Council, after deliberation, made a statement that they were in fact in favour. They resolved that the three women should be admitted to the examination in midwifery. However a problem then arose in that Sophia Jex-Blake had not yet passed the examinations in medicine and surgery. The Obstetrical Society, who provided the examiners, William Overend Priestley and Robert Barnes, opposed the Council and refused to conduct the examination. They had previously declined to accept

Elizabeth Garrett as a member. Priestley and Barnes resigned from the examining body rather than have to confront women candidates. The Metropolitan Branch of the British Medical Association then joined in the opposition. And the College's diploma in midwifery was never in fact reinstituted and later the subject became part of the surgical component of the conjoint examination (discussed on page 17). In 1884 the College was still not accepting women.

The year following the attempt on the midwifery diploma, the Russell Gurney Enabling Act went through Parliament in 1886 and all medical bodies received powers enabling them to examine women for medical qualifications. Enabling, but not compelling. When the Act was initially proposed, it would have compelled all medical qualifying bodies to admit women to their examinations, but Council of the Royal College of Surgeons opposed this, saying that while they were in favour of admitting women – so they stated – their preference was for permissive powers and they objected to compulsion. The General Medical Council, after prolonged debate, admitted women to the register, with a reluctant statement that they were not prepared to say that women should be excluded from the profession. Not a ringing endorsement. But agreement would follow.

Edith Pechey, with all her Edinburgh certificates and examination successes, travelled to Dublin. She had come top of the list in chemistry but the university had refused to give her the prize for the highest marks, a situation matched in Cambridge University mathematics finals when the title Senior Wrangler was not awarded to a woman, Millicent Fawcett's daughter and Elizabeth Garrett Anderson's niece, when she came out top of the list. In Ireland, the King and Queen's College of Physicians (William & Mary) and the University of Ireland were beguiled by Miss Pechey's charm and impressed by her abilities, and agreed to admit her, and women in general, to their examinations and diplomas, the first such liberal open-minded institution and which redounds greatly to their credit. And so Edith Pechey and Sophia Jex-Blake and others, two of the Zurich Seven, and some with foreign degrees, were able to qualify and register. And as the newly formed London School of Medicine for Women, 1874, took shape, and adequate clinical experience for the women students was negotiated and obtained at the Royal Free Hospital, 1877, women doctors increasingly found acceptance in the life of the nation. Approval was voiced in *The Lancet*, in *The Times*, a general change of attitude, but which was not endorsed by the Royal College of Surgeons.

Twenty years later after this momentous time, Dr Elizabeth Garrett Anderson, as Dean of the London School of Medicine for Women, wrote a Memorial to the Council of the Royal College of Surgeons on 11 July 1895, asking that the students of her medical school be admitted to the examinations of the College. The Council of the College had after all declared that they were in favour. There were now two hundred women doctors and their existence was becoming accepted in society. They qualified as doctors by taking the university bachelor of medicine and surgery degrees, the MB BS, if they had matriculated and were eligible to take a university degree, or by taking the conjoint examination, becoming a Licentiate of the Royal Colleges of Physicians, LRCP, and a member of the Royal College of Surgeons, MRCS, and it was these London based examinations that still uniquely did not accept women, necessitating the women students who were qualifying by diploma to travel to Dublin or Scotland. (Nowadays in the twenty-first century, the qualifying conjoint examination has been abolished and the Royal College of Surgeons has become an entirely surgical college without a general practitioner membership – the GPs (general practitioners) have their own Royal College. Confusingly, the MRCS, the membership of the Royal College of Surgeons, is now awarded to aspiring surgeons early in their surgical training after a two-stage examination that exactly mirrors the old Fellowship – Part I in the Basic Sciences and part II Surgical and Clinical. The FRCS is taken as an exit examination signifying completion of surgical training).

In 1895, however, and for the next near hundred years, the College had a membership of many thousands of doctors who had qualified with the LRCP MRCS and an elite of several hundreds of surgeons who by this time had all sat and passed the FRCS, the Fellowship. The annual meeting of Members and Fellows, not a statutory body, resolved that, as so many portals were now open to women to obtain a medical and surgical degree, it was not expedient that the College should admit women to the examinations for the diploma of membership, the MRCS.

Council, the following week, resolved that the Court of the Royal College of Surgeons, although themselves in favour of granting the petition of the officers and teachers of the London School of Medicine for

Women, did not see their way to admit women to the conjoint examination in the face of the vote of the meeting of the Fellows and Members of the College and swayed by the expressed negative opinion of the Royal College of Physicians.

Weasel words… .

Dr Elizabeth Garrett Anderson replied most diplomatically, – although much regretting this decision, she greatly valued the assurance contained in the resolution of the Council that, had the matter rested solely with them, the prayer of the Memorial would have been accepted.

Shortly after, a meeting of just the Fellows of the College in January 1896, the opinion was expressed in fact that women *should* be admitted to the diplomas of the College, but nothing was done.

There was probably a general acceptance that women doctors would eventually be accepted, the Council had professed themselves in favour, the Fellows had similarly spoken. Why then did it not come about? The vehemence of those few who were hostile to the idea was extreme and expressed forcibly.

Sir William Jenner KCB MD President of the Royal College of Physicians and who had been physician to Queen Victoria (no relation to Edward Jenner of smallpox inoculation fame) was entrenched in his views, opposing the opening of medical, and indeed all degrees of the University of London to women, and stated publicly that he had one dear daughter and he would rather follow her to the grave than see her subjected to such questions as could not be omitted from a proper examination for a surgical degree. Jenner's stance, one of male hegemony, exercising power and control over his daughter, preventing her access to learning, found him not the first, nor would he be the last, to feel threatened by intelligence and education in a woman. His daughter later responded by rebellion which took the form of her becoming a militant suffragette. In the files at the College are similar handwritten letters to Council expressing vehement views.

Dr Henry Maudsley, the famed neurologist, wrote his gloomy opinion that the mental and physical strain of college studies might impair the development of the reproductive system in a girl preventing the ideal of a complete and perfect womanhood. The phrase un-sexing of women was used as a warning what might befall girls who took to book study, and was applied to Octavia Wilberforce by the Wilberforce family as they fought against her friendship with Mary Robins, the American actress and author, from whom she received encouragement to seek an education for herself and eventual medical training.

Sophia Jex-Blake's father, while content for his feisty and intelligent daughter to teach mathematics, had been totally opposed to her receiving payment for her work. A woman's work was acceptable to some only if philanthropic. Not if it were remunerative.

The opposition in the British Medical Association was fuelled partly by that same Professor Christisson who had been the chief opponent to the Edinburgh Seven, vehement in his opposition to women entering the medical profession. The extreme antagonism of the few was sufficient to deter the reasonable views of the many – and of course the voice of the women themselves could scarcely be heard.

In 1906 the Dean tried again. A further petition was received at the College from the London School of Medicine for Women. The Memorial was in copper-plate handwriting like a legal document on vellum, and couched in most diplomatic terms (see Appendix 1). It acknowledged the refusal a few years before, but felt that the main questions surrounding women doctors had been solved with time, and any doubtful points settled by experience. At the beginning of this present year, it went on to state, there were over seven hundred and fifty women on the Medical Register, of whom more than four hundred had trained at the London School of Medicine for Women. One after another, universities and examination boards had admitted women to their degrees and diplomas so that few now remained closed. Several medical schools had opened to women in Scotland and Ireland. Many women in this country and abroad had held appointments on the staff of hospitals for women and children, cases of all kinds of severity dealt with, some clinics and hospitals had been staffed entirely by women, and women doctors had held appointments on public bodies, the General Post Office, the Metropolitan Asylums Board, on County Councils, as Assistant Medical Officers of Health. The British Medical Association, the Medico-Psychological Association, the Society of Anaesthetists, and the Anatomical Society were all bodies that now admitted women and the women worked abroad in India, China, Persia, Africa and Egypt.

The petition was signed by a bevy of names of the great and good, Elizabeth Garrett Anderson MD as Dean, Julia Cock as Sub-Dean, A J

Norton as Treasurer, Isabel Thorne as Honorary Secretary and a medley of chairmen representing the Physicians and Surgeons of the Royal Free Hospital.

There followed a list of the hospital staff of the Royal Free, fourteen in all, only one of them a woman – Louisa Aldrich-Blake MD BS. Her statue can be seen in Tavistock Square.

Then followed a list of the Medical School Lecturers, eight in all, only two of them women - Mary Dowson with her Irish diplomas, and Mary Scharlieb MD BS. Six men followed, three of them Fellows of the Royal Society.

After that there were thirty-one supportive names, some still familiar to us today, including eleven further Fellows of the Royal Society, and several knights and famous names, Sir James Paget, Sir Spencer Wells, J Hughlings Jackson, Victor Horsley, Frederick Treves, Jonathon Hutchinson – but there were no woman amongst them considered influential enough to be included.

Who could refuse to be moved by such a petition?

Still the Royal College of Surgeons prevaricated and resisted the whole question of the admission of women. The Council had the powers to concede but declared instead, in 1907, that they would conduct a formal consultation with the Members and Fellows.

In 1908 the poll was undertaken, as briefly noted earlier in this chapter. To all Fellows and Members a post-card poll was sent out together with a halfpenny stamp for reply, and leaving sufficient time to get a response from all quarters of the Empire. It contained just the two questions, each requiring a Yes or No answer, whether women should be admitted as Members, and whether as Fellows. Numbers were roughly equally divided but overall the Fellows gave a Yes vote to both categories, the more numerous Members, who were mostly general practitioners, against. The Members, already disgruntled at their exclusion from standing or voting for Council, felt hostility to any access of women to the Fellowship the more keenly, even though the numbers who achieved it were likely to be very small.

At their meeting, the Council then decided to admit women to become Members and, after a further tussle, agreed as well that they should also be allowed to become Fellows.

Council then rapidly had to enact by-laws to ensure that no women should have a vote for Fellows to have accession to the Council, nor – perish the thought – actually stand themselves for election to Council, nor to the Court of Examiners. There was clearly still apprehension but the fear was unjustified; only Fellows were enfranchised and there was not going to be a floodgate of women applying to enter. There was some debate, hilarious to a modern viewpoint, as to which doors women would be allowed to use to enter College or use the museum, should they go round to the rear of the building in Portugal Street or could they enter the portals between the great stone pillars at the front in Lincoln's Inn Fields.

Lest it be thought that the Royal College of Surgeons had altogether lost its combative spirit, the fierce antagonism, employing King's Counsel, to the founding of the Royal College of Obstetricians and Gynaecologists in 1929, should reassure the world that the surgeons were still ready for a fight. See Chapter 17.

The decision to open the doors to women was conveyed to the London (Royal Free Hospital) School of Medicine for Women at the end of 1909 and a trickle of women began to take the conjoint examination in London rather than travel to Dublin or Scotland to qualify, LRCP MRCS. It was the Fellowship, however, that was all important, the FRCS, that puts the authentic stamp on a surgical career.

In 1911 Eleanor Davies-Colley took the examination and became the first female Fellow of the Royal College of Surgeons of England. She is the subject of the next chapter.

No further women doctors however were to join Eleanor Davies-Colley and gain the FRCS until after World War I. At the end of 1919, the Sex Disqualification (Removal) Act was passed through Parliament enabling women to hold any position and averred that they could not be excluded from any field, if they had the ability, on account of their sex. The Edinburgh Royal College of Surgeons wrote at once to the Government to inquire whether the new law applied to them. It did. In 1920 two women doctors passed their examination to be Edinburgh Fellows, Alice Hunter – who went at once to be a missionary surgeon, and Gertrude Herzfeld who assiduously befriended and shepherded future women surgeons into the Edinburgh fold.

The acceptance of women doctors to the Fellowship of the Royal College of Surgeons of England was at least yielded marginally, by a few years, before the Act enforced it. It would be another fifteen years that the bar against the women Fellows voting or standing for office on Council or as an Examiner would be reversed. In 1926, near to the time that women got the vote on the same conditions as men, the year of universal suffrage, women were accepted by the Royal College of Surgeons under the same terms as the men. It would be another fifty years before the first woman would be elected, 1979, to sit on the Council. (The Edinburgh College followed five years later in 1984).

CHAPTER 2

Eleanor, The First Woman Fellow
Eleanor Davies-Colley 1874-1934 FRCS 1911 MD

WHEN Eleanor Davies-Colley heard that the Royal College of Surgeons had agreed to accept women doctors into their august company, it was December 1909. She had been qualified for a year and a half as MB BS University of London in June 1908, and had completed her house appointments, in particular a very fulfilling six months as house surgeon at the New Hospital on the Euston Road where her consultant, Miss Maud Mary Chadburn, had encouraged her to gain excellent surgical experience. Miss Chadburn was only six years older than she herself and they had worked together harmoniously.

After the house appointments, Eleanor had returned to the medical school to teach anatomy to the students in the dissecting rooms. There was yet to be a professor appointed there (Frederic Wood Jones would be appointed to the chair in 1912) and the department was very dependent on young surgeons teaching, which had the advantage that it gave them a thorough grounding as they revisited the study of anatomy. Then she had gone on from there to the coveted surgical registrar post at the Royal Free Hospital and was enjoying rotating through the different firms experiencing each consultant surgeon's special area of expertise and idiosyncrasies. In 1910 Eleanor gained her MD, the higher degree in medicine.

On 5 May 1911 she took the first half of the FRCS exam, known as the primary, consisting of a three hour paper in each of anatomy and physiology (see Appendix 2). She was glad of her recent spell teaching in the dissecting rooms which had filled her with confidence. The College was in the process of moving out from their research buildings on the Thames Embankment which they had sold to the Institute of Electrical Engineers but the renovations of the new Examination Buildings in Queen Square, Bloomsbury were not quite complete and ready for occupation.

In November 1911, Eleanor was ready, had read through all her old lecture notes, and presented herself at the Royal College of Surgeons for the final fellowship paper, a four hour examination in pathology, therapeutics and surgery. There were four questions and she planned to spend an hour on each. They were: 1: Give an account of the causes, symptoms and treatment of extra-dural abscess. 2: Discuss the diagnosis, course and treatment of aneurysm of the right subclavian artery. 3: What causes may give rise to chronic obstruction of the common bile duct? Give the differential diagnosis and appropriate treatment in each case. 4: Discuss the differential diagnosis and treatment of the swellings which may occur under the gluteus maximum muscle.

The examination day passed in a blur and then it was over. She returned to hear the results on 1 December 1911 and stood in the inner hall of the College, the only female among clusters of anxious men grouped around. After a long wait, the head porter emerged from the Examiners' Room and stood in the rotunda just beyond the hall, received the list from the College Secretary and began to call the numbers of those who had passed – 'satisfied the examiners' was his phrase. As each number was called, a man stepped forward and passed into the committee room beyond him. But when numbers were passed over, one or another would detach himself from the group and slink away home, some despondent with hunched shoulders, some defiant – 'never expected to pass anyway' – 'damned unfair exam'. She checked her admission slip. There was nothing to do but wait for her number to be reached and hope it would be called. It was quite a nerve-wracking wait. Then at last she heard her number and walked past into the committee room to join the successful candidates. They were all required to sign their names in the massive book laid out on the table, the Fellowship Signatures Book, giving all their Christian names and a permanent address. The first entry in the book was 5 December 1844, sixty-seven years before. They paid their joining fee in guineas and then shuffled into the Council Room to stand in a row. Most of the examiners had stayed, some sitting at the long table, some standing behind. A homily was read out. They seemed to bow to each other. And the day was over.

It is one hundred years now since Eleanor Davies-Colley became a Fellow of the Royal College of Surgeons of England. She was the first woman surgical Fellow. No more women came to take the FRCS again for eight years until 1919 when the Sex Discrimination (Removal) Act was passed. It is uncertain whether the College expected a woman to take up the offer of joining the Fellowship quite so readily after they had agreed to open the doors. And between Eleanor and the subsequent women there was almost a generation gulf.

All those of us who have become women Fellows since, feel something of the same, relief to have passed and the exam over, disbelief in our good fortune that we are privileged to join the long line of surgeons, some with names as familiar to us as those of our own family – Percivall Pott, Benjamin Brodie, Astley Cooper, some known for the instruments that we call for as we operate, Travers, Spencer Wells, some for their operations first-in-the-field, Grey Turner, some with personalities that have quirkily captured our attention, Wilfred Trotter, and stretching back to the brothers Hunter, William and John, and more recently giving tribute to our own surgical masters. Eleanor Davies-Colley had her own pride and celebration that day. She was not a woman to lay claim on a unique achievement, to make a hullabaloo, to beat the drum, she was not seeking fame and status. Her satisfaction was in her achievement in joining the rest of her family. The previous year had seen her receive the MD. She knew her anatomy having taught in the dissecting rooms in the medical school. She had been a surgical registrar for two years and was confident in her operative skills. And now she was FRCS. She was thirty-seven years old and her future was before her.

Her thoughts, like all of us, would have gone back to her father. How proud he would have been. And then to her two younger brothers, both FRCS.

The boys had gone from Westminster School where they had received a first-rate education and gone up to Cambridge, Hugh to his father's College, Trinity, Robert to Emmanuel, and both had gone on to Guy's Hospital where their father had been such a highly respected surgeon and teacher. Their father had had to step down from work with his mortal illness while Hugh was a clinical medical student at Guy's and Robert still up at Cambridge and not yet started on his hospital training, but both boys had been shepherded through the wards in the beneficent shadow of a renowned father. The FRCS had been gained by both brothers as a matter of course within a year or two of qualifying.

Eleanor reflected on her own pathway. She had been happy at her day school, the Church of England High School for Girls in Baker Street, but her education did not compare with Westminster School and it was not clear that she would manage to matriculate from there. She went on to Queens College, Harley Street. Queens College had been founded by the Reverend Frederick Maurice, the Professor of English History and Literature in King's College, London in 1848 to provide access to an academic education for girls and women, schoolgirls aged thirteen years and over, teachers and governesses, and female members of the public who could sign up to evening lectures six nights a week. The school had been an inspiration in education to generations transforming the standards of the governess and schoolmistress. Countless teachers had passed through the rigorous learning programs. Both Frances Mary Buss and Dorothea Beale had attended and went on to inaugurate public school education for girls at the North London Collegiate School and Cheltenham Ladies' College. Here, at Queens College, Eleanor passed the necessary subjects and was able to matriculate.

At holiday time and at week-ends they all went down to the farm in Sussex. Her elder sister married and her father settled some money on her. Her mother was content for her other daughters to stay with her in the country or at their home in Harley Street but that did not satisfy Eleanor. Possibly she ventured a discussion with her father to raise the question of a medical training for herself. But he was bearing the expense of both boys at Westminster School, and looking on to Cambridge and perhaps Guy's. Perhaps some charity work was suggested for Eleanor. She took herself off to the East End whether her mother demurred or not. In the event she enjoyed it. The earthiness of the East End, the characters, her little flat in Wapping, the maid calling in from Harley Street with a covered basket of produce from the farm and bringing her fresh linen, the work in the Invalid Children's Aid, and then she landed a job as a School Board manager.

She soon would have heard the history of the School Boards and found herself following in the footsteps that Elizabeth Garrett Anderson herself had graced thirty years earlier. When the School Boards were first set up after the 1870 Education Act, election to them in each London Borough was made open for women to sit on the board as well as for men, and women had the vote as well as men in the Borough elections, though not nationally. Dr Elizabeth Garrett in 1870 was asked by the Marylebone constituency where she had set up her New Hospital for Women, to stand for the new School Board. Her women patients had turned out in massive gratitude canvassing the streets to vote her in and she won in a great landslide. The voting system was by cumulative vote, each elector being able to cast the same number of votes as there were candidates, even giving all to one candidate should they choose to do so. She harvested 47 858 votes polled from 1676 voters, a record. Thomas H Huxley was second, polling 13 494 votes cast by 4470 voters. Emily Davies, who was to found Girton College Cambridge, won Greenwich and so Elizabeth Garrett and Emily Davies took their seats alongside forty-seven men at the first meeting of the London School Board when it was held in Guildhall in December 1870. The two ladies had had to make it clear that they would sit around the table alongside the men when an attempt was made to seat them for propriety sequestered separately into a corner. The Board had sat daily and faced an enormous task and when it came to re-election three years later, Elizabeth Garrett, now Elizabeth Garrett Anderson had not stood again – she had married the year after her election and was to have her first child two years later, her hospital was moving to its new site in the Euston Road, and a year later she was one of the instigators founding the London School of Medicine for Women. Her sister Alice had taken over her seat on the School Board. Nevertheless, by the election of the two women to the School Board at its inauguration they had made an important point for the cause of feminism, that women could win public office and effectively fill the role when elected.

Now Eleanor became one of the School Board managers in the wake of Elizabeth Garrett Anderson thirty years before. She enjoyed the work. The East End had been transformed since the days when Henry Mayhew and Charles Booth had opened a window on to the dire poverty in the crowded industrial hovels that lined the streets and alleyways, the Black Streets, of Bethnal Green and Whitechapel. The 1870 Education Act had given universal elementary education to the nation's children, six years of compulsory schooling, taking them out of the Dickensian work-places and off the streets and enforcing literacy and improvement on to the deserving poor. There was much inspired school building with brick-built schools by architects like E R Robson to add to the National Society schools (Anglican), the British and Foreign Society schools (Wesleyan and Congregational), Catholic schools, Jewish schools, and the old Ragged Schools that were enlarged to accommodate the numbers. To meet this revolution in elementary education, a bureaucracy of planners, school boards, attendance officers, school inspectors, and teachers themselves grew up to enforce attendance, combat truancy, and monitor the teaching process. All came under the London School Board and it was here that Eleanor Davies-Colley worked as a School Board manager. There was still much poverty of course. But that is how things were. And pockets of charitable endeavour enlightened life in the East End with the university settlements such as Toynbee Hall and together with church groups, active in bringing education and culture, clubs and leisure activities, Friendly Societies and the like.

Then her father was taken ill. Aware at once of his diagnosis and the outlook, he tendered his resignation from Guy's Hospital. He had no wish to let his colleagues see him, he who had always been so vigorous and full of health. Eleanor spent time with him at the farm at Sussex and kept a cheerful face. It was sad to see such a strong large man waste away. She made no mention to him of her plans. They talked instead of his past. He had been a clever man, the son of a Chester surgeon. He had gone to King's School and from there to Trinity College Cambridge where he had become a scholar in both maths and classics, distinguishing himself as forty-first Wrangler and top of the second class in the classical tripos. He had rowed for his college and moved across to St Catharine's and been a Fellow both at Trinity and at St Catharine's. He had done well at Guy's as a student and an athlete and had gone on to great success as a surgeon, a popular teacher and an examiner. Now it was all over. The cancer had spread to his liver. He voiced no regrets. He had had a wonderful and useful life, put his work first, and enjoyed at the end some time with his wife and children of whom he was inordinately proud.

There was much to do at first when he died, the farm tenancy to see to, and another tenanted estate in Cheshire, the boys were still young, but her brother-in-law, her sister's husband was helpful. They rallied round their mother and made arrangements to move her up to a smaller place in London. Then Eleanor made plain her plans, claimed her 'dowry', and arranged her entry to the medical school. There was surprisingly little opposition. She was then aged twenty-eight and seemed unlikely to marry. Within two years of her father's death she was enrolled as a student in the London School of Medicine for Women.

By the turn of the century as Eleanor entered medical school in 1902, more than two hundred women had qualified as doctors and were on the

Medical Register, most of them trained at the London (Royal Free Hospital) School of Medicine for Women which had been substantially rebuilt in Hunter Street in 1900, and it was in the last years of Elizabeth Garrett Anderson's twenty years as Dean during which time she had transformed the medical school. The year 1902 also marked the formation of the Women's Suffrage Movement, holding their meeting in Caxton Hall and sending petitions to Parliament demanding the vote. Harriet Weaver, the co-publisher of The Freewoman and a feminist activist was a cousin of Eleanor's and discussion meetings were held in a lively environment, but she dissociated herself from more militant action.

Eleanor was not the only older student but with some of the young ones she felt she had little in common. Though reserved she was not shy. She just saw no reason to be convivial. A fellow student from the same year as Eleanor found her diffident and confessed herself surprised later that she had become such a successful surgeon. She was a tall slender woman, of quiet demeanour, confident and self-contained.

As had been the case for Elizabeth Garrett Anderson, her childhood and family background had provided her with a secure base for life, alongside brothers and sisters and with warm caring parents. She had been brought up in a professional family and had breathed a medical and hospital environment from her infancy, her father the distinguished surgeon at Guy's Hospital and his father before him a surgeon in Chester. Her other grandfather – her mother's father – was the treasurer of Guy's Hospital. By chance, or by serendipity as we look back, she was born in that year, 1874, the year that the London School of Medicine for Women was created and formed and started in the small building in Henrietta Street, later Handel Street, in London.

How easy are the lives of men! Hugh and Robert had gone from being schoolboys at Westminster, sailed up to Cambridge, on to Guy's, the FRCS one year later following in their father's footsteps. Eleanor tried to embark on her medical studies as calmly and with the same assured sense of entitlement as her brothers. As she started as a student at the London School of Medicine for Women in 1902, her brother Hugh was in his final year at Guy's. There were only two years between them in age but Hugh had six years of medical studies under his belt and Eleanor was able to consult him on various problems during her early time at medical school. Robert on the other hand, although seven years younger than Eleanor, was still up at Cambridge and he and Eleanor were to go through their medical training year by year almost in parallel, both graduating in the same year 1907. Their experience of their medical training was of course very different, Robert up at Cambridge and then having his clinical training at Guy's, and Eleanor at the London School of Medicine for Women and the Royal Free Hospital, but the comparison enriched Eleanor's perception of her studies. Within a year of qualifying BChir Cambridge in 1907, Robert had the FRCS 1908, just in time to take part in the Royal College's poll on the acceptance of women into the College, and had the higher academic surgery degree, the MCh, the year after in 1909.

As soon as Eleanor had started in the anatomy dissecting rooms she knew surgery was for her. The unpicking of the structure of the body was a forerunner of surgical practice. When she qualified in 1907 MB BS London at the age of thirty-three in the University of London, she was appointed house surgeon at Elizabeth Garrett Anderson's Hospital. The following year 1908 was the year of the great suffrage procession in London. Forty-thousand women marched to Hyde Park in the big parade accompanied by a hundred bands. Dame Ethel Smyth's *March of the Women* was composed for such an occasion. Regiments of women doctors, teachers, writers, actresses, musicians, society women, business women, nurses, factory workers, marched five abreast. The regiment of prisoners, seven hundred of them, dressed in white, gave pause for contemplation on the institutional brutality inflicted on defenceless women. The regiment of university women, a thousand strong, robed in their academic gowns, was led by the women doctors, most of whom had trained at the London School of Medicine for Women. Whether this display of feminist power had any influence one way or the other on how the Members and Fellows of the Royal College of Surgeons voted in their 1908 poll for the inclusion of women in the College would be hard to say.

It was while she was a surgical registrar that she had heard from her brothers about the post-card poll that the Royal College of Surgeons was embarking on and she was one of the first to hear of the outcome. Her resolve to achieve the Fellowship was born in that minute.

Like Elizabeth Garrett Anderson sixty years before, planning her route of study toward becoming a doctor, Eleanor set about her task to take the FRCS quietly and with determination, her path being the house surgeon's post with Miss Chadburn, lecturing in Anatomy in the dissecting rooms, the coveted surgical registrar job at the Royal Free, the MD, then the Fellowship itself. She was the only woman amongst all the men. She planned to complete her time as surgical registrar at the Royal Free Hospital, teaching anatomy also in the medical school but she was offered almost at once, and accepted, the consultant surgeon post at the Elizabeth Garrett Anderson Hospital, where four years before she had been the house surgeon. She also became consultant to the Marie Curie Hospital.

It was Miss Chadburn's dream to found south of the river a hospital staffed by women for women and children, just as the Elizabeth Garrett Anderson Hospital served north of the Thames. And amazingly, one anonymous donor came forward and the hospital was founded and built in Clapham and opened in 1912. Eleanor Davies-Colley was appointed also to the staff there.

Then World War I changed everything for the three Davies-Colley surgeons. Hugh and Robert were both in the Army. Hugh was surgeon to the Cambridge Hospital in Aldershot, at first a captain, then major and stayed on there for twenty years, his surgical life-time until 1936, specialising in urogenital surgery. He died soon after he retired. He remained single and his unmarried sister, Hilda, came and joined his household. Robert had been on the surgical staff at Guy's when war broke out and went first to France and then went as surgeon to the Mesopotamian Expeditionary Force with the rank of colonel and becoming CMG. After the war he returned to work at Guy's and he and his wife, a nurse from the Hospital for Sick Children, had three children, two daughters and a son who sadly lost his life as a young man in World War II.

Eleanor Davies-Colley and Maud Chadburn had their private consulting rooms in Number 2 Harley Street (later to be Number 16) at the southern end near Cavendish Square and where they also had their home. The housekeeper and friend of Miss Chadburn was Miss Agnes Forbes Merrylees who ran the household. She was a merry and vivacious lady who loved a party. The quiet Miss Davies-Colley and the jokey Miss Merrylees carefully put up with each other's differing natures as Miss Chadburn's special wisdom and good humour kept all peaceful between them.

Miss Chadburn's consulting room was on the first floor back, the partitioned rear of the main drawing room. Eleanor Davies-Colley had hers, a medium-sized room also on the first floor back, free of traffic noise and with a clear sky view over the roofs of the old stables, later garages. She had a high cabinet desk, polished wood table and chairs and a dark wood day-couch. Polished wood enclosed a wash-hand basin with hot and cold. She always had a flower bulb in a cup vase. Her room looked more study than medical.

They ran quite an establishment with five female servants to look after the household – a cook, and scullery-maid and housemaids, and later a nursemaid. In the mews behind Harley Street, Miss Chadburn's car was garaged, originally driven by a female chauffeur, later by Osborne, and available also for Eleanor Davies-Colley whenever she needed it. Miss Chadburn also had a nursing home, St Lawrence's, in Lancaster Gate.

During World War I Miss Chadburn adopted three children: first Elizabeth, then Margaret, and then, in 1918, Michael. Miss Chadburn bestowed the surname Forbes on them all; they were not related and she took the name from her housekeeper's second name. They formed a family group in the household. Miss Chadburn was their guardian, Miss Agnes Forbes Merrylees was godmother to Michael. To the three adopted children, Elizabeth, Margaret and Michael Forbes, Miss Maud Mary Chadburn was 'Aunt Mary' and Eleanor Davies-Colley was 'Aunt Elly'. The house-keeper was 'Miss Merrylees'. Aunt Elly's bedroom was on the third floor next to Michael's day and night nursery and she looked after him through nights of measles and the usual infectious diseases of childhood. 'Aunt Elly' was tall, slender, the children thought her beautiful, quiet and caring. She was highly intelligent, helping with Michael's Greek homework with no need to look up any words in a dictionary, retiring to her own room in an evening to read and do *The Times* crossword. They at first sent Michael to Westminster School, probably because Eleanor's two brothers had been educated there, but the whole public school ethos, the archaic traditional uniform, the classical Greek that bore no clear connection with a language spoken contemporaneously, the learning of Latin, did not suit him. He managed to avoid boxing by taking up fencing. They moved him to King Alfred School in Hampstead and he travelled up each day by bus, and there he thrived, acting a notable *Lear* there, an inspiration for his future career.

'Aunt Elly' made it her especial responsibility to buy the children's shoes, always from Daniel Neal's; Miss Merrylees did the rest of the children's clothes shopping. They had a country house which they escaped to at week-ends and holidays, getting out of London.

'Aunt Elly' was very practical, sewing wonderful patchwork quilts, wool rugs, and the curtains for their country house, The Thatch, and The Old Farm, in the village of Ugley Green, Patmore, near Bishop's Stortford in Essex, making furniture covers, showing Michael how to re-web chairs, mowing the lawns, and re-furnishing the Harley Street home in her inimitable good taste. She played golf and tennis. The family ate their evening meal together. 'Aunt Elly' initiated holidays in France and Italy and Spain. She was a reader enjoying Galsworthy, and taking part in the children's plays and dressing up. The children found her a gentle kind loving person.

Her work at the Hospital was of a high standard. Life went on for many years. Surgeons at that time were multi-skilled. Michael remembers her kindly words giving the anaesthetic through a mask before doing his tonsillectomy, 'Just one more breath, Michael' as he was about to struggle before going under, and the complete faith he had in her. And as a young actor, Michael had his appendix out before going off to Ireland in repertory with Sir Donald Wolfit, in case he should fall ill while abroad.

Then at the age of sixty, having worked as a consultant surgeon for over twenty years, Eleanor Davies-Colley died in 1934 unexpectedly in her sleep of heart failure. Eleanor's death was of course a great loss to the South London Hospital and to the family. Maud Chadburn, then sixty-six, had retired from the hospital the year before. Michael was only sixteen and was allowed the quiet of 'Aunt Elly's' consulting room to study and do his homework.

She left her share of their country house, The Thatch and The Old Farm, freehold, and St Lawrence's Clinic to her friend and colleague Miss Chadburn. She gave her personal possessions to her sister Hilda Sophia Davies-Colley who lived with her bachelor surgeon brother Hugh and kept house for him, and she gave a bequest to each of her nieces and nephews and cousin Marjorie of one hundred pounds (about five thousand pounds each by today's standard), clearly demonstrating her commitment to the Davies-Colley larger family, and leaving the residue of her estate between her sisters and brothers and their families. She left a substantial sum, three thousand pounds (perhaps one hundred and forty thousand pounds in today's money) in trust, the interest to be available to Miss Agnes Forbes Merrylees during her lifetime and then the interest to the three adopted children, Elizabeth, Margaret and Michael Forbes and after them to their offspring, clearly making a commitment to the family life that they had set up and enjoyed together over the years in Harley Street.

The love and friendship between women in the early years of the twentieth century was expressed differently from the friendship and camaraderie that existed between women at a later time. As women emerged from the oppression of the Victorian age, there was no ready language to express their feelings and the words they used to talk to each other or write to each other sound strange to us today. This was not in fact due only to the relative absence of men after the loss of life in the Great War. But rather it was the reaction of women feeling their release from the bonds which had confined them – the choice of matrimony, control by their parents, lack of education. The opportunity for learning, for meaningful work, remuneration, and intense female friendships, was part of the passport to freedom and choice.

The sharing of a household in 1910, indeed in the first half of the twentieth century, involved a domestic arrangement quite distinct from post-World-War-II Britain when refrigerators, vacuum cleaners, washing machines, the electric iron, even breakfast cereals and the dishwasher, had taken the place of servants. I smile when I read, as one frequently does, that Florence Nightingale became a recluse in later years, *living alone*. Living alone, that was, with a cook and three maids. Eleanor Davies-Colley and Miss Chadburn had, in addition to their housekeeper, Miss Merrylees, five female servants and a chauffeur. One imagines, cook and scullery-maid, a housemaid, a parlour-maid, a nursemaid, and probably also a charlady to come in to scrub and do the household wash. Quite possibly there were other servants at the country house or came in from The Old Farm when the family were staying in The Thatch.

Dr Christine Murrell and Dr Honor Bone set up, in 1905, a general practice together in Porchester Terrace Bayswater which became a thriving practice employing other doctors. Dr Murrell was a pioneer of the infant welfare clinics, was the first woman to be on the Council of the BMA and the first to be elected to serve on the GMC and a busy public lecturer for the London County Council. She was a large flamboyant figure, clothed in emerald and purple, full of energy. Dr Bone was diminutive, quiet and patient. They each had brought one thousand pounds to set up the practice. Their friendship lasted over thirty years cemented by their professional partnership as doctors. Before the practice took off, they took alternate week-ends off and annual holidays at different times. Later they shared a country house motoring down for relaxation at the week-end, walking their dogs, together with a third person, a business woman who had become a friend.

Dame Louisa Aldrich-Blake, the surgeon who was the Dean of the London (Royal Free Hospital) School of Medicine, rented a house, 17 Nottingham Place in W1 where at first she lived alone (albeit with staff: cook and devoted maid Florence Small who was with her for twenty-five years, and devoted chauffeur Everett – though she loved to drive her car herself and was an accomplished mechanic) but was later joined by her friend Miss Rosamund Wigram, a Colonel's daughter, and while both went their own ways, the companionship was congenial. She was never troubled by housekeeping. Work was her greatest pleasure. It was surgery that she regarded as her main work. As Dean, she doubled the size of the medical school, greatly increased the number of beds at the Royal Free Hospital, founded the midwifery unit and put the finances of the medical school on a sound basis.

And there are countless other examples of women joining forces in a practical way to manage and share their households. The necessity of the support that domestic servants gave persisted and continued in ever diminishing amount until World War II, and took a long time to disappear.

The adoption of the children is an added aspect of the Davies-Colley/Chadburn household. It was Miss Chadburn who was their guardian. It was she who was on the Friends of King Alfred School listed as Michael Forbes' guardian when he was a pupil there (and nor did his adopted sisters attend the school) and there is no record of Eleanor Davies-Colley visiting the school. However as 'Aunt Elly' she was as close to the children and as committed to them as their actual guardian, 'Aunt Mary', and looked with foresight to their future wellbeing.

The desire to include children to complete the family circle was not unique. Indeed, the first woman doctor, Elizabeth Blackwell MD 1849, did the same. As is well known, she was born in England, in Bristol, and the family emigrated to America, where the Blackwell girls worked hard to procure a good education for themselves and a livelihood, teaching school. The persistence with which she obtained practical experience and completed her medical studies at Geneva College, New York State is a familiar story. She had obtained further experience at St Bartholomew's Hospital in England, with Sir James Simpson in Edinburgh, and worked in Paris at La Maternité. She had been qualified with the MD for five years and had opened her small hospital in New York City and, realising that she might not marry and coming from a warm supporting vibrant family herself, she decided to adopt a child. In 1854, back in New York, she visited the great immigrant depot of Randall's Island where there was a pauper nursery for unwanted orphaned children. A little red-headed Irish girl tugged at her skirt as she walked by and she picked her. It turned out to be a good choice. She was a girl with a sunny temperament who became daughter, and later companion, secretary, housekeeper, and Kitty cared for her in her old age.

And others of our women surgical Fellows who were single made family life for a child. Eileen Whapham, the renowned gynaecologist in the Southend-on-Sea unit with Flora Bridge (herself a mother), adopted a daughter when Doreen was twelve years old, and who later became a midwife herself. Enid Rockstro, the surgeon at the New Sussex Hospital, Brighton adopted first one, then a second baby boy, bringing them up conventionally with a nanny, then sending them to preparatory and boarding school. One later followed in her footsteps and became a doctor. Anne Bayley in her first foray to Africa took an interest in the education of a small girl in Ghana and later brought her to school in England. Her 'unadopted daughter' as she calls her is now married and settled here with children, her 'unadopted grandchildren'. Kate Fussell, the surgeon at Wigan and one of the exceptional few who made it to become a consultant general surgeon in England, offered to sponsor a child, expecting a small girl from Africa; instead she has supported a boy, now a young man, a graduate, from the Tibet region.

There is a saving grace in women's friendship. The love and friendship springs from a sense of identification with other women – not experienced as fellow-sufferers, but as fellow fighters, fellow-achievers in the public domain. On this the feminist movement depends: that women regard other women as 'we'.

CHAPTER 3

The Great War Students – FRCS 1919 to 1930

TWENTY-THREE women surgical Fellows followed the path pioneered by Eleanor Davies-Colley, the first woman Fellow of the Royal College of Surgeons, FRCS 1911. These twenty-three who became Fellows in the twelve years from 1919 to 1930 were women who were medical students during World War I. Among them were two Dames of the British Empire, three professors, the first woman to give a Hunterian Lecture at the College of Surgeons, the first to become president of a Royal College, the first to be a professor in any subject at Oxford University.

Among them they earned one DSc – doctorate of science for original work – seven MS (Master of Surgery) degrees (including an Edinburgh ChM), one with a gold medal. Five received the higher medical degree, MD. One came from a ranch in Canada to study in London and took her FRCS out to a Zenana mission in India before returning to Canada. Two Indian women returned to work in their own country with their FRCS. A British woman domiciled in India returned to India to be professor in a medical school. One did epidemiological and anthropological work spanning the Australian aborigine, Papua New Guinea and Taiwan. One in retirement worked in Uganda. Eight were general surgeons. Two did both gynaecology and general surgery. Four specialised purely in gynaecology and obstetrics. In addition there were an orthopaedic surgeon, two eye surgeons and two ENT – (ear, nose and throat) surgeons. One nurtured a special interest in female urology, although advised by her male colleagues that there was no money in it.

On average two new women doctors won the FRCS and were made Fellows each year. Usually it was two in a year, sometimes only one, occasionally three. There were twenty-three in all, after Eleanor, over the twelve years, 1919 to 1930.

The reason why there were no new Fellows from 1911 until1919 remains a mystery. Possibly the College, having accepted Eleanor Davies-Colley, thought better about the inclusion of women until the 1919 Sex Disqualification (Removal) Act was passed and the acceptance of women became compulsory, though there was a small number taking the membership as a qualifying examination. More likely the years leading to the Great War were a time of extreme unrest and instability, with perhaps a dampening effect on social change, as Austro-Hungary annexed Serbia, Italy invaded Tripoli, Germany attacked Tangier and then Agadir. Russia, the Balkans, Germany, Austro-Hungary, Italy, France, and Great Britain all experienced threats to their territory. Then the war years themselves followed 1914 to 1918 with the exodus of male doctors from the home country to serve on the battlefields.

During the years of the Great War there was a steady increase year-by-year in the number of women students enrolling in medical school to train as doctors. (The same increase took place in Germany, the policy being reversed in the 1930s when the rise of fascism opposed the freedom of women to be in the workplace). More entered indeed than could easily be accommodated and trained in the London (Royal Free Hospital) School of Medicine. At the same time, however, there was of course a dearth of potential male students to present themselves – and pay the fees – to the all-male medical schools of the great London teaching hospitals because the young men had volunteered and gone to war as soldiers, and later there was conscription. One by one, the old established medical schools succumbed to welcome - welcome was not quite the word, rather to accept - young women as students. The Royal Free was careful to pick girls to second over for part of their training who were both clever and had decorum, guaranteed not to ruffle the delicate sensitivities of the misogynous professors and teaching staff of St Mary's, St George's, and the London Hospital Whitechapel, and a few also received mostly postgraduate teaching at Guy's and Barts.

Of the twenty-three women surgeons who became FRCS in these twelve years, all were born in the last decade of the nineteenth century, from 1891 to 1898. So all reached young adulthood and were of an age to become students and receive their training during the war years. They qualified MB BS between 1916 and 1926. They received the accolade of the FRCS becoming surgical Fellows between 1919 and 1930. All practised their surgical skills. Each climbed a ladder of unique achievement. And amongst them were some outstanding women, first in the field.

The half who persevered as consultants in general surgery achieved their posts either in their own teaching hospital, the Royal Free Hospital, or in affiliated hospitals, the Elizabeth Garrett Anderson, or in one of the hospitals founded by women for women and children, the South London

Hospital and the New Sussex Hospital. Those who specialised in gynaecology and obstetrics had a slightly wider choice though most were also working in the women's hospitals. The eye surgeons, ENT surgeons and the orthopaedic surgeon were not so confined and were appointed outside that narrow range. At least nine of the women surgeons married and, between them, they had twelve children and six step-children.

The Great War Students – FRCS 1919 to 1930
Women Fellows into General Surgery

Those surgeons who stayed solo in general surgery were Catherine Lewis, Geraldine Barry, Gwen Smith, Alfreda Baker, Constance Ottley, Eleanor Partridge, Esther Rickards and Hetty Ethelberta Claremont.

Catherine Lewis and Geraldine Barry were appointed to the Royal Free Hospital where they had trained, Gwen Smith to the South London Hospital for Women to join Eleanor Davies-Colley, Alfreda Baker to Elizabeth Garrett Anderson's New Hospital, Constance Ottley to the New Sussex Hospital for Women in Brighton, Eleanor Partridge stayed within the purlieus of the Royal Free as lecturer teaching anatomy and practising surgery for fifteen years until she moved into the psychiatric field. Esther Rickards, as one who had been seconded to St Mary's for her student training and was said to be an excellent technical surgeon, then found it hard to achieve an established post. She held an appointment at the Lock Hospital (venereal disease) in the Harrow Road and was Vice Chairman of the Regional Health Board and was active in local government. Hetty Ethelberta Claremont, after a brilliant early career and poised to achieve more, died at a young age of typhoid fever.

Catherine Lewis loved music and as a young woman was making a success of a career teaching the piano. Her father was a lieutenant in the Royal Navy. She was a quiet self-contained young woman in her late twenties and her circle of friends were surprised when she abandoned her music just before World War I and entered the London School of Medicine for Women to train to be a doctor. Being a mature student, she was serious in her studies and qualified both with the conjoint board in 1917, LRCP, MRCS, and went on the next year to take the London University degree of Bachelor of Medicine and Surgery, MB, BS with honours. She was thirty-six and wasted no time in sitting for the FRCS which she passed the following year, the second woman to achieve this. A year later she added the MS, the Master of Surgery degree, the higher degree in surgery.

She was soon to join the staff of three hospitals, the Royal Free where she had done her training and where she set about teaching the students both clinically on the wards and in the anatomy dissecting rooms, the Marie Curie Hospital, and the South London Hospital for Women and Children where she supported Eleanor Davies-Colley in the practice of general surgery. She felt that her training as a pianist, and indeed her embroidery, had contributed to her technical skills in the operating theatre which were generally considered to be superb.

At the Royal Free, Catherine Lewis developed an interest in female urology in spite of warnings from her (male) surgical colleagues that there was no money in it! But it may be that her choice of an unpopular side-line made her an acceptable fellow-worker, that – and her exceptional technical skill. She did consider plastic surgery but was not attracted by the cosmetic aspect. She founded the female urology department at the Free and wrote a well-received text-book, a small green book of seventy-five pages, on the subject that ran to two editions. Her book, *Urology in Women, A handbook of Urinary Diseases in the Female Sex*, 1932, was published by Balliere Tindall and became a small classic. It begins with a description of the anatomy in the female and goes on to discuss the treatment of urethral caruncle whether by excision or diathermy coagulation, the use of a glass catheter, a rubber tube, and graduated dilators and probes, then going on to more modern-sounding instruments with a self-retaining catheter and the use of a cystoscope to look inside the bladder. She described treatment for prolapse, hernia, and diverticula of the bladder. The medical side of treatment sounds more strange, with hot vaginal douches, instilling 5-10 cc Gomenol daily with belladonna pessaries and suppositories for cystitis, the familiar Mist.Pot.Cit, then antisepsis with Pyridium i-ii tablets three times a day, Cystast Helmitol gr.xv three time a day, hexamine, normal saline and mercury oxycyanide diluted 1 in 6000, and protargol 1 in 500. She also published papers, for example, 'Incontinence of Urine in Women', in the Postgraduate Medical Journal(1944) 20, 346.

Catherine Lewis worked all her life and then enjoyed a long retirement, living to age eighty-three, with her music, arts, books and a later interest in studying gems.

Geraldine Barry joined Catherine Lewis some ten years later at the Royal Free Hospital. They were the two women surgical Fellows amongst the general surgeons on the teaching staff, where Cecil Joll, J Cunning and Clement Shattock were the establishment. Geraldine Barry had been a brilliant student graduating with honours in medicine and surgery and winning the University Gold Medal; even so it was with reluctance that Cecil Joll gave her his house surgeon post. Cecil Joll was the unrivalled authority on thyroid surgery and a rapid and dexterous general surgeon who had served in the war in France and the military hospitals in London.

The daughter of an Anglican minister Geraldine Barry had gone up to Cambridge from Queen Anne School, Caversham, to read mathematics. As a mathematician, she had never considered medicine as a career. During World War I, she came across Professor Winifred Cullis, the Professor of Physiology at the London (Royal Free Hospital) School of Medicine. Winifred Cullis was an ardent feminist who felt it incumbent on herself to gather intelligent educated women into medicine. She was the first woman to hold a professorial chair in any British medical school; during the war, the Colonial Office had sent her out to give lectures to the troops in Malta and Gibraltar. No matter whether their first subject was mathematics like Geraldine Barry (or Icelandic studies like Gladys Hill, FRCS 1936), Professor Cullis was a persuasive advocate for the medical life.

Geraldine Barry was convinced by Professor Cullis to consider becoming a doctor. She graduated MB BS from the London (Royal Free Hospital) School of Medicine with honours in medicine and surgery in 1922 and winning the University Gold Medal. After Cecil Joll's house surgeon post, she worked also for J Cunning and Clement Shattock, and with Percival Cole at the Cancer Hospital (the Marsden) and took the FRCS in 1926 and the MS in 1929. She was fortunate in her surgical teachers. Joseph Cunning was a self-described 'ardent gastrectomist' and excelled in the surgery of the upper abdomen; he was an Australian from Ballarat and Melbourne where he qualified and came at first to Barts to study and take the Fellowship; an inspiring teacher, debonair and charming, and his wife was a doctor so perhaps he was in sympathy with the Royal Free students. Clem Shattock was the foremost surgical teacher of the time; a true generalist and rejected for war service because of a polio-damaged leg. Percival Cole, experienced in the surgery of war injuries, particularly of the head and face, was a forthright man.

Geraldine Barry in her turn became an accomplished surgeon doing all abdominal surgery, She was consummately skilful in thyroid surgery and was appointed first as assistant surgeon to the Royal Homeopathic Hospital in 1929 and then to the Royal Free Hospital in 1930, where she then spent her working career, doubtless an important role model for generations of young women medical students. She never married. She was interested in and supportive of all the house surgeons and registrars who worked for her, following their careers and keeping in touch by Christmas letters. Her sister, Frances, was also a doctor, a general practitioner, and occasionally her juniors were sent out to do locums in her sister's practice. They retired together to Yateley where they had a large and beautiful garden and enjoyed dispensing hospitality.

Not all the women surgical Fellows came out of the Royal Free. Gwen Smith trained at University College London, UCL, and University College Hospital, UCH, Alfreda Baker in Belfast, and Constance Ottley in Oxford and the London Hospital, Whitechapel.

Gwen Smith got the surgical registrar post at the Royal Free because she was a woman. There was plenty of prejudice around, she said later, from the 1920s to the 1940s but for once it was in her favour. She was FRCS in 1929 and became a consultant at the South London Hospital for Women and Children and also to the Marie Curie Hospital and had a private practice in Harley Street. She operated over the full range of general surgery and published an interesting paper on a case of leiomyosarcoma of the rectum in the *British Journal of Surgery* in 1963.

Alfreda Baker did her training in Belfast, at first in the Belfast College of Technology where she took honours in chemistry, then at Queens University, where she graduated again with honours MB, ChB, BAO the Belfast qualifying degrees, followed by house posts at the Royal Victoria Hospital where she was also a lecturer in anatomy. She was proud that three of the students that she taught in the dissecting rooms later became professors of anatomy.

She came to the Royal Free Hospital from Belfast on a Riddell research fellowship and her work on the causes of foetal death led to the MD with commendation in 1926. Alfreda Baker also did a house post at the Cancer Hospital (the Marsden) with Ernest Miles. She took the FRCS in 1927. Her published papers included 'A case of primary adamantinoma of the tibia', 'Acute duodenal obstruction due to neonatal volvulus', and 'A case of megalo-duodenum with various vascular abnormalities' with John Kirk, showing the breadth of her surgical experience.

Alfreda Baker became consultant first to the Hounslow Hospital in 1930, then was appointed to the Elizabeth Garrett Anderson and the Marie Curie Hospitals in 1937 and had a private practice in Wimpole Street. Subsequent women Fellows recall working for her as registrar at the EGA and gaining valuable operative experience.

During World War II Alfreda Baker took the Royal Free medical students out to Oster House at St Albans, previously a Poor Law Hospital where part of the hospital had been evacuated. There they had a wealth of clinical experience and few students would forget her upright figure, deep blue eyes, and white hair, insisting on high standards and good record keeping. She took the students also across to Hill End Hospital, formerly a Mental Asylum, which Barts had used for their war-time evacuation...Barts in Herts. In retirement, she enjoyed travel, had many friends and living in Essex took up painting both in oils and water-colour as do many surgeons; indeed her father had been an artist. She remained single.

Constance Ottley went up to St Anne's, Oxford University, which was then the Society of Oxford Home Students, after private education at home in Hampstead where her father was an Anglican Canon, the Reverend Robert Ottley. From Oxford, she won a scholarship to the London Hospital, Whitechapel, where she worked under James Sherren and A J Walton. She became consultant surgeon to the New Sussex Hospital for Women in Brighton.

James Sherren was an interesting man. He loved the sea. He had served as an apprentice to a ship's doctor which inspired him to follow in his footsteps, and after qualifying and taking the FRCS, he had been appointed in 1900 to the surgical staff of the London Hospital where, among other contributions, he described Sherren's triangle, an area of hyperaesthesia of the skin of the right iliac fossa in acute appendicitis, and also the Ochsner-Sherren conservative management of the acute abdomen. The diagnosis and operative treatment of acute appendicitis, sometimes called acute typhlitis, only gradually became acknowledged and accepted. Elizabeth Garrett Anderson's sister, Louisa, died of appendicitis, unoperated; the operative treatment of King Edward VII by Frederick Treves in the early years of the century delayed his coronation but was successful. Sherren had also worked and published with Sir Henry Head and William Rivers, the neurology shell-shock physicians. Soon after the time that Constance Ottley studied under him, he returned to sea as a ship's surgeon.

Her other surgical teacher and mentor was A J Walton, a young consultant with broad general interests. Many years later, Leela Kapela, FRCS 1968, learnt her surgical craft under his tutelage.

Constance Ottley qualified BA BM BCh Oxford in 1922 and became house officer in the receiving room at the London Hospital, house physician in York, and house surgeon at the South London Hospital for Women. She took the FRCS in 1928. She was appointed consultant surgeon to the New Sussex Hospital for Women in the Brighton group of hospitals where she spent all her working life. She joined the surgeon Elsie Visick, the wife of J R Griffith, a surgeon at Hove, and they were later joined by Enid Rockstro FRCS. She played the cello. She remained single. She died in Hove age eighty-two.

Eleanor Partridge was an anatomist and a surgeon and then had a second career as a psychiatrist. She came from Devon and was a countrywoman at heart. She did her medical training in the London (Royal Free Hospital) School of Medicine for Women qualifying at the age of twenty-five in 1917 with the conjoint diploma and did house surgeon posts at the Elizabeth Garrett Anderson and the Royal Free Hospital. She taught anatomy as demonstrator and as lecturer and went on to publish papers in the Journal of Anatomy, one on 'The relations of the glossopharyngeal nerve at its exit from the cranial cavity', the other on 'Joints, the limitations of their range of movement, and an explanation of certain surgical conditions'. She was surgical clinical assistant to the West London Hospital as well as the Elizabeth Garrett Anderson and the Royal Free Hospitals and took the FRCS in 1921, when after practising surgery and anatomical research for fifteen years, she turned toward psychiatry. After being a clinical assistant at the Institute of Medical Psychology (the Tavistock Clinic) and studying Jung, she was appointed psychiatrist there, and was a member of the British Psychological Society, and the Society for Analytical Psychologists.

Eleanor Partridge contributed to a Maternity and Child Welfare Conference in 1938 where there was discussion on the falling birth-rate, comments on the maternal mortality-rate being the lowest for the century but with no concomitant decline in the death rate of infants under four weeks of age, papers were presented on the school medical service, posture and diet, the provision of sex education in girls' and boys' clubs, where she communicated a prescient statement on the attitude to sex passed on by parents to their daughters, a statement perhaps advanced for the time. There were calls for day-nurseries and nursery schools, and for emergency nursery residential schools for infants and toddlers when parental illness or domestic crisis occurred and recommendations for an increase in home-visiting. The future need for holiday-homes under the Air Raid Precaution scheme was mooted, recommending that homes of fifty children be presided over by a matron and a nursery school teacher, four staff nurses and fifteen probationers. Of note was the fact that this discussion took place more than a year before war was declared.

Eleanor Partridge left London and went to live in Exeter with her husband, Edward Wenham, an American, and her daughter. She practised as a psychiatrist from consulting rooms, and at the Withymead Centre, Exeter and was medical director of the Lympstone Grange Nursing Home. She published a small book of ninety-four pages with the title *Baby's point of view, the psychology of early babyhood.* She started by stating that medical psychologists, when they meet together, are wont to bewail the ignorance and mistakes of parents. The mismanagement of childhood foretells the case of nervous difficulties in adult life. Difficult children have suffered from difficult parents. She then went on to make five points. First, that a baby does have a point of view. Then that love is the primary need, the feeling of safety, the important achievement of sensory gratification, what she calls the three pennyworth of hot hands of the cinema fan, dancing, kissing, nuptial embrace. Thirdly she writes about instinct versus instruction: a genuine love, never leaving a baby to cry, never scolding when wet or soiled, the closeness of breast-feeding. Fourthly, she deals with deprivations, both necessary and unnecessary: birth itself, weaning, mother's absence, the arrival of the next baby, the importance of the first six years. Five, she calls for moderation.

Ill-health overtook her when she was ready to retire, enjoying taking part in meetings of the Soil Association, and seeing to her bee-keeping, and she died aged sixty-two a day after arriving in Switzerland for recuperation.

This making of a second successful career, this total change of direction, was not unique amongst our early women Fellows.

Esther Rickards had an excellent brain, became an exceptionally skilled operative surgeon, and was forthright in expressing her socialist convictions. Esther would like to have been a vet and would have made a good one. Her father was a veterinary surgeon but veterinary science and practice was even less open to women than a medical training. Aleen Cust was the first woman to obtain the MRCVS Diploma in 1922. Olga Uvarov who qualified as a vet in 1934 did eventually become the first woman President of the Royal College of Veterinary Science.

Esther Rickards studied at the Polytechnic in Regent Street and also at Birkbeck College in order to obtain enough higher education to matriculate before entering medical school. She was one of a group, together with Ida Mann, Erna Jebens and Sybil Mocatta, selected from the London School of Medicine for Women to do her clinical work at St Mary's. She qualified MB BS in 1920 and did several resident posts at St Mary's working for Clayton Greene, Sir Zachary Cope and Professor Charles Pannett. She was surgical registrar there. Octavia Wilberforce, who was house physician, unpaid and honorary, to Dr Wilfred Harris, the neurologist and head of the department of medicine, wrote of Esther Rickards that she was a first-rate surgeon, a beautiful operator, with a remarkable brain and inevitably of consultant timbre. However she commented that her work was valued in spite of her outspoken statements championing Labour. Esther took the MS in1923 and the FRCS in 1924. She became honorary consultant to the Lock Hospital in Harrow Road, Paddington.

Dr Charles W Brook in an address to the Socialist Health Association stated that Esther Rickards MS FRCS had undergone victimization for her political views when seeking surgical appointments at London hospitals. He did not mention whether she was rejected because of gender which was at least equally likely.

Forty years after Esther Rickards was not appointed when trying to be accepted into a surgical post, a women was appointed to be a lecturer, senior registrar, on the surgical unit at St Mary's. They had not had a woman on the staff before. Within the first week, the professor received a letter from one of his senior fellow consultants demanding her instant dismissal. Almroth Wright had long since gone but misogyny persisted.

Esther Rickards pursued an administrative career as Assistant Medical Officer for Finsbury Borough Council, and for Paddington, and was a member of the Central Public Health Committee with a special interest in maternity and child welfare. She stood, unsuccessfully, for Parliament as a Labour candidate. She was a member of the London County Council for Greenwich. She became an alderman. She was a brilliant debater and a first-class administrator, and a confident and able chairman of committees. She worked on the NW Metropolitan Regional Board, where she was vice-chairman, and sat on the St Mary's Board of Governors from 1947 to 1971. She was appointed OBE in 1966 for her administrative work.

Outside medicine, Esther Rickards was a founder member of the Windsor Gun Dogs Society, chairman of the London Cocker Spaniel Society and the European Spaniel Society. A fine, perhaps surprising, example of her skill was that she embroidered a gown for the President of the Royal College of Surgeons.

Hetty Ethelberta Claremont and Margaret Basden were both educated at King Alfred School in Hampstead, though Hetty was six years junior to Margaret and also always looked particularly youthful. It was an extraordinary thing that of the five earliest surgical Fellows, two should have gone to the same school. Hetty was a brilliant student, athletic, with wide interests, mountain climbing, walking, speaking several languages, the daughter of a J.P. and with many doctors in the family. She was practical with her hands, enjoying carpentry and gardening, as well as music. It was she who, as a schoolgirl, found the site in Manor Wood in North End Road where King Alfred School re-located from Ellerdale Road in Hampstead and played an active part in the move and building.

She qualified with the conjoint diploma in 1916 at the age of twenty-four and the university degree of MB BS the following year. She published a case-report on a case of mycosis fungoides in the Proceedings of the Royal Society of Medicine while still a medical student. Intent on a surgical career Hetty Claremont took and passed the FRCS in 1920 at the age of twenty-seven and followed it with the MS in 1922. She studied at the London School of Medicine for Women where the surgeon Mrs Scharlieb spoke highly of her intellect and her personal charm and her concern for the welfare of her patients, and also at St George's Hospital, in Hyde Park Square; again, it was war-time and the all-male medical schools were depleted of students and were therefore agreeable to receive some women students and the tuition fees that they brought with them. Although it was felt that leaving the Royal Free and going to St George's was at some risk to her career, she was keen to go in order to ensure that women students should be admitted to the other London teaching hospitals. In her final degree MB BS, she was awarded the John Hunter Gold Medal.

Good experience in house appointments, and as surgical and anaesthetic registrar at St George's, followed and again as curator of the museum where Sir Humphry Rolleston thought highly of her, and in the posts of casualty officer, and clinical assistant to the venereal diseases department. She had two papers published in *The Lancet*, one on shortening post-operative convalescence, a topic that retains its interest today, and one a case-report describing a patient where the pylorus had inverted and obstructed a gastrojejunostomy, giving an indication of the range of surgery that she was taking part in. She took the FRCS in 1920 and the MS in 1922.

Then, using her languages, she travelled to study for a year at the university clinic in Zurich, and visited centres in Vienna, Budapest, Frankfurt, and then Madrid. On her return she was appointed surgical registrar to the National Temperance Hospital, surgeon to the Bermondsey Medical Mission Hospital, and clinical assistant to the outpatients at the South London Hospital for Women and Children and to the female Lock Hospital for venereal disease in the Harrow Road, Paddington; as well as these appointments she set up in private practice at 31 Devonshire Place as a consulting surgeon. She was appointed to her old school to carry out medical inspection of the children.

However, at the early age of thirty-two, she contracted typhoid fever and perished. It was a great sadness to all who had known her. A broadcast was made through the London wireless station appealing for suitable blood donors that might save her but, though offers were received, none was of any avail.

The Great War Students – FRCS 1919 to 1930
Women of the Fellowship in General Surgery and Gynaecology

Two of the women surgeons practised both in general surgery and in gynaecology, one, Muriel Elsie Landau, predominantly on the gynaecological side but also active in general surgery, the other, Gladys Sandes, a general surgeon but particularly committed to working in gynaecological disorders of women and children.

Muriel Elsie Landau, FRCS 1920, was among the first half dozen women surgical fellows. Highly intelligent and formidably energetic, she was the complete woman. She was Miss Muriel Landau MD (London) FRCS (England) in her practice at 14 Harley Street, always Elsie in the family. Her marriage to Dr Samuel Sacks, an East End GP of similar renowned energy, formed a formidable partnership, a beacon of Jewish culture, education and medicine; they had four sons, Marcus, David, Michael and Oliver, three of them doctors. Her husband termed himself with humour 'the original Dr Sacks' and he continued to practise and see patients until the age of ninety-three. If their youngest son's autobiographical account of his childhood in *Uncle Tungsten: Memories of a Chemical Boyhood* is to be strictly believed, his mother allowed Oliver dissecting practice at an early age, only rivalled by his uncle's chemical experiments. In fact, it was one of her former students, Professor Ruth Bowden, FRCS, who supervised her son's dissection of a leg.

Muriel Landau was educated at the Dame Alice Owen School in Islington and entered the London (Royal Free Hospital) School of Medicine for Women with a scholarship, qualifying in 1918 at the age of twenty with the London University MB BS. She came from an enterprising family, her father had invented the Landau safety lamp for coal-miners. She did house jobs at the Royal Free and at Queen Charlotte's, a measure of the general acknowledgement of her exceptional ability, and was registrar at the Hospital for Women, Soho Square, again an indication of how her work was perceived, passing the FRCS examination in 1920 at the age of twenty-five and taking the MD in obstetrics and gynaecology in 1921.

By the age of twenty-six Muriel Landau was on the staff of the Elizabeth Garrett Anderson Hospital for Women where she was senior casualty surgeon covering general surgery and obstetrics and gynaecology, and her marriage the year after to Dr Samuel Sacks in no way diminished her professional commitments. She served also at the London Jewish and the Marie Curie Hospitals. Her help was frequently sought in cases of difficult labour and obstetric problems. Her services to the Elizabeth Garrett Anderson Hospital over forty years from 1921 to 1961 added considerably to its traditions and prestige. She was a good colleague, loyal and supportive and was elected President of the Medical Women's Federation.

Muriel Landau worked for forty-five years in the hospitals. In World War II she went out, often through the blackout, to Oster House, the former Poor Law Hospital in St Albans, Hertfordshire to where the Elizabeth Garrett Anderson Hospital had been partially evacuated. She was an outstanding person not only because of her professional skills which were seen to be of a high standard, but also for her warm interest in others and sympathetic consideration to colleagues, junior doctors, students, nursing staff as well as patients. She was the doctor that medical and nursing staff sought when they had a personal problem.

She wrote a helpful book, a little brown book of only forty-nine pages, *Women of Forty*, and she begins the book with the words: 'Life begins at forty'. She encourages women as they lay down the possibility of further motherhood, to take up a new career whether in the community or in public life, and to find renewed zest in professional life. She describes the phases of a woman's life through childhood and adolescence, comparing the 'curse' of menstruation for girls as comparable to the necessity to shave for boys. For the climacteric with its hot flushes, vasomotor changes, palpitations, nervous anxiety, hair loss, digestive problems, and weight gain and obesity, she recommends attention to diet, judicious rest and exercise, care of the skin, and medically – barbiturates, Largactil (chlorpromazine), thyroid hormone, and stilboestrol (synthetic oestrogen). In the last chapter of her book, she deals with employment of women in the over forties, recommending it. She produced publications. Over the years she attracted an extensive private practice, predominantly in obstetrics and gynaecology but also doing general surgery. She died suddenly age seventy-seven while on a visit with her husband to Israel.

Neither Muriel Landau nor Gladys Sandes were members or fellows of the college of obstetrics and gynaecology and therefore may be regarded as primarily general surgeons.

Gladys Sandes was a surgeon who was active in many spheres of social morality, giving support to liberal causes. A special interest became the infective gynaecological disorders of women and children and their sociological impact. She was consultant surgeon at Queen Mary's Hospital Carshalton and at the Mothers' Hospital Clapton where she was in charge of the VD and vaginal discharge clinic and where the medical and nursing staff and patients had the highest regard for her. She gave expert unobtrusive support to patients with venereal disease and was particularly sensitive to the needs of children who had been the victims of sexual assault, not a new problem though some would imagine it so. She played her expert part in medical officer of health committees for the LCC on special diseases in children in paediatric and general hospitals, in nurseries and residential care homes. She sat on the many relevant committees and boards of inquiry and was a co-signature to reports. She was expert at holding her ground with charm and wit in debate even when her views were unpopular.

Her motivation to become a doctor arose in childhood. As a schoolgirl attending Wimbledon High School, a Girls' Public Day School Trust school, Gladys Sandes was taken by her headmistress to meet Elizabeth Garrett Anderson herself, who must have been then in her seventies. She held that meeting as a life-long inspiration.

She was born in Dublin and was interested in Irish genealogy all her life. In fact, she always took a wide and lively interest in all things and all people. She studied at the London (Royal Free Hospital) School of Medicine qualifying MB BS in 1922 and taking the FRCS in 1930. She wrote a popular textbook with Dr Evelyn Hewer while still a registrar *An Introduction to the Study of the Nervous System.* She was surgical registrar at the South London Hospital and a first assistant in urology at the Royal Free, a valuable training for her later work, and became consultant at Queen Mary's Hospital, Carshalton and the Mothers' Hospital, Clapton where she spent her working life and she was also surgeon to the Lock Hospital (at the venereal disease dispensary in London's Harrow Road which closed with the advent of the NHS in 1949) and the Marie Curie Hospital. At the Mother's Hospital, Clapton, in the East End of London, consultant in charge of the VD department and vaginal discharge clinics, she gave an exceptional service.

She was chairman of the editorial committee of *Mother and Child*, chairman of the Marylebone division of the BMA, on the executive of the

Freedom of Medicine Fellowship, on the Women's Advisory Committee of the British Standards Institution, and was active with the Apothecaries in their history of medicine section.

Gladys Sandes was a charming generous doctor, witty and a good speaker, given to hospitality, always ready to help juniors and foreign postgraduate visitors. Sir Alexander Haddow, the cancer biology scientist, wrote a eulogy indicating that she possessed enormous personal charm and a great capacity for friendship. She ran a successful private practice in Portland Place and Devonshire Street. She continued to work in retirement both privately and doing locums when needed. She travelled extensively all over Europe, to America and Canada, to Russia and to South Africa. She was married to Dr Maxwell Alston MD FRCP, the pathologist, and they had a daughter, Lilac.

The Great War Students – FRCS 1919 to 1930
Women Fellows in Gynaecology

Of the four women surgeons with the FRCS who made obstetrics and gynaecology their sole speciality, Dame Hilda Lloyd is the most celebrated name, born Hilda Shufflebotham in Birmingham and destined to reach the heights of her field, and joined by Margaret Basden, Alice Bloomfield and Sybil Mocatta.

Dame Hilda Lloyd, later Dame Hilda Rose, was born Hilda Nora Shufflebotham and was a Birmingham schoolgirl, educated at King Edward VI High School for Girls, the daughter of a grocer who had many high class stores in the city and suburbs, and who was reluctant for his child to study medicine, which she did none-the-less at Birmingham University, taking a BSc in 1914 and the MB ChB, the qualifying examination, in 1916. She had the opportunity of a wealth of clinical experience in the Birmingham & Midland Hospital for Women and the London Hospital, because it was war-time (World War I) and many of the medical staff were away in the Forces. She took the FRCS in 1920.

She became consultant to the Maternity and Women's Hospital in Birmingham, took the MCOG in 1935, the FCOG in 1936 and was soon elected an Examiner and on to the Council. In 1949 she was elected President of the Royal College of Obstetrics and Gynaecology, the first woman to be president of any Royal College, and became the college representative on the General Medical Council. She was honoured with the title of Dame of the British Empire, DBE, in 1951.

In Birmingham, she demonstrated excellent administrative and organizational skills, setting up the flying squad and running her department as Professor of Obstetrics and Gynaecology, teaching the students, doubtless acting as an important role model. She married Bertram Lloyd, a fellow doctor, a pathologist, who became Professor of Forensic Medicine in Birmingham University. Theirs was a happy marriage, and when he died, she later married again, happily, Baron Theodore Rose, a fellow surgeon who had also been alongside her as a medical student. She lived with full energy into her nineties, organizing her own ninetieth birthday party. She died later in that year. Her local fame and popularity when in active practice in the Midlands bore witness to the demand that existed for a woman surgeon to treat, particularly in the field of obstetrics and gynaecology, women patients. She had a large practice, and was particularly valued by the wives of her colleagues.

In fact, though, she was not the first women surgeon to work in the Birmingham hospitals, though she was the first of course with the FRCS, being in the first half dozen women ever to attain the Fellowship. Fifty years earlier, in 1872, Dr Louisa Atkins MD Zurich had been appointed to the staff of the Birmingham Hospital as resident medical officer and was much valued there. Fifty years is a long time, particularly from the 1870s to the 1920s, when life in Britain had undergone a total transformation. It would not be surprising if the Birmingham hospitals failed to recall to memory Louisa Atkins when Hilda Lloyd made her impact on the medical scene. But they were two pioneering women.

Margaret Basden took and passed the fellowship in 1919. Together with Catherine Lewis, they were the first two surgical fellows after Eleanor Davies-Colley. She had been a medical student at the London (Royal Free Hospital) School of Medicine when the Royal College of Surgeons had opened its doors to women and she lost no time in taking the first part of the FRCS, the primary, in anatomy and physiology, as one could then, after the second MB, before clinical studies, while still a student. She had been educated at King Alfred School in Hampstead, along with Hetty Ethelberta Claremont, and where she was called Margery.

She qualified with the London University MB BS in 1913 and took the MD, higher degree in medicine, a year later. The war was wreaking its effect on the staffing of the great London teaching hospitals and there were unfilled posts as the young men volunteered. Margaret Basden was an imposing figure and her skills were well regarded and she went on to house surgeon posts at the London Hospital, Whitechapel, serving under Sir Hugh Rigby and Dr Russell Andrews, and being impressed by the teaching and kindliness of Russell Howard, availing herself of all the opportunities offered for surgical training under these renowned figures. She took the FRCS in 1919 and was appointed to the staff of the Bethnal Green Hospital as well as to the Mothers' Hospital in Clapton in the East End, and the Mildmay Mission Hospital and the South London Hospital for Women and Children. She worked all her life.

Having benefited in World War I from the enhanced opportunities for surgical experience, she re-paid this by a doughty contribution in World War II. In charge of the Clapton Maternity Hospital, in the thickly populated East End of London, a hospital abandoned by the EMS (Emergency Medical Service) after the first three months of the war as a non-general hospital unsuitable to receive casualties, she was left as the sole consultant with her former colleagues deputed away to other services, and she took up residence in the hospital with the trainee medical officers, staying throughout the bombing-raids – sometimes as many as eight in a night, transferring the hundred patients – and their babies (who were deposited on to a shelf over the bunk of each mother) in to the underground shelter throughout the air-raids. By her organizational skills, she and the night-shift nurses and midwives could achieve the whole transfer in seven minutes. These were still the days of a lying-in period of ten days post-partum. Her report in the British Medical Journal makes the penetrating observation that the early ambulation required of the patients to transfer to the air-raid shelter had the beneficial effect of less morbidity, better involution of the uterus, a marked reduction in deep vein thrombosis, and generally improved morale and strength of patients. The practice finds resonance today with the domino effect when most patients after childbirth are not only ambulant but going home the same or first day after giving birth. She voiced a small concern that such early mobilisation might later increase the incidence of prolapse.

Margaret Basden enjoyed being busy at her work and found retirement at age sixty-five in 1951 difficult so she took herself off to the Mengo Hospital in Kampala, Uganda, where she continued to offer her surgical expertise. She lived to a good age, eighty-eight. Her compassion and sense of responsibility were illustrated by her travelling to America to bring back a Czech lady who had once worked in her household and who was terminally ill. It was said in her family that an ancestor had attended the King, George III, in his illness, the malady depicted by Alan Bennett in *The Madness of King George*. With her stately appearance and dignified carriage and formal apparel of an earlier age, her deep contralto voice and chuckle as she recounted humorous anecdotes, she would have been a match for any such illustrious forebear.

Alice Bloomfield was born in India where her father, a merchant, was murdered by terrorists, and she was brought home in infancy by her mother to Britain. She did her medical training in Edinburgh. She was a brilliant student and seemed to have no problem breaking into the London scene.

She graduated with first class honours, a silver medal in chemistry, the Annandale gold medal for surgery, the Leckie Mactier postgraduate scholarship, and the William Gibson research fellowship. She took the MD in 1921 and the ChM in 1925, Edinburgh's higher degrees in medicine and surgery, and the FRCS in 1922. She was resident at Queen Charlotte's and at the Hospital for Women in Soho Square and became consultant surgeon in gynaecology at the South London Hospital for Women at the early age of twenty-eight where she worked, a deft and speedy surgeon, all her life and also at the Marie Curie Hospital. She presented case reports at the Royal Society of Medicine, of a cyst occupying the utero-vesical space, persistence she felt of a urachal cyst, and a case of a patent Wolffian duct, clearly demonstrating both her anatomical knowledge and operative expertise. In another paper, a consideration of the after-results of the abdominal operation for correction of retroversion of the uterus, with notes of fifty cases, she demonstrated the breadth of her surgical experience. In yet another paper she recounted two cases of excessive uterine hypertrophy following on prolonged oestrogen administration, illustrating her rejection of ill-considered therapy and her commitment to conventional responsible treatment only.

She was a founder member of the College of Obstetricians and Gynaecologists, was on the Council, becoming Chair of the Examining Board, and an FRCOG when it became a Royal College.

When she reached retirement age, she studied law and was called to the Bar at age seventy at Gray's Inn and practised as a criminal barrister in the SW Circuit. She was an expert alongside Josephine Barnes in a highly publicized case involving intersex, annulment and non-consummation, marriage and divorce.

Her interests were wide, including golf, bird-watching, cross-country walking, playing bridge, and travelling with the select Women's Gynaecological Visiting Club of twenty-two members, and learning and speaking languages, a polymath.

Sybil Mocatta was one of the small cohort of women who studied at St Mary's during the war years when the medical school was short of men medical students due to conscription. She qualified with distinction in midwifery in 1922 and was awarded the university medal in diseases of women when she took the MD and also passed the FRCS the following year, 1923. She worked at Queen Charlotte's, the Elizabeth Garrett Anderson and the Marie Curie Hospitals and in private practice, pursuing a career in obstetrics and gynaecology, adding the MRCOG comparatively late in her working life in 1945 when she was forty-seven. Married to A S Diamond, she lived to a grand old age, dying aged ninety.

The Great War Students – FRCS 1919 to 1930
Women of the Fellowship who came from abroad

Four of the twenty-four early women surgical Fellows came from abroad and returned there to live and work.

Gladys Marchant was an English woman domiciled in India who did her medical training in Calcutta and came to England for further training. She was born in Calcutta and at the age of seventeen embarked on a two year teacher training course at the Isabella Thorburn College. She then joined the Calcutta Medical College and graduated in 1916 with top marks in pathology and ophthalmology. She did house posts at the Lady Hardinge Hospital in Delhi and was lecturer in anatomy and surgeon to the outpatient department. She came to London and took the Edinburgh fellowship and on her return to India was made superintendent at the Dufferin Hospital, Meerut and resident surgeon at the Bangalore Maternity Hospital over the next five years. She came again to England and achieved the FRCS in 1928. She also took the Eye Diploma of the College, the DOMS, and presented her thesis for the MD in Lausanne in French, and spent some time in clinics in Vienna. Returning to India, she was Professor of Anatomy in the Lady Hardinge College in Delhi and then medical superintendent at the J A Hospital at Gwalior where she became renowned as a skilful operative surgeon which led to her appointment as the first full-time Professor of Obstetrics and Gynaecology at Queen Mary's Hospital, Lucknow which she occupied for the next fifteen years with great distinction. She returned to England from time to time to obtain first the MRCOG in 1937 and then the FRCOG in 1943 and visited the United States. When she was age sixty-three, her life-long friend Begum Farooqui died and she came back to England and adopted the son of her old friend and returned to India to live with him and his family. She was seventy-eight when she died.

Satapriya Ghosh also underwent her initial medical training in Calcutta and came to England to train further during World War I and took first the conjoint diploma, then the FRCS, in 1921, and returned to India to work. *Annie Pichhaimuthie* similarly came for further training, got the FRCS, 1930, and returned to Madura in South India.

Marian Bostock came from a pioneering family who had settled in Canada; she came to London at the beginning of World War I to enter medical school and train, and left, with the FRCS, to work amongst the women in a Zenana mission in India before returning home to Canada.

She came from a remarkable enterprising family. Her paternal grandfather had made a fortune in the mid-Victorian boom and lived in The Hermitage in Walton-on-the-Hill near Epsom in Surrey. Her father, Hewitt Bostock, after a mathematics degree at Cambridge, embarked as a young man on an intrepid world tour, a Wanderjahr, with his sister (another Marian) but it was not the conventional tour of the European capitals. They travelled across Canada, where Hewitt, age twenty-four, bought a ranch which was later to become the childhood home of his children, including our Marian Bostock, the surgeon. Her father and aunt, as young people on their extended 'gap-year', went on travelling from North America to visit the Antipodes, China and Japan. Returning to England and being called to the Bar, Hewitt married and took his bride on a visit to stay at the Canadian ranch on honeymoon. Marian, their first- born child, was born in England, the eldest of four daughters and three sons, and the family went to settle in British Columbia when Marian was a small child; they lived in Vancouver and on the ranch at Monte Creek on the South Thompson River, east of Kamloops in British Columbia. Marian's mother was a quiet free-thinking individual who was well-read and committed to the education of women. Marian's father, Hewitt, served in both houses of the Canadian government and was a delegate to the League of Nations, owned a newspaper, and had mining, railway, lumber and property interests. The seven children brought up on the ranch had a vigorous free outdoor life, experiencing round-ups, branding, ploughing, sowing, haying, harvesting, and gardening, watching the blacksmith and carpenter at work. Of her six brothers and sister, Alex, the next in line to Marian, volunteered and lost his life in World War I, two brothers became engineers, two sisters, Nan and Jean, ran the ranch after the parents were no longer able to. Hugh, the next brother, became the geological engineer who surveyed and mapped the Yukon in twenty seasons, travelling from May to September each year on foot, by dog-sled, pack-horse, canoe and river-boat, across wilderness territory habited by bears and wolves, returning each winter on the Canadian Pacific Railway to Ottawa, to write his reports, and when hearing by moccasin telegraph at a trading-post that his wife was taken ill, relying on his surgeon sister Marian to look to her recovery in a Vancouver Hospital. He was not only concerned with a survey of the mining and oil prospectors, but also collected botanical specimens, and a mammoth tusk 16 500 years old. His ranch childhood had clearly well prepared him for this life and the contribution he made is described in his best-selling books *Pack-Horse Tracks* and *Bostock's Memoirs*.

So it was not surprising that his sister Marian, too, after her hardy childhood was intent on making her mark in life. She travelled back to England, the country of her birth, just before the outbreak of World War I, studied to be a doctor at the London School of Medicine, at the Royal Free and at St George's Hospitals and qualified with the conjoint diploma in 1917, being awarded the MD Canada the same year and she became a Fellow of the Royal College of Surgeons in 1921.

After surgical experience, Marian Bostock went to work in India in the Zenana Bible and Medical Mission Hospital in Patna, one of a large cohort of women doctors who went to India and other parts of the British Empire, particularly motivated to help other women. After four years in India, Marian was back in Ottawa giving a talk with slides in the presence of Viscountess Willingdon the wife of the Governor-General, who herself, when her husband moved later to become Viceroy of India, was to show a real concern for the health and medical care of women in India.

Marian became Marian Noel Bostock Sherman after her marriage and had a daughter Ruth (later Mrs Ruth Lindsay). Canada, at that time, was of course very much part of the British Empire, soon to be the British Commonwealth of Nations, and Marian Bostock made the point that the people of India had taken part in supporting Great Britain in the Great War, and that she, in going to succour the women of India, was in some way re-paying that debt.

The Great War Students – FRCS 1919 to 1930
Women of the Fellowship into ENT practice

Two of the group of early women surgical Fellows eventually specialised toward an ENT practice. Mildred Warde trained first as a general surgeon and had a successful career and later concentrated on ENT. Dorothy Hall chose ENT as her speciality.

Mildred Warde came from a medical family, her father was a doctor and an MD. After school at Hamilton House in Tunbridge Wells, she studied at Manchester University for three years, and then completed her medical training at the London (Royal Free Hospital) School of Medicine for Women, graduating with the London University MB BS in 1921 and the FRCS the year after, 1922.

Mildred Warde was surgical registrar at the Royal Free Hospital. She wrote a fascinating paper on an account of a patient she had treated, a woman with haemophilia (or related inherited blood dyscrasia), a condition rare in itself in a female, a patient in a family with a disastrous record of morbidity and deaths from bleeding, whom she took through mastectomy for carcinoma of the breast, and described her management with pre-operative oral 30 grains of calcium lactate every other night, and artificial anaphylaxis induced by a subcutaneous dose of 5 cc of horse serum, followed thirteen days later by ½ c.cm. She noted some urticaria around the injection site and headache and malaise. At the end of the operation, she swabbed the wound with horse serum before closing, and although there was drainage from the tube for several weeks, healing and recovery was uneventful and complete, though slow.

She took the MS in 1929 and became the first woman to be awarded a gold medal in the MS, the higher degree in surgery. She never was aware of any prejudice against her as a woman in surgery.

She went on to have an ENT practice in Harley Street and presented cases at the ENT Section of the Royal Society of Medicine, a tuberculous ulcer of the septum of the nose with infection of the antra showing the histology of the polyp she had removed, with caseation, giant cells, epithelioid cells, and defended her case in discussion giving tuberculosis as a diagnosis. A further case was presented of abductor cord weakness and Sir James Dundas-Grant made an interesting contribution in the discussion of the possible diagnosis.

After working ten years in surgery, she met and married Mr O T Faulkner and gave up her surgery to mother his two sons, Denis and Alan, and went on to have two more sons of her own, Henry and Tony. He was in the Colonial Agricultural Service and it was not practical to both accompany him on tour and practice surgery. She took up painting as many surgeons did and joined and became chairman of the Norfolk and Norwich Art Circle. She was a member of the council of the Medical Defence Union. She was a 'Samaritan', manning the phone-lines of distressed people who phoned for support.

Dorothy Hall was a Liverpool graduate who came to London to do a postgraduate course at St Mary's in the 1920s and became a registrar and first assistant at the Central London Nose and Throat Hospital which started her on her specialist career.

She was the only child of a professor of music. She went to Aigburth Vale High School in Liverpool and on to Liverpool University where she was Holt Fellow in Physiology and qualified with MB BCh Liverpool in 1919. She took the FRCS Edinburgh in 1925 and the FRCS England in 1928.

She was appointed ENT surgeon to the Mildmay Mission Hospital, Shoreditch, and the Western Hospital, Fulham. She also worked at the Elizabeth Garrett Anderson Hospital, and gave her specialist ENT services to the Eastern Hospital, Homerton, St Ann's Hospital Tottenham, and the Clare Hall Hospital, South Mimms and in her private ENT practice in Queen Anne Street and in Harley Street.

The Great War Students – FRCS 1919 to 1930
Women of the Fellowship into Orthopaedic Surgery

One of the early women surgical Fellows studied and taught anatomy and became an orthopaedic consultant surgeon.

Erna Henrietta Jebens was driving her own car in France as the hostilities broke out and having encountered early war casualties she volunteered as an ambulance driver. As a twenty-four-year-old, she spent the early part of World War I driving an ambulance in France and it was ferrying the wounded from the front to the base hospitals that motivated her to a medical, then a surgical – and orthopaedic – future. She had been educated privately in Paris and London and had her own car from an early age and loved to drive. She drove the ambulance for two years, one of many intrepid women, some working under the Red Cross, some with maverick units, collecting wounded soldiers and transporting them from First Aid posts and field surgical units to base hospital, and was thus inspired to enter medicine.

Along with Ida Mann, Esther Rickards and Sybil Mocatta, she was one of the London School of Medicine students who was picked to be seconded to St Mary's and who were selected for their intelligence and maturity and sense of decorum so as not to upset any misogynist staff or ruffle the feathers in St Mary's. She qualified in 1922 and after house surgeon posts at St Mary's, she became a lecturer anatomy at the Royal Free, work which she continued alongside her surgery right until she reached retirement age at sixty-four. She took the FRCS in 1926 and became a clinical assistant in surgery at the Battersea General Hospital, and eventually a consultant founding the orthopaedic department there and establishing a private practice from 56 Wimpole Street. She published original anatomical research with Mrs Monk Jones MSc on the pH and viscosity of synovial fluid. There is a further account of her work and the hospital in Chapter 10 on women Fellows in orthopaedic surgery.

During World War II she also manned the East Ham General Hospital for the EMS, the Emergency Medical Service, and the Royal Free Hospital.

The Great War Students – FRCS 1919 to 1930
Women of the Fellowship in Eye Surgery

Two of the early group of women surgical Fellows chose to become eye surgeons. Ida Mann and Philippa Martin carefully chose rather than picked an easier pathway than the hurly burly of general surgery. Ida Mann, as she approached the end of her student years gave a lot of thought about her future. She did not want to be a general surgeon in spite of the enjoyment she had had as a first year student assisting in hernias and digging out shrapnel from the POWs. Medicine she thought seemed rather pointless. Neurology intrigued her. Skins fascinated her. Eyes were clean and obvious in view of the anatomical dissections she had made on the embryo eyes in the St Mary's anatomy department.

Ida Caroline Mann made legendary contributions to eye surgery which is enlarged on and expanded in the chapter of those FRCS women who chose eye surgery as their speciality, but some of her achievements as first in the field will be recounted here.

She was a schoolgirl at a small independent school, Wycombe House, and left at age sixteen for Clarke's Business College and a post-office clerk's job. Chance intervened. She donated sixpence from her meagre earnings to the London Hospital, Whitechapel and was invited on a group guided tour of the hospital where she was bowled over by the equipment, the laboratories and the x-ray machines. Directed to the London School of Medicine for Women, she enrolled, assuring them that she would matriculate before the start of term and by dint of evening classes and tutorials, achieved it. She trained at the London School of Medicine for Women and was one of those girls hand-picked to pursue clinical studies at St Mary's during World War I, chosen by their intelligence and sensible decorum not to ruffle the sensibilities of the all-male medical establishments that had temporarily let them in.

Ida Mann was a prize-winner and used the access to St Mary's to entrench herself in the anatomy department, embarking on research of outstanding work on the development of the human eye which was to be her field of abiding interest. She qualified MB BS in 1920, took the DOMS in 1922 and became the consultant eye surgeon to the Elizabeth Garrett Anderson Hospital in 1922. She spent some necessary time with two general surgeons and managed the FRCS in 1924, describing in her viva the use of the slit-lamp to her examiner, Sir Arthur Keith, of which he knew nothing. She had travelled to Germany to do a course with Professor Vogt to learn about this innovation, the brainchild of a Swedish physicist, Gullstrand. She was appointed to the Central London Ophthalmic Hospital and the Royal Free Hospital and finally to Moorfields where the chairman of the selection board announced her successful appointment with the words, 'I did my best to keep you out but as you have won, I will say no more.' She worked at Moorfields from 1925 to 1949 and in private practice in Wimpole Street. The hospital appointments were of course honorary (unpaid). She wrote her DSc thesis on *The Development of the Human Eye* and *Development Abnormalities of the Eye* in 1931 and a book *The Science of Seeing* in 1946 and of course numerous research papers and many presentations to the Anatomy Society.

During World War II she was instrumental in keeping Moorfields open. Without her stalwart intervention, her fierce and determined efforts to keep the hospital as an institution going, Moorfields might have been closed as a non-general hospital unsuitable to fit in with the funding of the EMS, Emergency General Service Hospitals, required for the war effort to receive casualties in the Blitz. She was also instrumental in extracting Josef Dallos from Hungary as it was about to be invaded by Nazi Germany and enabling him to join Hamblins on corneal lens work.

At the start of World War II, she signed that she would go anywhere, do anything, as directed and needed, and was sent to Oxford (as was Diana Beck who became a neurosurgeon, and Josephine Barnes intent on obstetrics and gynaecology) to rejuvenate the Eye Department and set up a research laboratory with Nuffield money. She also worked at Mill Hill on BAL (British anti-Lewisite) and the eye. At Oxford, she was first made reader, then given a titular chair in January 1942, the first women ever to hold a professorship in any subject in Oxford University. (After her, Agnes

Headlam-Morley was a full professor in October 1948, the Montague Burton Professor in International Relations).

In 1944 Ida married the Oxford professor Dr William Ewart Gye, an FRS and an eminent research scientist, she at the age of fifty-three, he, a widower, due to retire in 1947 and they went to live in Perth in Australia for his health's sake. She was devastated when her husband died and took a few years to recover an aim in life, but went on to do seminal work on trachoma in the aborigine population traversing the outback, and then repeated the surveys in Papua New Guinea and in Taiwan and wrote two books under the name Caroline Gye, *The Cockney and the Crocodile* and *China 13*. She was honoured with the DBE. Ida Mann travelled extensively. There are further accounts of her life's work in the chapter on eye surgeons. Her full autobiography is in the Archives at St Mary's Hospital and extracted versions in the books *The Chase* and *Ida and the Eye*.

Philippa Martin, the other Eye surgeon amongst these early women surgical Fellows, was born Philippa Parry Pughe in Australia. Her father was Canon Thomas St John Pughe. She went to Toowoomba High School, Australia and then to St Felix School Southwold and after a year in Switzerland, she went up to Newnham College, Cambridge but left after only three weeks because she found life at Cambridge stifling, like being back at school. She went instead to University College London which she felt suited her better. In London, there was more freedom. Going on to University College Hospital she qualified with the conjoint diploma in 1921 and the MB BS with honours in surgery in 1922. She became house surgeon at UCH and married her consultant Edward Kenneth Martin at the age of twenty-six.

She then went on to make a tremendous success of her career, and her life, taking the FRCS in 1930, the MS in 1932 only the fifth woman to get this higher degree in surgery; she gave a Hunterian lecture at the College in 1936, the first woman ever to be a Hunterian Professor. Her oration was on 'The effect on the eye of radium used for the treatment of malignant disease in the neighbourhood'. She was ophthalmic registrar at UCH and became the consultant at the Elizabeth Garrett Anderson Hospital, the Maida Vale Hospital for Neurology and Neurosurgery, and the Western Eye Hospital. They had a happy marriage, three daughters –

two of them doctors, and one an architect, and they enjoyed travelling, driving all over Europe. Philippa Martin was still operating in her eighties. Her husband was ninety-six when he died and she eighty-three, dying within a year of each other.

An outside observer might have wondered whether a promising surgical career might have been about to be jeopardised by her early marriage when a house surgeon to her consultant; far from it. She made a great success of her surgical career, her marriage and as an inspiring mother to her daughters.

The liberal instincts of the 'godless institution of Gower Street', University College, London, prevailed similarly with *Gwen Hill* who qualified in 1924 (FRCS 1955), two years after Philippa Martin at UCH. She married Reginald Hilton the following year after graduating and none-the-less went on to specialise and founded the radiotherapy department at UCH, becoming its first director, and working all her life. Their daughter, also a doctor, followed in her mother's footsteps.

Summary of The Great War Students – FRCS 1919 to 1930

Of the twenty-four earliest women Fellows, twenty-three became consultant surgeons. Ten continued as consultant general surgeons, Eleanor Davies-Colley herself at the South London Hospital, Catherine Lewis at the Royal Free and developing a special interest in female urology, Muriel Elsie Landau at the Elizabeth Garrett Anderson Hospital, Marian Bostock in India in a Zenana Mission and back to Canada, Eleanor Partridge in general surgery and anatomy and having a second career in psychiatry, Mildred Warde (Faulkner) doing general surgery and developing a special interest in ENT, Geraldine Barry on the Staff at the Royal Free following Cecil Joll's footsteps, Alfreda Baker at the Elizabeth Garrett Anderson, Constance Ottley a consultant surgeon at the New Sussex Hospital for Women in Brighton, Gwen Smith a general surgeon at the South London, Gladys Sandes at Queen Mary's Carshalton and the Mothers' Hospital, Clapton. Seven went into Obstetrics and Gynaecology, two of them becoming Professors, Dame Hilda Lloyd in Birmingham and Gladys Marchant in India where she had originally trained, and five as consultants in obstetrics and gynaecology, Margaret Basden, Muriel Elsie

Landau, Alice Bloomfield, Sybil Mocatta and Gladys Sandes. One became an orthopaedic surgeon, Erna Henrietta Jebens. Two were Eye Surgeons, Dame Ida Mann and Philippa Martin. Two became ENT surgeons, Dorothy Hall and Mildred Warde. One went into public service and administration, Esther Rickards. One died untimely, Hetty Claremont. Two returned to their native India to practise there, Sataypriya Ghosh and Annie Pickhaimuthie. Nine were known to have married; six had children, Marian Bostock a daughter, Elsie Landau four sons, three of them doctors, Eleanor Partridge a daughter, Gladys Sandes a daughter, Mildred Warde (Faulkner) two sons and two stepsons, Philippa Martin three daughters, two of them doctors.

The Great War Students – FRCS 1919-1930

Eleanor Davies-Colley 1874-1934 MB BS 1907 MD 1910 FRCS 1911

Emily Catherine Lewis 1882-1965 MS FRCS 1919

Geraldine Mary Barry 1897-1978 FRCS 1926 MS 1929

Beatrice Gwendoline Smith FRCS 1929

Alfreda Helen Baker 1897-1984 MB ChB BAO 1921 Belfast FRCS 1927 MD 1926

Constance May Ottley 1898-1981 BM BCh Oxford 1922 FRCS 1928

Eleanor Joyce Partridge 1893-1956 FRCS 1921

Esther Rickards 1893-1977 FRCS 1924 MS 1923 OBE 1966

Hetty Ethelberta Claremont 1892-1924 FRCS 1920 MS 1922

Muriel Elsie Landau 1895-1972 FRCS 1920 MD 1921

Gladys Maud Sandes 1897-1968 FRCS 1930

Dame Hilda Lloyd (Dame Hilda Rose, née Hilda Nora Shufflebotham) 1891-1982 FRCS 1920 FRCOG 1936 PRCOG 1949 DBE 1951

Margaret Mary Basden 1886-1974 FRCS 1919 MD 1924 FRCOG 1931

Alice Bloomfield 1895-1977 FRCS 1922 MB ChB 1919 ChM 1925 FRCOG 1935

Sybil Grace Mocatta 1898-1988 FRCS 1923 MD 1923 with medal MRCOG 1945

Gladys Marchant 1894-1969 MB BS Calcutta 1916 MRCS & DOMS 1922 FRCS 1928 MD Lausanne 1927 MRCOG 1937 FRCOG 1943

Satapriya Ghosh d.<1986 FRCS 1921 MB Calcutta 1914 MRCP LRCS England 1917

Annie Pichhaimuthie FRCS 1930 MB 1924 Madura, South India
Marian Noel Bostock 1891-1975 FRCS 1921 MRCS 1917 MD Canada 1917
Mildred Warde (Mildred Faulkner) 1897-1982 FRCS 1922 MS with Gold Medal 1929
Dorothy Winifred Hall 1896-1958 MB BCh Liverpool 1919 FRCS (Ed) 1925 FRCS 1928
Erna Henrietta Jebens 1890-1964 FRCS 1926
Dame Ida Caroline Mann 1893-1983 FRCS 1924 DOMS 1922 DSc 1929 CBE 1950 DBE 1980
Philippa Parry Martin 1897-1981 FRCS 1930 MS 1932

CHAPTER 4

The Inter-War Years – FRCS 1931 to 1939

THIRTY new surgical Fellows were added during the nine inter-war years 1931 to 1939.

Nineteen-thirty-one was a bumper year with seven new Fellows but the increase was not sustained and in the following years, there were three, two, two, four, four, one, two and five in each of the next eight years. These women had been born in the Edwardian years, the first years of the new century. They were schoolchildren during World War I and were young adults entering medical school after the war was over.

Society had changed since the Great War. The work that women had been seen to do during the war years, in factories and munitions, in the Land Army, driving ambulances and nursing as VADs had created a new respect and warmth and tolerance in the whole of society for the contribution that women could make in the field of work. Women themselves had a new confidence in their ability to hold down an important job. They could choose not to marry and still feel that they were not a drain on their families, nor be expected to stay at home and look after elderly parents. They could work and support themselves. They could live independently.

This group qualified as doctors between 1922 and 1936. Full franchise nationally came in 1928. The Royal College of Surgeons in 1926 had lifted the restrictions originally imposed on their women Fellows and given them the same rights as the men to vote on to Council. They attained the FRCS between 1931 and 1939.

It was notable also that some of the consultant appointments were starting to be made to posts outside the small tight circle of the women's hospitals. However, as they obtained the FRCS and began to look to practice as surgeons, the whole structure of the medical world and indeed of society was once again to be disrupted by World War II and in some cases occupied the whole span of their working life.

Of those thirty new Fellows, only six practised as consultants in general surgery in this country, Margaret Louden in the South London Hospital for Women, Enid Rockstro at the New Sussex Hospital, Muriel

Long at Llandudno, Doris O'Doherty in Carshalton, Gertrude Toland at Dover, Beatrice Willmott Dobbie in Birmingham and the last two had a surgical practice that somewhat embraced gynaecology as well as general surgery. A further four practised general surgery abroad, Joyce Ludlow with a lifetime's missionary endeavour in Nigeria, Doris Brown holding the fort during World War II in the Lady Hardinge College in Delhi, Muriel Hulke in Simla/Lucknow in India, and Margaret Shepherd in Madras. The largest contingent, eleven in all, became specialists in obstetrics and gynaecology, foremost among them Dame Josephine Barnes, and also Margaret Salmond, Edith Hall, Flora Hargreaves, Margaret White, Jocelyn Moore, Ruby Sharpe, Gladys Hill, Gladys Dodds, Mary Mayeur, and Dorothy Sharpe. Two Fellows became ENT surgeons, Dorothy Collier and Winifred Wadge, one an eye surgeon, Jean Dollar, one an orthopaedic surgeon, Eugenie Willis, one went into public health, Hilda Linford, and one into private general practice with an obstetric speciality, Keren Parkes, one returned to South Africa, Ruby Sharpe, and one to Australia, Muriel McIlrath, and one returned to her home country of India, Venketeswaraiya Sankarambal. One uniquely became a neurosurgeon, Diana Beck, and was appointed to a London teaching hospital.

The Inter-War Years – FRCS 1931 to 1939
Women of the Fellowship in General Surgery in England and Wales

Of the six who achieved consultant posts in general surgery in this country, two were appointed to the hospitals established by women for women and children, Margaret Louden to the South London Hospital where she was a power-house for good, and Enid Rockstro to the New Sussex Hospital in Brighton and Hove where she joined Constance Ottley and Elsie (Visick) Griffith.

Margaret Louden was very talented and a tall good-looking woman and was confident in her ability and ambition and as a young doctor was invited into Guy's to demonstrate on the FRCS course where Sir Heneage Ogilvie was her inspiring surgical teacher. She wrote leaders for *The Lancet* and felt well encouraged. She points out in a letter that of course at that time as there was no intake of women *students* into the big teaching hospitals, you could say discrimination abounded, but she did not experience it personally. On the contrary, she was given enormous help and support in her surgical career. She was educated at St Paul's School, London where she was captain of cricket and swimming and went on to the London (Royal Free Hospital) School of Medicine on an exhibition scholarship from the St Dunstan's Foundation, London University and from her school, St Paul's.

Qualifying in 1934 MB BS London Margaret Louden passed the FRCS in 1938 and became a consultant at the South London Hospital for Women and Children. She wrote that even in the women's hospitals, there was a certain amount of discrimination against *married* women but, married though she was, again she didn't feel it. She writes with humour that 'in any case, I'm afraid there has to be discrimination both "for" and "against".' 'This anti-discrimination business' she says, 'I regard as boloney – and counter-productive.' She goes on to say 'Experience is everything in medicine and every reduction of working hours reduces the chances of gaining it.' The relevance of her opinion finds resonance today.

During World War II she treated casualties of all sorts, soldiers, pilots and civilians, describing the Crush Syndrome and its treatment. If she had written her work up, she would have been recognised as having made this notable contribution. She was a highly respected operative surgeon and battled to keep the South London Hospital from closure.

Margaret Louden married Derek Martin, the museum curator of the Hospital for Children, Great Ormond Street and they had two daughters. She had two full-time resident helps when the children were small and variable other domestic help. She married a second time, Bernard Simpson, a consulting engineer.

In the fullness of time, the South London Hospital, like all the other women's hospitals, was to close. It had made an important contribution for fifty years providing a women-for-women's service to patients at a time when there were few women consultants but, although it was the largest of the women's hospitals, having two hundred and sixty-three beds, it was probably too small in the days of specialisation and increasing technology to be viable in the shadow of St James's Balham with its five hundred and fifty-five beds, which in turn was overshadowed when St George's Hospital came out from its Hyde Park site, two hundred and sixty-nine beds, to be re-built at Tooting, initially two hundred and ninety-eight but destined to increase, on the old Fountain Hospital site. At the end, when the South London Hospital was being closed in 1984, a posse of forty women police officers was sent in to evict a nine month sit-in and occupation. The hospital remained boarded up for years, unoccupied apart from the South London Hospital ghost, before demolition and replacement by a Tesco superstore.

Enid Rockstro was appointed consultant surgeon to the New Sussex Hospital for Women and Children, Brighton in 1937 and Cuckfield Hospital where she spent her working life. She wrote that it was very hard to get established at first but once she had achieved her consultant post, she had no difficulties.

Educated at Cheltenham Ladies' College Enid Rockstro went on to train at University College London, UCL, where she won the chemistry prize and to University College Hospital, UCH, graduating MB BS in 1927. She was house surgeon to Hamilton Bailey and to W B Gabriel at the Royal Northern Hospital and got her surgical experience there and at the South London Hospital, taking the FRCS in 1932. Her father was a GP, and her grandfather a well-known flautist and musician and her great uncle Sir William Rockstro, the musician. She herself remained single. Once established in her consultant post, she adopted two sons, the first when she was aged thirty-two and then the second when she was aged thirty-five and each when they were only a few weeks old. She had a live-in nanny when her children were babies and young children, and the boys went to prep and boarding school when they were older and she had daily help. The younger of her two sons, Richard Frank Rockstro, became a doctor and was a consultant forensic psychiatrist. Enid Rockstro lived to a good age, dying aged ninety-four in retirement at Milford-on-Sea.

Of the six who were appointed as consultants in general surgery in this country, four were to hospitals outwith the women-for-women hospitals, Llandudno, Carshalton, Dover and Birmingham.

(Muriel) Hilary Long was to have gone to the Lady Hardinge College in India as professor of surgery. Instead Hilary Long became for nineteen years the only woman surgeon in Wales.

Hilary Long was educated in Lewisham Prendergast Grammar School and King's College Hospital, taking the BSc in 1928 and graduating MB BS in 1931. She was house surgeon to Sir Cecil Wakeley and won a University of London travelling scholarship and visited Vienna, Budapest and Berlin. She took the FRCS in 1934 and became reader in surgery in Leeds in 1936 working there for three years where the professor of surgery clearly thought very highly of her – but not highly enough to overcome his prejudices! In his written testimonial (which bit of paper she treasured) Professor E R Flint stated that had she been a man she would have been appointed to the staff of Leeds Royal Infirmary but that was not possible because of her sex.

As it turned out she says herself that she was really helped by the 1939 war. She served in the RAMC as a major, the first woman major surgical specialist in the RAMC. Amongst other posts, she worked in the Royal Hospital, Bolton. During the war, aged thirty-six she married a lieutenant-colonel in the RAMC, Dr Thomas Knowles Boney, who had been a consultant physician in Wales and they had a son Guy born 1944. After the war, both husband and wife became consultants in Llandudno in North Wales, he as a physician, she as a consultant general surgeon. They spent their working lives there for twenty years as physician and surgeon. Hilary did the full range of general surgery including prostatectomies and all emergency work and trauma and serving as a capable chairman of the medical staff committee thus giving a great deal to the hospital and area. She wrote: 'As a woman with a house to run and family, one needs dedication – unusual ability and a cast-iron constitution. One hasn't only to cope with the routine work – but with emergencies. The provision of registrars in the more out-lying areas is a dicky affair and it isn't funny when you are sixty and have creamed your face and pinned up your hair to have to turn out and have to face a more than dire emergency with the worst (she means a thinner night-time staffing) theatre staff and porters etc. This is why I gave up at age sixty-one. It is difficult to be able to compete with male colleagues and still maintain a happy family home. I managed it, with luck - I suppose Dame Josephine Barnes – for whom I have a very deep regard – did it better – but it isn't easy. I think surgery or marriage – the combination is difficult.'

Those were her words – but colleagues spoke in shining terms of her capability and all that she contributed to the hospital and the area.

In retirement they spent some years in Malta and were the soul of hospitality to those who visited. They returned home and retired again to Guernsey where she died at age seventy-eight.

Doris O'Doherty was appointed surgeon to the Carshalton, Beddington and Wallington War Memorial Hospital where she worked all her life. She was at school at the Mary Thatcher Girls' School, Camberwell, from where she won a St Dunstan's Science Exhibition to the London (Royal Free Hospital) School of Medicine where she won a prize in surgery. She was house surgeon to Clement E Shattock and Lionel Norbury and house physician at the Queen Elizabeth Hospital for Children in Hackney and further resident posts where she got good experience. She took the FRCS in 1935. She married C J Chapman in 1945 when she was forty-three.

Gertrude Beatrice Mary Toland (née Morgan) was consultant surgeon in Dover. With the evacuation of the Expeditionary Force from Dunkirk in May 1940, she worked tirelessly for nine days, spending long hours in the operating theatre, operating on the severely-injured troops that landed in Dover, and throughout the war she carried a heavy operative load as the channel ports were bombed.

She was educated at Edinburgh Ladies' College and went up to Newnham College, Cambridge, completing her clinical studies at St Mary's when they were still accepting a few women in training, though shortly they were to close their doors again. She took the conjoint board exam in 1925, the MB BChir Cambridge in 1927, the MD in 1930 and the FRCS in 1931. She worked on the surgical unit at St Mary's, and held posts at Queen Charlotte's.

Gertrude Toland was appointed honorary consultant at the Royal Victoria and Buckland Hospital Dover at first in surgery, and then covering also as consultant gynaecologist and obstetrician in the south-east Kent hospital group.

She had married Dr Charles Patrick Kirk Toland, a GP and anaesthetist, and they worked together and had a son, Gordon. With the outbreak of War, however, she was working on her own in Dover, her husband having being called away as a major in the RAMC serving as a specialist anaesthetist. Her contribution in the war years was exceptional.

Mrs Toland lived to a good age and died age eighty-three on the forty-fifth anniversary of the small boat evacuation 21 May 1985.

Beatrice Willmott Dobbie was to follow in the foot-steps of the illustrious Dame Hilda Lloyd who was ten years her senior.

Beatrice Marion Willmott was a Birmingham schoolgirl and her surgical working-life throughout was centred in the Midlands. Her father was a company secretary. From Devon Lodge, Sutton Coldfield, she went on to King Edward VI High School for Girls like Dame Hilda Lloyd before her, and then went up to Girton College Cambridge on a Carlyle scholarship. She returned to Birmingham to study for the clinical years and graduated MB BCh Cambridge in 1929.

She was only the second woman to be allowed a house surgeon's post at the Birmingham General Hospital. She took the FRCS in 1931 and added a diploma in radiology and electrology with the aim of effectively using radiotherapy after surgery for cancer. Taking the diploma course in that same year was Dr Joseph Dobbie whose name she was later to add to her own.

Beatrice Willmott was appointed consultant in 1934 at the age of thirty-one to the Birmingham & Midland Hospital for Women founded by Lawson Tait. She developed a special interest in the use of radium for cancer of the cervix. She had a private practice in the Harborne Road, along from Dame Hilda Lloyd. She was small in stature, hair short in an Eton crop, and had a boyish enthusiasm, with twinkling eyes and was a determined conversationalist. Known as Betty at school and to her friends, she had a strong sense of fun. Once on a cold snowy night at a function requiring full evening dress she lifted the hem of her long gown to reveal to everyone's amusement sensible and incongruous fur boots. She was a quick and dexterous surgeon, which was just as well as the vascular surgical list preceded hers and they frequently over-ran their time into her list which she took in good part professing to admire their intrepid surgical skills.

She wrote in 1948 a text-book intended for general practitioners and junior doctors, particularly aimed at the obstetric registrar taking part in the emerging flying squads and conducting domiciliary midwifery, *Obstetrics & Gynaecology: a Synoptic Guide to treatment*. Josephine Barnes, reviewing the book, wrote in the *British Medical Journal* that 'Miss Dobbie shows her wide experience in this book…it will prove a valuable addition to current medical literature'. Another reviewer wrote 'this is a very readable and highly commendable book and an invaluable vade-mecum to anyone taking up obstetrics and gynaecology'.

She married Dr Joseph Leslie Dobbie in 1940 when she was thirty-seven. He was a consultant radiotherapist and Deputy Director of the

Holt Radium Institute in Manchester. Working apart in two different cities, they were together at week-ends. Beatrice Dobbie was a swift surgeon and Pamela Ball, the plastic surgeon, recounts as a junior doctor giving a series of anaesthetics for Mrs Willmott Dobbie's radium list of patients with cancer of the cervix and remembers the necessity for speed.

In retirement she carried out historical research and wrote a book *An English Rural Community: Batheaston with St Catherine*, an in-depth study of the area in north Wiltshire from early times, and also a small piece of written work on a group of early suffragettes in that area, and she also researched and wrote a learned study of maternal mortality in the sixteenth to the eighteenth centuries that makes fascinating reading today, *An Attempt to Estimate the True Rate of Maternal Mortality, Sixteenth to Eighteenth centuries*.

The author wrote in the introduction to that piece of research: 'Exact truth is unattainable; most of the data are flawed; nothing better than an informed estimate can be hazarded, using such solid facts as can be gathered, and not scorning crumbs of evidence.' A piece of reassuring advice as this study is pursued. She also co-wrote and edited the History of the King Edward VI High School for Girls. The foundation of the boys' school of course dates back five hundred years to its founder King Edward VI, the young son of King Henry VIII. The sister school was started alongside the boys' school in 1883.

When, in retirement, she came to take a course on the Open University, newly founded by Harold Wilson as Prime Minister and Jenny Lee MP, she was amused to find one of her own books on the syllabus reading list. She lived to a good age, ninety-two, a useful and fulfilled life.

The Inter-War Years – FRCS 1931 to 1939
Women of the Fellowship in General Surgery abroad

Four women surgeons worked in general surgery abroad.

For *Joyce Woods (Joyce Ludlow)*, her vocation was to be a medical missionary, an aim in life which she magnificently fulfilled. The missionary society's communication to its workers ominously read: 'When a missionary in active work dies, funeral expenses up to twelve pounds will be paid and should be claimed by next-of-kin; a great deal of trouble is caused if a missionary on the field dies intestate and the enclosed form will facilitate the making of a will.' Yellow fever in particular decimated the missionary endeavour.

Joyce came from a large and warm family, staunchly Methodist. Her younger brother, like her a doctor, had been sent to a hospital in Yunan in South-west China. Her elder sister was in Madras, south India, where the Methodist minister husband was in charge of the English church and she worked at training girls in needlework in the Ikkadu Centre for Indian Women. Joyce trained at the London (Royal Free Hospital) School of Medicine and qualified with the conjoint diploma and the London MB BS in 1929 and took the FRCS two years later in 1931.

She was interviewed by the Methodist Missionary Society, the MMS, who accepted her for Ilesha, the Wesley Guild Hospital in Nigeria. She was to join Dr Edward Hunter who had re-opened the mission hospital and after the usual eighteen months work (a short period because of the harsh health conditions of work in West Africa) was due for his six months furlough. Joyce was needed to cover the much needed furlough, but Joyce was intent on not going out there until she had the accolade of the Fellowship of the Royal College of Surgeons. Accordingly at the Royal Free Hospital ball she sought a colleague who would stand in for her until she had the Fellowship and found a friend in Dr Helena Gambrell who offered to go to in her place. Helena met out there a young agricultural officer Jim Pudney and returned to Nigeria as Dr Pudney, such are the chance happenings of life.

The journey to Nigeria took two to three weeks on an Elder Dempster line cargo and passenger ship. Life on board as ever was dominated by meals, early tea brought to the cabin, cooked breakfast, fish or cold luncheon, elevenses of beef tea and trays of afternoon tea brought out to the deck-chairs or served in the saloon bar, dinner in formal dress. A small canvas swimming pool with sea-water was set up once the weather grew hot and deck quoits played. Liverpool, Madeira, Las Palmas, the Gambia, Freetown in Sierra Leone, off shore for Accra in the Gold Coast, Monrovia for Liberia, Lagos in Nigeria, train and truck 180 miles north to Ilesha.

When Joyce Woods arrived at Ilesha Hospital, the hospital staff, in addition to Dr Hunter, was Stella Liony who was of mixed African and English parentage and had worked there as matron for twenty-three years, five African girls who were nurses in training, Jacob the interpreter at clinical interview, Solomon the untrained dispenser, and Michael the untrained night nurse and guardian of the girl nurses. Joyce's pay was three pounds a week.

The dry season was November to February, with harvesting and farm work over by Christmas and a dry wind, Harmattan, bringing fine sand from the Sahara desert covering the houses and contents with a white dust. Then the season of tropical storms followed which threw rain down usually in the early evening, but with a respite during the day, but which filled the rain-water tanks. The hospital was on the outskirts of Ilesha and had electricity but in her thatched mud hut she had Tilley lamps only and was looked after by a steward and a cook. Joyce found that many of the patients who were eventually carried to the hospital in hammocks after long treks through the bush and forest came too late and damaged by treatment by the local medicine men or witch doctors. Once they had adequate staff in the hospital, she embarked on treks accompanied by an African nurse and an interpreter to set up dispensaries in the villages with the aim of encouraging the people to trust the hospital. Increasingly she matched her medical visits with those of the Reverend Nelson Ludlow as he visited outlying schools and churches. He was the Methodist missionary in charge of the large Ilesha circuit, four ministers, one-hundred-strong staff of catechists and teachers, manager of many schools and forty-five churches.

Joyce Woods and Nelson Ludlow made a formidable team, partners in pioneering. After marriage on their first furlough home, they embarked on a joint enterprise making regular visits to villages with car and trailer converted to a dispensary and operating theatre, setting up dispensary, managing the schools and church. When necessary, she roped her husband in as anaesthetist. They liaised with local government officers and with local chiefs and emirs, with district officers and assistant district officers and magistrates. West Africa is the home of many hundreds of tribes, each with its own language. Together they were concerned with literacy using the Dr Frank Laubach method and were involved in schooling for girls as well as supporting the boys' schools. In time they were able to place nurses or midwives in the village dispensaries, supported by regular visits. Infant mortality had been appalling high, as illustrated by Joyce asking one mother who came for treatment how many children she already had.

Eleven was the reply. Joyce commented that surely she ought to be satisfied with that. The reply came back, 'I have only one alive.' Measles vaccination was inaugurated for the under-fives in conjunction with the World Health Organisation. Smallpox outbreaks necessitated a vaccination programme. Leprosy patients lived in an isolation village. Their joint work was carried out over more than twenty years. They achieved a furlough home just before World War II and had a hair-raising sea journey back to Africa dodging torpedoes but later, needing a holiday in Nigeria they twice had a wonderful respite on the northern Nigeria central plateau, high enough above sea-level, 3000 feet, to have a temperate climate, and where the young schoolgirl, Delia Cothay, later to become an FRCS, holidayed with her parents who were engaged in the tin-mining industry. A subsequent furlough was spent in South Africa. In order to maintain continued good health, it was important to have breaks. The inoculation at the London Hospital for Tropical Diseases prevented them from contracting the yellow fever that had carried off series of missionaries and their wives in former times, but they both suffered typhoid fever in their time in Africa, and this of course in the pre-antibiotic era.

In order to continue her surgical vocation in tandem with her missionary husband's commitment to Africa, Joyce had to leave her children at home in England for their education, a heart-rending decision, but she felt a right one. Her three children were born in 1939, 1943 and 1949, two sons and a daughter. It was the end of World War II before the days of speedy air travel that first Peter, age seven, was left, then Anthony for a time at the age of two-and-a -half and again later. Her daughter Elizabeth was born six years after Anthony. She took great pains to seek the right schools and families to give stability and security to her children.

In 1949 at the end of one furlough, Joyce was invited by the interdenominational Nigerian Christian Council to be the Medical Secretary and to survey the whole country with Dr C (Sir Clement) Chesterman, travelling long train journeys to document the hospitals and dispensaries set up originally by missionary endeavour. The Queen awarded Joyce the MBE in 1952 for medical services to Nigeria.

Joyce Ludlow lived to a great age dying in England age one hundred. At her memorial service in Bournemouth, a bishop of the Methodist Church in Nigeria travelled especially to be present. Resplendent in brilliantly colourful robes against his black skin, he spoke eloquently of the long-lasting influence the Ludlows had had on the education and life of the area. The bishop's father had been the young house-boy in the mission compound and had progressed to be surgical dresser to Mrs Dr Ludlow and then pharmacy assistant accompanying her on her visits to hold clinics in outlying villages from the hospital at Ilesha. The house-boy's son had thus been enabled to have an education and had made the journey to England to honour his own father as well as to give thanks for the life of Dr Joyce Ludlow. The MBE was well merited for services to medicine in the Commonwealth.

Doris Barbara Brown had a remarkable war in India, marooned when other staff were compulsorily evacuated, re-registered therefore necessarily as a man and given jungle equipment and training in warfare, running the hospital without skilled assistance, and then operating on the wounded soldier that she subsequently married.

Doris Brown went to school in Harrogate, the clever daughter of a draper, and went on to Leeds University where she took 1st class honours in the BSc and qualified with the conjoint diploma and graduated MB ChB in 1932. She did house surgeon posts at Leeds General Infirmary and the Women's Hospital, Leeds and was tutor in obstetrics at the Queens University, Belfast. She took the FRCS in 1935. Her sister also became a doctor, a gynaecologist.

In 1939 Doris Brown was the medical officer at the Lady Hardinge Medical College in New Delhi. This was on the route of the expected Japanese invasion of India and all female staff were evacuated. As the sole medical officer she was asked to stay, and was re-classified as a man, and given jungle equipment and training. She ran the hospital solo without skilled medical assistance. A British officer brought in a posse of exhausted soldiers who had escaped from a prisoner-of-war camp and she treated them, operating on the officer – who later became her husband. They married later on in the war in Calcutta in 1944 and had a daughter Elizabeth.

Her husband Reginald Wallace joined the Colonial Office after the war and served as secretary to the governor in the Gold Coast (Ghana gained independence in 1956). She suffered ill-health in her mid-forties, a stroke, from which she made a slow recovery and was not able to work again. She died in her sixties.

Muriel Hulke was one of the dedicated women who went out to serve in India. She became Superintendent at the Lady Reading College in Simla and later at the Dufferin Hospital, Lucknow. Her father was an FRCS, a surgeon and a GP, and a great-uncle had been President of the Royal College of Surgeons.

Muriel was educated at the Welsh Girls School in Ashford, Middlesex, then at University College London taking the BSc in 1925 and at University College Hospital, qualifying with the conjoint board LRCP MRCS in 1928. She did house appointments in the Elizabeth Garrett Anderson Hospital and the Royal Northern where she worked for McNeil Love. She took the FRCS in 1933. She married in 1935, Lawrence Brander, university lecturer, writer and publisher and they had a son, William Lawrence Brander, who qualified at Guy's and became a Consultant Histopathologist. He worked for a time in New Zealand , later returning to work in Maidstone. Like many surgeons, Muriel Hulke enjoyed painting as a hobby.

Margaret Shepherd went to India and worked as consultant surgeon at the King George Hospital, Vizagapatan in Madras. She was a Manchester graduate, she was educated at Owen's College, Manchester and graduated MB ChB in 1930 and stayed on as a lecturer in anatomy and was then resident surgical officer at the Christie Hospital and the Holt Radium Institute taking the FRCS in 1938. She married James Forrest Shepherd in 1937 at age thirty He worked in the India Medical Service and she went with him to India working in several stations and as consultant surgeon at the King George Hospital, Vizagapatan, Madras.

During World War II, Margaret Shepherd worked as a surgical specialist in the RAMC. After the war, she continued an interest in orthopaedic surgery and, on behalf of the British Orthopaedic Association, she investigated the results of hip surgery and established a procedure for hip assessment. Her husband became consultant surgeon to the Sutton Coldfield Hospital. When they moved to Farnham, Surrey, Margaret continued her studies at the Royal National Orthopaedic Hospital and for the Institute of Orthopaedic, looking at the results of different hip operations. After her husband's death, Margaret Shepherd joined the Geriatric Department of the Norman Day Hospital in Farnham, Surrey and went on working as a clinical assistant until she was over seventy years of age, much valued for her commonsense approach and her sense of humour.

The Inter-War Years FRCS – 1931 to 1939
Women of the Fellowship in Gynaecology

Eleven of the inter-war year Fellows turned to Gynaecology and Obstetrics with their FRCS, foremost among them, Dame Josephine Barnes. She was a major figure in many fields, highly respected, and an important role model to many.

Josephine Barnes had her early education scattered through many schools as her minister father who, by the tradition of the Methodist Conference, was peripatetic, moved the family to a new church and to live in a new manse in a new town every few years. The Reverend Walter W Barnes had a committed nonconformist family history that stretched back to John Wesley himself. Josephine Barnes, Jo or Josie, as the medical world came to know her, was the first-born child of five and all the family names were bestowed on her. Her mother was Alice Mary and the name of Taylor amongst her given names harked back to her mother's grandfather, John Francis Taylor, a prominent Victorian Yorkshireman who founded a bank and an insurance company in York and was the pioneering chairman of the city's gas and electricity companies. Her mother was a talented musician and one of the first women to gain the fellowship of the Royal College of Organists.

After schools in Exeter and Scarborough, Josephine fortuitously found herself in Oxford High School and decided there and then to go on to the science side and to become a doctor. She went up to Lady Margaret Hall, Oxford to read for a degree in natural sciences and in the anatomy dissecting rooms, a right-of- passage for many a medical student, she came under the influence of Alice Carleton, one of the demonstrators, who fired her with a desire to take the primary FRCS. She took first class honours in physiology in her BA in 1934. She played a vigorous game of hockey at school and also at university where she was an Oxford hockey blue. She went on to University College Hospital with a Goldschmid scholarship for her clinical years, where she got excellent training and graduated MA BM BCh Oxford in 1937 with a clutch of prizes and medals.

Dame Josephine Barnes, like many other successful women medics, would sometimes deny that she had ever experienced prejudice as a woman in medicine. The facts hardly bear this out. In spite of her first class honours and prizes and medals, she failed to land one of the coveted house jobs at her own teaching hospital and went out to a district general hospital where she doubtless got excellent clinical surgical experience at the King Edward VII Hospital, Windsor. She did manage then to get a house physician post back in UCH and her interest on that medical side led her later to the subject of her MD thesis, DM Oxford 1941, on Tuberculosis and Pregnancy.

The war gave opportunities to women doctors that they might not otherwise have had. Josephine worked at the Samaritan Hospital for Women, as resident medical officer at Queen Charlotte's, and other posts and took the FRCS in 1939. Initially in the war, she was sent to Oxford (as were Ida Mann, the eye surgeon and Diana Beck who became a neurosurgeon). She worked as first assistant to Chassar Moir, who pioneered the use of ergometrine in obstetrics, at Oxford and she taught the first cohort of clinical students at the Radcliffe Infirmary in Oxford and took charge of the maternity work of women evacuated in the war and was able to sit for the MRCOG.

At last she was able to re-enter UCH on the obstetric and gynaecology side, working as registrar for F J Browne and during the World War II she was extremely busy holding the fort as part of the flying squad. Never one to miss the opportunity of further qualifications, she took the MRCP as well as the MD. David Innes Williams relates how surprised he and his friends were to come across the clever and efficient blue-stocking obstetric registrar sitting on the knee of their fellow house officer, Dr Brian Warren. They were married for over twenty years, though the marriage did not finally survive, and had three children, two daughters and a son who became a GP like his father, later Sir Brian Warren. Josephine Barnes was always ready in the future to give advice to younger women doctors on combining motherhood and work, strongly advocating getting all qualifications under ones belt before embarking on a family and then being prepared to spend the whole of one's salary on the care of babies and children.

Josephine Barnes took on consultant duties at the Elizabeth Garrett Anderson Hospital and the Marie Curie, as well as at University College Hospital but when F J Browne came to retire, his successor Professor W C W Nixon terminated her employment at her own teaching hospital which she had served with such commitment through the war years and where she would have liked to have been appointed. She took sessions at the West London Hospital where the maternity services of Charing Cross Hospital medical school were based.

She was a speedy surgeon, respected by the staff, often feared by student nurses and sometimes by juniors, kindly and supportive of younger women doctors. She sped around London in her sports car, an open white Mercedes, which students believed had been given her in gratitude by the Middle Eastern husband of one of her grateful patients. She invariably carried a signature red leather-lined handbag of the best quality. She ran her private practice from Wimpole Street.

She was a member of Council of the Royal College of Obstetricians and Gynaecologists and became Vice-President, and was said to have missed by only one vote following Dame Hilda Lloyd to be the second woman to be President. She claimed to be the first FRCOG to give birth. She was a member of the Lane committee on the working of the Abortion Act, the Royal Commission on Medical Education, the Warnock committee on in-vitro fertilisation, she sat on the Council of the Medical Defence Union for twenty-one years, and the National Association of Family Planning Doctors for seventeen. She was an examiner for universities in the United Kingdom, the West Indies, Nigeria and Uganda. She sat on all manner of other august bodies, President of the Women's Nationwide Cancer Control Campaign, President of the Medical Women's Federation and she was the first woman to be President of the British Medical Association, an annual appointment. She became a Dame of the British Empire, DBE.

Josephine Barnes found great happiness with the success and lives of her children and grandchildren. When looking after the grandchildren she advocated keeping the same hours as the small children, going to bed soon after they did in the knowledge that she would probably be woken early by them and thus conserving her energy.

Margaret Salmond was a consultant with the RAMC in World War II with the rank of major and worked at Bexhill with the EMS and at the military hospital Tidworth. She was awarded the MBE (Military). Her father had been a major in The Royal Scots .

She was educated at St Paul's Girls' School, and went on with a St Dunstan's Foundation Exhibition to the London (Royal Free Hospital)

School of Medicine where she was a prize-winner in gynaecology and in operative midwifery and obstetrics, and played hockey and swam for the University of London. She graduated in 1922 and worked under Dame Louise McIlroy and Gertrude Dearnley. The Royal Homoeopathic Hospital gave her a scholarship in obstetrics, gynaecology and radiotherapy and she took the London MD in 1925 and was registrar, then working up to first assistant at the Royal Free Hospital. She held a BMA research grant to investigate scarlet fever and puerperal fever and the relevance of the Dick test. She held the A M Bird scholarship for further work at the Free. She took the FRCS in 1936 and was appointed to the Bermondsey Mission Hospital and the Marie Curie.

With the outbreak of World War II, she was in charge of the EMS hospital at Bexhill, then joined the RAMC at Tidworth with the rank of major. After the war she was the consultant in obstetrics and gynaecology to St Olave's Hospital Bermondsey and the Marie Curie Hospital.

Looking back on her working life, she did feel that she had experienced some prejudice as a woman – 'somewhat' is the word she used. Commenting on the idea of part-time working or training, in her own words she said: 'If you have the FRCS, I take it consultant practice is the aim. You can't work school hours as a consultant. What about night calls?' She retired at sixty and went to live on the Isle of Mull, gardening and bird-watching.

Edith Hall was appointed consultant gynaecologist at the South London Hospital in 1935 and obstetrician when they opened the midwifery section. She had already been consultant to the Mothers' Hospital, Clapton since 1923 and was Chairman of the Medical Committee there. She was appointed also to the Marie Curie Hospital and the London Homeopathic where she was the first woman on the consultant staff. She had taken the FRCS in 1931. She had a private practice from Devonshire Place. Her speciality was obstetrics and gynaecology and she was an FRCOG.

However, when war broke out she joined the EMS, the Emergency Medical Service, and treated casualties of all sorts from the air-raids throughout the war from 1939 until 1945.

She qualified from the London (Royal Free Hospital) School of Medicine in 1920, MB BS with honours in surgery and took the MD in midwifery and gynaecology in 1922 winning the university gold medal. She had house appointments at the Royal Free and was junior and senior resident medical officer at Queen Charlotte's and returned to the Royal Free where she rose to senior assistant before her consultant appointments.

She enjoyed travel and had an interest in archaeology. She suffered ill-health and died age sixty-one before retiring and was cared for by her friend Dr Olive Rendel and sister Dr Marjorie Hall.

Flora Bridge (née Hargreaves), together with her colleague Miss Eileen Whapham FRCS founded an outstanding obstetric and gynaecology unit in Rochford General Hospital in Essex serving the Southend area where, amongst other innovations, they formed the flying squad for home deliveries and their maternal death-rate was admirably lower than the national average. They set up a school for pupil midwives. Forty of the medical junior staff who passed through their hands as trainees got the MRCOG. They were in the news too when quadruplets were born and survived, unusual at that time.

Flora Hargreaves was born in Rochdale, Yorkshire where her father was a commercial traveller selling flannel and clothing and her mother a teacher. She was the youngest of three and said to be not strong as a child, belied by her later formidable career. She was a great reader and educated at Harrogate Girls' School from where she won a scholarship to University College London, UCL, and University College Hospital, UCH, where she was one of the early girl students and won a fistful of prizes, qualifying MB BS in 1930. She got good and varied experience at the Hospital for Women in Leeds, at the Mile End Hospital and at the Cancer Hospital (the Marsden) and took the FRCS in 1931.

While at Mile End she met Dr Raymond Bridge, a New Zealander, who had come over to take his Fellowship and they married and set up a practice together in Chesterfield and had a son and daughter, Mary and Michael. With World War II Raymond joined the New Zealand RAMC and was posted to North Africa and to Europe and the marriage did not survive. Flora was at Rochford General Hospital and was appointed consultant in obstetrics and gynaecology and she and Eileen Whapham made an admirable team. Miss Whapham adopted a twelve-year-old daughter, Doreen, who later became a midwife. Flora was an energetic person who enjoyed work and life, smoking a pipe, dancing, camping, walking, and, like many surgeons, painting in water-colour. She lived to age ninety-one.

It was *Margaret White*'s intention to be a paediatric orthopaedic surgeon. After leaving Belmont School, Derby and the Tremarth School in Hampstead she went to Birkbeck College to matriculate. She trained and worked first as a physiotherapist at St George's, at the National Hospital for Nervous Diseases in Queen Square, and at the Royal National Orthopaedic Hospital, Stanmore. She did her medical training at the London (Royal Free Hospital) School of Medicine winning the junior and senior anatomy prizes and taking and passing the primary Fellowship, Part 1 of the FRCS, while still a student. She qualified MB BS in 1930, and completed the FRCS the following year in 1931. She was house surgeon at the Royal Free to Cecil Joll and to Hamilton Bailey and got good experience there and went on to the West Norfolk Hospital and Kings Lynn where her ambition to be a children's orthopaedic surgeon crystallised but she could find no openings for such a career.

Accordingly she came back to the Royal Free Hospital where her next post was as registrar but to the gynaecology unit and from there she went on to Willesden General Hospital and took the MD and the MRCOG. At the Royal Free Hospital she founded one of the first infertility clinics with a colleague Miss Gertrude Dearnley in 1937 - most of the problems of infertility at that time were thought to be due to tuberculosis in the pelvis.

World War II intervened and she worked at the Three Counties Hospital in Arlesley, Bedfordshire where the Royal Free had been evacuated as surgeon and in gynaecology. After the War, she became consultant gynaecologist to the Lister Hospital, Hitchin, the Letchworth Hospital, the Three Counties Hospital and the Royal Free. She presented work at international conferences in Cairo, Stockholm, Mexico, Israel, Japan, the United States and Holland.

She married Dr Leonard Page, a psychiatrist, in 1942, at age forty and they had two sons, one becoming a doctor.

Jocelyn Moore became a consultant in obstetrics and gynaecology at the Royal Free Hospital. World War II intervened and she served in the war as a major in the RAMC. She turned up in khaki in the outpatient clinic at the hospital. Her father, Sir John Moore CB, was a Major General in the Royal Army Veterinary Corps. She married David Symon, a journalist, during the war in 1942 at age thirty-eight.

After the war, she returned to the Royal Free as consultant and was much involved in the teaching of medical students, chairman of the education committee and serving as vice-dean of the medical school.

Later, at retirement age, she was invited to go out to West Africa as the foundation professor of obstetrics and gynaecology and head of department in of the new University of Ahmadu Bello in Zaria, Nigeria in 1971. She also chaired the medical advisory committee there and served on the library committee.

Jocelyn was educated at Wycombe Abbey and trained at the London (Royal Free Hospital) School of Medicine graduating MB BS in 1929 and took the FRCS in 1933 and the MRCOG in 1934. She became FRCOG in 1948.

Ruby Sharp came from South Africa to do her FRCS in England and returned there to a busy and distinguished surgical life in Cape Town. There is a sculptured head of her in the department of obstetrics and gynaecology in the Medical School of the University of Cape Town.

Ruby was the daughter of a surgeon and educated at Wynberg Girls' High School where it was reported that she needed a wheelbarrow to carry away her winnings on Prize-Days. As an undergraduate in the University of Cape Town she won medals in anatomy, bacteriology and public health and graduated MB ChB in 1930 with a first in Surgery. After house appointments in Cape Town in surgery and in gynaecology, she came to England and, after several posts, took the FRCS in 1935 and the MRCOG the year after.

Back in South Africa, she was appointed consultant to the Woodstock Hospital and to Groote Schuur when it opened in 1938. During the World War II when many men from the hospital served with the allies in the Forces, her capacity for work was highly valued. When asked if she had ever experienced any prejudice against her as a woman in medicine, she wrote '– rather the reverse! I never felt the slightest prejudice on the part of patients or colleagues'. She added with humour, 'If one had a family, I can see that one might not always be ready to rush out at night.' She was unsparing in her work and was much revered and admired by her colleagues, the nurses and patients. After the war, she received the FRCOG and served on the South African reference committee of the RCOG and she was increasingly involved in postgraduate teaching and headed one of the firms in gynaecology.

Living and working in South Africa, she had domestic help living in and also coming in from outside during the week.

She retired at age sixty-two and, as many surgeons in South Africa do, went to spend a year in a Mission Hospital in the Transkei.

Gladys Hill became a distinguished consultant at the Royal Free Hospital and the Elizabeth Garrett Anderson and a stalwart of the Royal College of Obstetricians and Gynaecologists which august body threw a hundredth birthday luncheon party for her, their first centenarian.

She was said to be a terrifying examiner with a horror of slovenly thought and shoddy work and whether that was due to Icelandic studies, her time in MI5, or her surgical training was hard to be sure.

Gladys Hill was educated at Cheltenham Ladies' College, when Miss Dorothea Beale, the founder, was still headmistress and went up to Somerville College Oxford to read Old Icelandic studies, and where she was a contemporary of Dorothy Sayers and Vera Brittain. She took a half-blue in hockey. She was an energetic person, keen on games, on mountain walking, archaeology, and amateur dramatics.

When she had graduated in the humanities at Oxford, she went to work for MI5 in 1916 during World War I. Like Geraldine Barry, she met Professor Winifred Cullis, the professor of physiology, whose self-appointed mission it was to proselytise intelligent educated young women toward further study to become doctors. Gladys Hill was persuaded and she entered the London (Royal Free Hospital) School of Medicine after the war was over and where she was a prize-winner, qualifying MB BS in 1923 at the age of twenty-nine. She worked for Cecil Joll, Lionel Norbury, Clement Shattock and Dame Louisa Aldrich-Blake. She took the MD in 1925 and went to Paris to the Curie Centre to study the use of radium in treatment. She passed the FRCS and the MRCOG in 1936 and was consultant in obstetrics and gynaecology at the Elizabeth Garrett Anderson Hospital in 1935 and the Royal Free Hospital in 1940 where she spent all her working life. She visited clinics in Canada and the United States and wrote up her work for publication.

She was sometimes found to be unhelpful to young Royal Free women doctors who were looking toward a career in gynaecology when they approached her hoping for constructive advice and a helping hand toward a job. In that, she was not alone then or since in being a disappointment as a woman in not being found to give sisterly support to other women. She was a formidable role model for the Royal Free students.

Gladys Dodds was a Scottish graduate who came down to London for consultant practice. She was educated at the Dunfermline High School and then went on to Edinburgh University where she qualified MB ChB in 1922 and took the MD in 1927 after posts at the Royal Maternity Hospital, the Simpson Memorial Hospital and the Royal Hospital for Sick Children. She obtained good obstetric experience in Dublin and obtained the licence in midwifery from the Coombe Lying-In Hospital and the Diploma of Public Health, then came to London to work as first assistant in obstetrics at University College Hospital. She worked at various times at the Hackney and Mile End Hospitals, the Bermondsey and Tottenham Hospitals, Annie McCall's Maternity, Bushey Heath, the Mothers' Hospital Clapton and Queen Charlotte's and ran a practice from Upper Wimpole Street.

She wrote a highly popular book, *Gynaecology. A Handbook for Nurses*. The review in *The Midwife*, was adulatory: 'This very comprehensive work on gynaecology should be sought by nurses and midwives as a real acquisition to add to their bookshelf, and a good companion for reference in this wide field of nursing.' There were chapters on anatomy, physiology, fertilization and implantation of the ovum, development of the foetus and placenta, illustrated with excellent drawings. Then chapters followed on ante-natal care, diet, post-natal care, pregnancy toxaemias, venereal disease. In the diet section, there were interesting words about vitamin B 'In these times of rationing …the Ministry of Food recognized [this] early in the war and at first ordered the addition of vitamin B to flour, and then the use of a national Loaf. The average diet furnishes about 250 to 500 international units daily, and the requirements are believed to be twice this amount. polyneuritis, cramps, and pain in the lower extremities, which are common in pregnancy, are often due to deficiency of vitamin B1. Calcium influences the absorption of iron, and vitamin B2 helps its utilization. Vitamin B complex is present in milk and milk products, yeast, whole-grain cereals, liver, eggs, root vegetables and some fruits.'

In the chapters on childbirth, in the post-natal section, it recounts that while 95% of women were accessing ante-natal care, only 30% receive post-natal care. There are interesting comments on those who did come to be seen in the post-natal period, a third presented because they had pelvic complications, incompletely involuted uterus, retroverted uterus, torn eroded and infected cervix, prolapse, pelvic inflammation, and sometimes urinary incontinence. There is also an interesting discussion and classification on toxaemia of pregnancy.

Mary Mayeur was educated at St Paul's Girls' School, like Margaret Louden with whom she must have been a contemporary, and like Elaine Salmond, though she must have been at the school many years earlier. Her father was an actor. At the Royal Free Hospital, she won scholarship and prizes, and graduated MB BS in 1933. She did house posts under Victor Bonney and Charles McIntosh Marshall and was MD in 1934 and FRCS and MRCOG in 1938.

In World War II she was working in the Liverpool Maternity Hospital where she gave heroic service under frequent bombing raids attracted by the docks nearby. She looked after patients and casualties. She was appointed to Wigan Infirmary and the Stanley Hospital in 1944, and later to Liverpool Women's Hospital and Liverpool Maternity Hospital. After the war there was a need for a consultant unit at Ormskirk General Hospital and she worked there for twenty years giving yeoman service becoming FRCOG in 1953. She took retirement at age sixty and went to live in Sussex, growing roses and joining the Women's Institute.

Dorothy Sharpe was educated at Skipton Grammar School before being sent to board at Roedean School. Subsequently at the London (Royal Free Hospital) School of Medicine for Women she qualified MB BS in 1930, did house posts at the South London and the Elizabeth Garrett Anderson Hospitals and took the MRCOG in 1938 and the FRCS in 1939 being appointed to the staff of the Royal Free Hospital as assistant gynaecological surgeon and obstetrician.

In World War II, Dorothy Sharpe worked for the EMS, the Emergency Medical Service, at the Elizabeth Garrett Anderson Hospital. After the war, she was a Borough Councillor (Labour) for Marylebone and must have worked alongside Esther Rickards. Her grandfather, Sir John Brigg, was for many years Liberal MP for Keighley.

Her father was a rheumatologist, Dr William Cecil Sharpe, treating his patients in Smedley's Hydro in Skipton. She herself was afflicted early with rheumatoid arthritis and suffered chronic persistent pain and retired early at age forty-nine, living to age seventy-five.

The Inter-War Years – FRCS 1931 to 1939
Women of the Fellowship in ENT Surgery

Two women Fellows became ENT surgeons, Dorothy Collier and Winfred Wadge.

Though herself an ENT surgeon, *Dorothy Collier* became famous for rescuing Professor Joseph Trueta, the orthopaedic surgeon, in the Spanish Civil War 1936-1939 and bringing him and his family from Barcelona to England.

She was also one of the small handful of women Hunterian professorial lecturers.

She was a highly educated discerning elegant lady, and an intrepid traveller. She made hazardous trips up the Orinoco in Venezuela with a woman friend and maintained that her fascination with the river was that it had two right-angled bends like the seventh cranial nerve, the facial nerve, her particular field of interest in otology.

Educated at the Convent of Notre Dame in Southport, Lancashire Dorothy Collier went up to Oxford University subsequently doing her clinical studies at University College Hospital, UCH, in London, qualifying MB BCh Oxford in 1922. She did a house surgeon post in King Edward VII Windsor and then went into ENT training, house surgeon, registrar and first assistant in ENT at UCH, then registrar at the Central London Hospital for Throat and Ear. She took the Fellowship in 1932 and became Consultant ENT surgeon at the Royal Free and the South London Hospital and assistant lecturer in the Institute of Laryngology. She carried out private practice from Harley Street and Upper Wimpole

Street. She gave a Hunterian lecture on reparative surgery for the facial nerve at the Royal College of Surgeons in 1939. Her professorial dissertation was entitled 'Facial paralysis and its operative treatment'.

During the World War II she served with the Forces in North Africa and Italy as a specialist otologist in the RAMC with the rank of major.

Winifred Wadge was surgeon to the ENT department at University College Hospital, UCH, and surgeon to the Diseases of Throat, Nose and Ear at the Nelson Hospital, Wimbledon. She worked full time until retirement at age sixty-five.

Her sentiments, when asked, of the position of women in the medical profession, were that there was no prejudice whatsoever in her own teaching hospital, UCH, either as a student or as a full member of staff. She felt that there had been prejudice before 1945 in other hospitals and her impression was that it had existed more in small peripheral hospitals.

She had a live-in au pair when she was working and a daily twenty-two hours a week. She trained at Cambridge and University College Hospital, taking her MA Cambridge in 1930, her MB BS London in 1936 and the FRCS in 1939. She lived in Walmer, Bucks, and practiced from Devonshire Place.

The Inter-War Years – FRCS 1931 to 1939
Women of the Fellowship into Eye Surgery

Jean Dollar became an eye surgeon, and made an original and important contribution in her field describing a new technique after exenteration of the orbit, an immediate reconstruction procedure with a prosthesis, a boon particularly to young patients with sarcoma to help them to adapt to their situation.

She presented her work as a dissertation to the College as a Hunterian Professor in 1945 and the work was also published in *The Lancet*, and was entitled 'The use of plastics in ophthalmology'. She was known as a deft and gentle surgeon.

Her father and grandfather were veterinary surgeons with a city practice based in Bond Street. She trained at the London (Royal Free Hospital) School of Medicine and qualified MB BS in 1927, took the DOMS in 1929 and the FRCS in 1936. She was consultant to the Royal

Eye Hospital which was her main concern, but also gave service to St Olave's, the Elizabeth Garrett Anderson and the Royal Free Hospitals. She practised all her working life.

During World War II, she was one of the few surgeons not on active service and so concomitantly busy. For a short time the Royal Eye amalgamated with King's College Hospital but separated again and her diplomacy was influential at that time. She was a good teacher and colleague with a fund of clinical anecdotes and quiet wit. She declared herself to be a reluctant housekeeper and gardener. In retirement she travelled and enjoyed visiting places of archaeological and wild fauna interest and was a great reader.

The Inter-War Years – FRCS 1931 to 1939
Women of the Fellowship into Orthopaedic Surgery

Eugenie Willis became an orthopaedic surgeon and treated hundreds of casualties during World War II. Her father was a captain in the Royal Navy. She went from Blackheath High School, a Girls' Public Day School Trust school, up to Girton College Cambridge where she got a first class honours degree and then went on to do her clinical training at the London (Royal Free Hospital) School of Medicine. She qualified MB BCh in 1936 and after house surgeon posts at the Royal Free, she was resident surgical officer at the Royal Oldham Hospital where she specialised in orthopaedics. She took the FRCS in 1939 and was chief assistant to the orthopaedic department at Manchester Royal Infirmary all through the war, treating hundreds of casualties, and was appointed lecturer in anatomy and orthopaedic surgery to Manchester University. She was orthopaedic registrar to the Duchess of York Hospital for babies at Manchester and consultant to Woods Hospital, Glossop, and to the Oldham Municipal hospitals. She was taken ill in September 1948 and died in hospital within a short time.

The Inter-War Years – FRCS 1931 to 1939
Women of the Fellowship in Public Health

Hilda Linford became the first woman to run the Public Health Department in the Isle of Wight.

The daughter of a marine engineer, she went from Wyggeston Grammar School, Leicester to Manchester University where she was a prizewinner in 1921 and graduated MB ChB in 1924. She became lecturer in physiology and did research work including a year in Paris as a Dickinson Research Scholar at the College de France in neurophysiology, taking the MD in 1930. She returned to clinical work doing an anaesthetic registrar post at the Royal Newcastle-upon-Tyne and a maternity post in Sheffield where she took the FRCS in 1934. She then went into public health, the first woman to be appointed to the Isle of Wight Public Health Department with special charge of maternity and child welfare and where she spent her working life.

She was an inveterate traveller , interested in pre-history, traveling to archaeological sites. She died age eighty.

The Inter-War Years – FRCS 1931 to 1939
Women of the Fellowship in General Practice/Obstetrics & Gynaecology

Keren Parkes was keen to study at a medical school that accepted both men and women and went from Streatham High School for Girls and Somerville House, St Leonards-on-Sea to King's College London, KCL, and King's College Hospital, KCH, where she was one of only five girls in her year. She had decided to be a doctor at age twelve. She was a prize-winner taking many scholarships and medals, entrance and first and second year scholarships, two Jelf medals and seven further prizes. She qualified MB BS in 1929, MD in 1931 and the FRCS in 1932 and was both house surgeon and registrar in obstetrics and gynaecology at Kings where she was obstetric tutor, and surgical registrar at the Elizabeth Garrett Anderson and the Kingston and District Hospital.

She did not practise as a surgeon after the surgical registrar years which finished in 1937 when she had had the fellowship for five years and looking back she felt that there was prejudice against her advancement as a woman surgeon at that time. It is possible that being outside the network of those who trained at the Royal Free left her with fewer connections to land the all-important consultant position, and KCH was not yet ready to appoint a woman at that time to their own or to an affiliated hospital. But she set up as a GP and ran a successful private practice and in 1938 went out to deliver a son and heir to a Rajah traveling by flyboat to Karachi and by special train. She worked until age sixty. She was a magistrate and a Soroptimist, holding high rank.

The Inter-War Years – FRCS 1931 to 1939
Women in the Fellowship returning abroad

Three women surgical Fellows returned abroad to work: *Ruby Sharp* returned home to be a gynaecologist and obstetrician in Cape Town, South Africa, *Muriel McIlrath* to Australia and *Venketeswaraiya Sankarambal* to India.

Muriel McIlrath qualified and worked at St Mary's Hospital Whitworth Park Manchester and took the FRCS in 1935. She went to work in Australia in New South Wales.

Venketeswaraiya Sankarambal came from India, took the MRCS in 1935 and the FRCS in 1939 and returned to work in the Maharajah's Hospital, Pallusuthe, in Cochin State, India.

The Inter-War Years – FRCS 1931 to 1939
Women in the Fellowship in Neurosurgery

Diana Beck is the first neurosurgeon amongst our women Fellows. She was also the first woman to be appointed to a consultant post at one of the major London teaching hospitals (1947).

She worked for a few years as a general surgeon taking the FRCS in 1931. Then in 1939 with the outbreak of war she went to work with Sir Hugh Cairns in Oxford on the William Gibson research fellowship from the Royal Free and thus started her career as a neurosurgeon.

She had been educated at the Queen's School, Chester and went on to the London (Royal Free Hospital) School of Medicine where she was a prize-winner and qualified MB BS in 1925. During World War II, she worked at first in Oxford under Sir Hugh Cairns, an Australian who had learned his neurosurgery under Harvey Cushing himself at Harvard, and who held the Nuffield Chair at Oxford, then in Enfield and in Bristol and in 1943 was appointed consultant neurosurgeon at the Royal Free Hospital. In 1947 she was appointed to the Middlesex Hospital, the first woman to hold such a post on the teaching staff of a major London teaching hospital, and worked there for a brief nine years. She published some papers in *Brain*, in the *British Journal of Surgery*, the *Journal of Neurosurgery*, in the *Archives of the Middlesex Hospital* and in *Transactions of the Association of Industrial Medicine*. She died prematurely at age fifty-four after surgery, a thymectomy, in the Royal Free Hospital.

Diana Beck's career was at that time a unique achievement, to have been appointed a woman with the FRCS to the consultant staff of a major London teaching hospital and an analysis of the significance of the event is important. She entered into an esoteric speciality, one not heavily populated with practitioners, nor in the main stream of surgical work. And when she was appointed it was into a medical school that did not even accept women *students* to study, though that was shortly to change. There might be thought to have little or no immediate or later impact on the acceptance of women into the Middlesex Hospital. However as she worked in the early 1950s, one young women medical student was aware of her in the operating theatres, though more preoccupied by the fierce reputation of Sir Gordon Gordon-Taylor and impressed by the meticulous surgical technique of the kindly David Patey. She did none-the-less register the presence of Diana Beck, and the student Jennifer Haley did go on to become a neurosurgeon. A woman physician neurologist, Dr Pamela (Paddy) Fullerton, was appointed to the Middlesex staff in the 1960s.

The essential need for the achievement to have a lasting effect as a breakthrough is the necessity for there to be *other women* – they need the presence of other women – otherwise, like Diana Beck, they stand alone as one exceptional person, and when that meteor has streaked across the sky – all too briefly – it is gone, and leaves no pathway for others to follow.

Summary of the Inter-War Years Women Fellows – FRCS 1931 to 1939

Of these thirty women doctors who became FRCS from 1931 to 1939, six became consultants in general surgery in this country, Margaret Louden at the South London, Enid Rockstro at the New Sussex Brighton, Muriel Long at Llandudno in Wales, Doris O'Doherty at Carshalton, Gertrude Toland at Dover and Beatrice Willmott Dobbie at Birmingham. Four became consultants abroad, Joyce Ludlow as a missionary surgeon in

Nigeria, Doris Brown holding the fort at the Lady Hardinge in Delhi, Muriel Hulke in Simla/Lucknow and Margaret Shepherd in Madras. Eleven went into obstetrics and gynaecology, Dame Josephine Barnes, Margaret Salmond, Edith Hall, Flora Bridges (Hargreaves), Margaret White, Jocelyn Moore, Ruby Sharp – in South Africa, Gladys Hill, Gladys Dodds, Mary Mayeur, and Dorothy Sharpe. Two went into ENT, Dorothy Collier and Winifred Wadge. One became an Eye surgeon, Jean Dollar. One went into Public Health, Hilda Linford. One into private practice with an obstetric/gynaecology interest, Keren Parkes. One returned to South Africa, Ruby Sharp. One to Australia, Muriel McIlrath. One returned to India, Venketeswaraiya Sankarambal. One became a neurosurgeon, Diana Beck.

The career destiny of these thirty women doctors who achieved the FRCS between 1931 and 1939 reflects the range of opportunities open to them. Six as consultants in general surgery in this country, albeit two with a speciality interest also in gynaecology. Of those six, two were appointed within the inner circle of women's hospitals that women had founded, the South London and the New Sussex Hospital Brighton. A further four though were outside that tight circle, laying claim to Llandudno, Carshalton in Surrey, Dover, and Birmingham. Abroad, one was in Nigeria fulfilling missionary endeavour and three in India. The largest group were those who went into obstetrics and gynaecology, eleven in all, and all but one choosing the speciality rather than entering by default. The two ENT surgeons and one eye surgeon also chose their speciality. The one who went into public health, while committed to getting the FRCS eventually, tried anaesthetics for some years, and obstetrics before opting for the public health role where she found a satisfying career. The one in general practice had had a successful career up to the final step but somehow – perhaps because the war was imminent – had failed to achieve the final goal of a consultant post. She had chosen a medical school out of the common path. Those who trained within the Royal Free did have a network of senior support and contacts to help them toward future jobs. The one in the speciality of neurosurgery had, because of the war, been directed to Oxford to work under Sir Hugh Cairns and the opportunity was found. At least thirteen of the thirty married and between them they had more than eighteen children.

The Inter-War Years Women Fellows – FRCS 1931 to 1939

Margaret Mary Crawford Louden 1910-1998 FRCS 1938
Enid Helen Rockstro 1902-1996 FRCS 1932
M Hilary E Long (Muriel Hilary Eileen Long, Mrs Boney) 1906-1984 FRCS 1934
Doris Ethel O'Doherty 1902-1980 FRCS 1935
Gertrude Mary Beatrice Morgan (Mrs Gertrude Toland) 1901-1985 FRCS 1931
Beatrice Marion Willmott-Dobbie 1903-1995 FRCS 1931
Joyce Rewcastle Ludlow (née Woods) FRCS 1931
Doris Barbara Brown died 11 06 1972 FRCS 1935
Muriel Sydney Hulke 1904-1975 FRCS 1933
Margaret Mary Shepherd (née Ferguson) 1907-1982 FRCS 1938
Dame Josephine Barnes (Alice Josephine Mary Taylor Barnes) 1912-1999 FRCS 1939
Elaine Margaret Katharine Salmond 1897-1982 FRCS 1936
Edith Mary Hall 1896-1957 FRCS 1931
Flora Bridges (née Hargreaves) 1906-1997 FRCS 1931
Margaret Moore White 1902-1983 FRCS 1931
Jocelyn Adelaide Medway Moore 1904-1979 FRCS 1933
Ruby Grace Sharp 1906-1989 FRCS 1935
Gladys Hill 1894-1998 FRCS 1936
Gladys Helen Dodds 1898-1982 FRCS 1937
Mary Helen Mayeur 1910-1988 FRCS 1938
Dorothy Anderton Sharpe 1903-1978 FRCS 1939
Dorothy Josephine Collier 1894-1972 FRCS 1932
Winifred Joan Wadge FRCS 1939
Jean Marguerite Dollar 1901-1982 FRCS 1936
Eugenie Leeson Willis 1910-1948 FRCS 1939
Hilda Margaret Linford 1900-1980 FRCS 1934
Keren Isabel Parkes 1904-1993 FRCS 1932
Muriel Betty McIlrath FRCS 1935
Miss Venketeswaraiya Sankarambal FRCS 1939
Diana Jean Kinloch Beck 1902-1956 FRCS 1931

CHAPTER 5

Women Fellows in World War II – FRCS 1940 to 1945

THE College was bombed in 1941 causing major disruption. During the heavy nightly air-raids from September to November 1940, the College had roof-watchers to put out incendiary fires. On 15 September 1940, fifty windows were shattered when a bomb came down in Holborn; and on 14 and 16 October more damage was done to ceilings, doors and windows. Toward the end of 1940, the Barbers' Hall was totally destroyed and the Barbers accepted the invitation to hold their quarterly Court in Lincoln's Inn by courtesy of the Royal College of Surgeons. In 1941, on the night of 10 May, ten incendiaries and a high-explosive bomb made a direct hit on the College and caused great destruction.

The Council of the College had, with admirable prescience, begun in the mid and late 1930s to consider plans for their strategy on a likely future European political disruption. The Director-General of the RAMC came to address the Council in 1937. Regulations to receive medical students and doctors who might be fleeing from European countries were discussed and quotas contemplated. Modifications of the arrangements for the examinations of the College were introduced, particularly the necessity to hasten the qualifying membership examination if and when more doctors were needed. The possibility of holding the clinicals outside London was considered: Birmingham, Cambridge, Bristol and Manchester were to be approached.

Once war was declared, all ordinary committees were suspended. The Management Committee however continued to meet in order to organize the storage and disposal of books, paintings and museum specimens.

There was a slight increase in the numbers of women doctors taking the Fellowship during the early part of the war. Four in 1940 and six in 1941. Then the College received that direct hit in the bombing of an air-raid and for the rest of the war years the numbers were very small. There were none in 1942, one in 1943, one in 1944, and two in 1945. Perhaps they were too busy filling hospital posts vacated by the men who were serving in the Forces, or were themselves working in the EMS, Emergency Medical Services hospitals, and the RAMC. Seven women surgeons became majors in the RAMC, one a captain in Anti-Aircraft Command and two became squadron leaders in the RAF. Of the seven who were majors, Dorothy Collier FRCS 1932 served in North Africa and Italy, Jocelyn Moore FRCS 1933 did general and spinal surgery, Hilary Long FRCS 1934 served in the Royal Bolton and other sites, Margaret Shepherd FRCS 1935 in Anti-Aircraft Command, Elaine Salmond FRCS 1936 served in the Military Hospital Tidworth and was awarded the Military MBE, Janet Bottomley FRCS 1941 was deployed in the British General Hospital, Hanover, Katharine Liebert FRCS 1941 was with the Forces in the Middle East. Mary Richardson was the Captain in Anti-Aircraft Command and got her FRCS after the War in 1956. Two further women served in the RAF, Elisabeth Simpson and Agnes Bartels, and took the FRCS after the war in 1952 and 1953. It was not until the early 1950s that numbers of new women Fellows began to pick up.

The fourteen new Fellows who joined the College during the war included six who were gynaecologists, one a general surgeon who returned to Scotland and worked in a woman's hospital, one who returned to India and was Director of her hospital, one who was gravely injured in a bombing raid in London and made her career in research neuro-otology, one who did valiant general, spinal, neurosurgical and orthopaedic surgery on casualties and alongside prepared herself for a distinguished career in radiotherapy once the war was over, and one who, dedicated to a career in ENT, revolutionised the diagnosis and treatment of the deaf child and one further who trained in ENT becoming a consultant after the war.

Women Fellows in World War II – FRCS 1940 to 1945
Women of the Fellowship into Gynaecology

Six women went into gynaecology. Some had already served in the Forces.

Eleanor Mills became consultant gynaecologist to the North Manchester and Stretford Memorial Hospitals and had a successful career. She qualified with the MB ChB Manchester in 1936 and took the FRCS in 1940 and the MRCOG in 1942. After the war she became FRCOG in 1958. She published a paper in the *British Journal of Obstetrics and Gynaecology* (2005) 52 278. 'Peroneal palsy as a complication of parturition'. Two of the cases were her own patients and she had gathered seven cases in all from local hospitals. She was married to a medical husband and when the children were small had a resident full-time housekeeper and a daily who came in for 15 hours a week. She was a member of the North of England Obstetrical and Gynaecological Society.

Kathleen Robinson had a distinguished career in obstetrics and gynaecology, being the first woman to be appointed to the consulting staff of Queen Charlotte's. She was also consultant at the Royal Free Hospital.

Kathleen Robinson was educated at Penhros College and the Royal Free Hospital, graduating in 1936 MB BS London, and got excellent experience with house posts at the Royal Free, the Royal Cancer (the Marsden), the Samaritan and Queen Charlotte's, working then at a very busy district general hospital, St James', Balham, and taking the FRCS in 1940 and the MD in 1941. She went on to work at the City of London Maternity Hospital, Bearsted and in the outpatients of the South London Hospital. She was resident in obstetrics at Queens Charlotte's and later was appointed to the consultant staff at Queen Charlotte's. In 1946 she also joined the staff at the Royal Free, being an inspiring woman teacher to the medical students. She married Vincent Sherry and had a son and two daughters, one following her into the medical profession.

Janet Bottomley had the distinction of being the first woman on the consultant staff at Addenbrooke's Hospital Cambridge and had an impressive career in World War II. She served with the rank of major in the British General Hospital, Hanover.

Educated at Putney High School and Wimbledon High School, two GPDST schools, Janet Bottomley went on to the London (Royal Free Hospital) School of Medicine where she was a prize-winner, graduating MB BS London in 1938. She had posts at the Royal Free Hospital, was senior resident at Queen Charlotte's and the Chelsea Hospital for Women and was first assistant at the London Hospital. She worked for Victor Bonney and Charles Reed. She took the FRCS in 1941, the MD in 1943 and the MRCOG.

After the war, she was appointed consultant in gynaecology and obstetrics at Addenbrooke's Hospital Cambridge, the first time a woman had been appointed to their consultant staff, and where she spent her working life. When she was working she had resident domestic help. She was on the Council of the Royal College of Obstetricians and Gynaecologists and an examiner for her college and for Cambridge and for the Central Midwives Board.

Janet Bottomley was an enthusiastic traveller and photographer, visiting the Great Wall of China and Antarctica before visits to those parts were common and, nearing retirement, she went to do a locum in Borneo. As medical officer to an archaeological dig, she met Carson Ritchie, a senior lecturer in history at Thames Polytechnic and they were married in 1979, she at age sixty-four. She had a stepson and stepdaughter who is Dr Jean Horton, a consultant anaesthetist.

Dorothy Knott worked for the EMS, the Emergency Medical Service, during World War II at the Royal Free, Sheffield Royal Infirmary and the Three Counties Hospital, Arlesley, where the Royal Free Hospital was partially evacuated.

Educated at St Felix Southwold she did her medical training at the London (Royal Free Hospital) School of Medicine graduating MB BS in 1938. She went on to take the FRCS in 1941 and the MS in 1944. After the war she re-joined the Royal Free in 1946, and was appointed consultant in general surgery and urology in 1948, succeeding Miss E C Lewis. She was in charge of teaching the introductory surgical rounds to the students and taught vividly with clinical anecdotes from her own experience. She married the following year, 1949, age thirty-five, Dr Oliver Barclay, the Secretary of the Intervarsity Christian Evangelical Fellowship, and continued to hold the appointment as surgeon for a further eight years after her marriage and later gave up surgery to look after their four children. She died at the early age of fifty of breast cancer.

Katharine Liebert was a Manchester graduate who became a consultant in Withington and was a warm-hearted popular surgeon. In World War II she worked at first as a general surgeon at Manchester Royal Infirmary and then was a major in the RAMC and served for a year and a half in the Middle East.

Katharine Liebert was educated at Manchester High School for Girls. Her family were highly educated and lovers of the arts and music and had come from Germany in the previous century to work in the cotton and woollen industries. She went on to Manchester University where she took a BSc in 1934 and graduated MB ChB in 1937. She was house surgeon at the Royal Infirmary, Manchester and St Mary's Hospital for Women and Children, at the Duchess of York Hospital for Babies and at the Christie. She took the FRCS in 1941 and the MRCOG in 1943 and became FRCOG in 1959.

After the war Katharine Liebert became consultant in 1947 in obstetrics and gynaecology at Ancoats Hospital and at Withington Hospital in Manchester, and at Leigh Infirmary and she covered many smaller maternity units and worked there for nearly twenty years, all her working life. She was a devoted attender at the Hallé Orchestra. She died early at the age of fifty-three of multiple sclerosis.

Eileen Whapham became consultant in obstetrics and gynaecology in Southend and was a skilled and rapid operator, well respected. She worked in harmony with Flora Bridge FRCS (née Hargreaves) q.v. ten years her senior, and together they formed an excellent unit.

Before that, however, in World War II she worked for the Emergency Medical Service, the EMS, throughout the blitz in LCC hospitals and later in Essex. She worked at Runwell, the Mildmay Mission Hospital, and the Bethnal Green Hospital and was appointed consultant gynaecologist to the Mildmay Mission Hospital in 1945.

Eileen Whapham was educated at the Dame Alice Owen School. Her mother was a teacher. And her sister also became a doctor and went into general practice. She trained at the London (Royal Free Hospital) School of Medicine graduating MB BS London in 1932 with Honours in Surgery. She did house posts at the Royal Free, the Elizabeth Garrett Anderson Hospital, Kings Lynn and the Oldchurch Hospital, Romford Essex, taking the FRCS in 1941.

She said when asked that she never experienced any prejudice as a woman in medicine – she was too busy and occupied to notice any such thing!

After the war, Eileen Whapham joined Flora Bridge as fellow consultants in obstetrics and gynaecology at the Southend group of hospitals, Southend and Rochford, where she spent her working life over the next twenty years. Together they inaugurated the flying squad for home deliveries. Their trainees were numerous, forty of them passing through their department and emerging with the MRCOG. They hit the headlines with quadruplets delivered and surviving which was a rarity at that time. Her anaesthetist, Dr Alfred Lee who did her lists for twenty years described her as a skilled and rapid operator. She published a thoughtful and comprehensive paper in the *British Journal of Obstetrics and Gynaecology* (2005) 67 473-477, 'Extended use of the Le Fort operation for vaginal prolapse in the elderly', describing the results of two hundred and ninety-five patients.

Eileen Whapham was a member of the United Reformed Church. She was a single lady and adopted a daughter Doreen at the age of twelve who later trained and became a midwife. They always had full domestic help – a resident housekeeper and daily help – and also a secretary and receptionist. She maintained that she did not think it possible to be competent in consultant practice without being completely free of domestic duties. Eileen Whapham retired at sixty and had a very rewarding and useful life.

Women Fellows in World War II – FRCS 1940 to 1945
Women of the Fellowship in General Surgery and into Radiotherapy

Two women general surgical Fellows became FRCS during World War II, Kathleen Branson and Margaret Snelling.

Kathleen Branson became a consultant surgeon in Bruntsfield and Longmore Hospitals, Edinburgh. Bruntsfield was a small women's hospital, started originally by Sophia Jex-Blake as a dispensary (outpatient clinic and pharmacy). Elsie Inglis[1] worked there at one time. It developed into a small hospital for women and children, 80 beds, and a children's ward, with three resident staff and a number of consultants. Longmore was a hospital for chronic patients ('incurables' was the old parlance). Kathleen Branson did feel that she had experienced prejudice as a woman in medicine and that had limited her opportunities of advancement.

Educated at the Hall School Weybridge and St Felix Southwold, Kathleen Branson did her medical training at the London (Royal Free Hospital) School of Medicine where she graduated in 1938, MB BS. She had

[1] Scottish pioneer surgeon who manned the battlefield hospitals.

house posts at the Royal Free working for Cecil Joll and at the Royal Cancer Hospital (the Marsden). She took the FRCS in 1941 and the MS in 1946.

She was appointed to the Bruntsfield and Longmore Hospital in Edinburgh where she spent her working life. She took the Edinburgh Fellowship in 1956 because she was working in that city. When she was working she had resident domestic help and after retirement, at age sixty-two, she had a daily. She was a Soroptimist. She was interested in campanology and in ornithology. She lived to a good age, dying at eighty-nine.

Margaret Snelling had two careers; first as a surgeon then as a radiotherapist. She became Director of the Myerstein Institute at the Middlesex Hospital. Her greatest pride was that she was the first woman to be President of the European Association of Radiology and that in her international work she had encouraged emerging radiotherapy units in developing countries world-wide.

Educated at Wimbledon High School, a GPDST school, and the London (Royal Free Hospital) School of Medicine she graduated MB BS London in 1938. The difficult disruptions of hospital training in World War II intervened as she did her early posts. She did house jobs at the Royal Free and at Chelmsford and Essex. Then the war intervened and she spent a year in 1940 as assistant radiotherapist at the Myerstein Institute of Radiotherapy at the Middlesex Hospital, during which time she took the MRCP and the Diploma in Medical radiology. From 1941 to 1944 she was surgeon at Chase Farm Emergency Hospital, becoming experienced widely in surgery, taking the FRCS in 1944. She was assistant neurosurgeon at the South London Hospital for Women and Children. Then she was seconded to Haymeads Emergency Hospital, Bishop's Stortford, where she did both general, orthopaedic and thoracic surgery, and from 1946 to 1947 was doing neurosurgery in Sheffield. She became aware that at the end of the war the previous post-holders would return from service and lay claim to their jobs and as a woman in surgery she was not sanguine about her chances of getting a consultant's post.

Margaret Snelling returned to the Middlesex Hospital and embarked on her future career in radiotherapy. She became FFR in 1952 and FRCP in 1968. She was consultant at the Marie Curie Hospital and at the Middlesex Hospital where she worked for Sir Brian Windeyer, eventually succeeding him there. Her special contribution was on the treatment of carcinoma of the cervix and of the uterus.

She developed a treatment for carcinoma of the cervix that was a combination of intra-cavity radium with arc therapy that had advantages over planning a conventional multi-field technique. The technique was especially developed for treatment of the parametria when supplementing the intra-cavity radium treatment of carcinoma of the cervix since the poor depth dose obtained in the larger patients made it impossible to give adequate irradiation to the pelvic glands through conventional anterior and posterior fields. With the introduction of arc therapy it was possible to give an additional 3000 to 4000 rads to the parametria and glands without approaching the tolerance level of the skin. She pioneered the use of computers in radiotherapy and this was the subject of her Presidential address to the British Association of Radiology.

Renowned for teaching overseas postgraduate students she visited centres in India, Egypt and the Sudan, and generously shared her experience of treating carcinoma of the cervix and gynaecological cancers with a view to helping those in under-developed countries without sophisticated equipment and where the cost of effective treatment was prohibitive. Her work was sponsored by the International Atomic Energy Authority.

Margaret Snelling was a single lady, sociable and gregarious, a keen tennis player and was in the Fencing team for the University of London. She mothered her nieces when her sister-in-law died.

Women Fellows in World War II – FRCS 1940 to 1945
Women of the Fellowship back to India and abroad

Perin Kavasji Mullaferoze had qualified with the MB BS Bombay and with the MRCS in 1937 and took the FRCS in 1940. Although it was war-time and travel was difficult, she got back to India to practise in Bombay. She was consultant surgeon and medical director in the Children's Orthopaedic Hospital, Bombay. She was a single lady. In India, she had two resident servants. She worked all her life finishing up as medical director of the hospital.

Women Fellows in World War II – FRCS 1940 to 1945
Women of the Fellowship in Research Neuro-otology after Grievous Injury in the Bombing

Margaret Dix had an unusual career as a neuro-otologist in research and was directed into that career because of injuries received in the blitz.

Educated at Sherborne and the London (Royal Free Hospital) School of Medicine, she graduated MB BS London in 1937. She was house surgeon to Douglas McLaggan and intent on a surgical career taking the FRCS in 1943. In World War II she received injuries in a bombing raid causing facial disfigurement; she was a beautiful young woman and was treated by Sir Archibald McIndoe. Jean Dollar, the eye surgeon, removed fragments of glass from her eye. She had to give up the idea of a surgical career.

After the war, Margaret Dix went to work in the Medical Research Council, MRC, Otology Unit at Queen Square, the Hospital for Neurology and Neurosurgery, and specialised in the neuro-otology of the inner ear and central nervous system, publishing more than 100 papers. She won the W J Harrison prize for otology in 1954, the RSM Dalby prize in 1958, the Norman Gamble prize in 1958 and took the MD in 1957.

There is a Dix Memorial window to Margaret Dix in the old church in Badger, a Shropshire village , where her father, the Reverend Archibald Dix, had been rector. Designed by Jane Gray ARCA of Shrewsbury, it is a roundel with a representation of the middle ear referring to Dr Dix's life of healing, a celtic knotwork, the four elements: the sun as fire, the cloud strata as air, green fields, trees and ploughed fields as earth, a surging wave as water with droplets of spray. There are seven guiding stars near the sun. She willed the old rectory to the Dix trust on her death.

Women Fellows in World War II – FRCS 1940 to 1945
Women of the Fellowship into ENT – treatment of the Deaf Child

Edith Whetnall revolutionised the treatment of the deaf child in her inspiring career as an ENT surgeon. She stressed two important concepts. Firstly that there is almost always some residual hearing in the deaf child and it is vital that the diagnosis is made and amplification provided early to utilise the small residual hearing. Only then can speech be encouraged to develop normally. Secondly she realised the importance of mother (or family) being taught to interact with the deaf baby and deaf child to work toward good intelligible speech.

For the first, Edith Whetnall was fortunate that technological advances in amplification coincided with her work. For the second, she set up mother and baby clinics and residential hostels where they could stay while undergoing diagnostic tests and being taught the techniques of communication.

Her career is marked by a lecture named after her, the Edith Whetnall lecture, given in the ENT Section of the Royal Society of Medicine.

Edith was born in Hull and did her medical training in King's College Hospital (KCH) where she knew at once as she qualified MB BS in 1938 that it was in ear, nose and throat surgery that she wanted to pursue her career. She was house surgeon at the Horton and Surrey Hospitals, part of the KCH Group, and then was registrar at King's. She took the FRCS in 1940 and the MS in 1944.

She was clinical assistant and did otological research at the National Hospital for Nervous Diseases, Queen Square. She then became consultant otologist to the LCC (London County Council) School Medical Services succeeding Sir Terence Cawthorne at Horton. She was assistant surgeon to the Royal National Throat, Nose and Ear Hospital.

Edith Whetnall established a clinic in Golden Square, London to detect deafness in young children in 1947 and from that many other clinics were developed. She founded a hostel in Ealing for mothers and deaf babies where they could stay while they had their tests; and then another hostel for older deaf children while they had their investigations. She was the pioneer of realising the importance of the mother, and the family, in the treatment of the deaf baby and deaf child. While always showing empathy and encouragement to her small patients and their families, she demanded high standards of the staff who worked with her who sometimes felt a frisson approaching terror that they might not measure up to the exacting standards she wanted from them. In recognition of the importance of her work, the Nuffield Foundation gave £100,000 to fund the Nuffield Hearing and Speech Centre in 1963.

Edith Whetnall was appointed consultant aural surgeon at St Giles Hospital, Camberwell and at Queen Mary Hospital Carshalton and practised from Wimpole Street. She published the definitive work *The*

Deaf Child with D B Fry in 1964. And posthumously her husband, Dr Robert Niven MD FRCP, always a great supporter of her work, carried on her work in a book called *Learning To Hear* with Niven. She had had a serious car accident in 1945 which impaired her health. She died in 1965 at the early age of fifty-five.

Carolina Mathilda van Dorp took the MRCS in 1941 and the FRCS the same year and was Carolina Mathilda Sim in 1946. She later trained in ENT becoming Consultant as Mrs Carolina Lessington-Smith at Kings College Hospital. Career unknown, possibly returned to Leiden.

Women Fellows in World War II – FRCS 1940-1945
Women of the Fellowship into Thoracic Surgery

Two of our surgical Fellows became thoracic surgeons, Doreen Nightingale and Betty Slessor, very much contemporaries of each other, though Betty Slessor received her FRCS England in later life as one who had been in practice for over 20 years – before that she had the FRCS Edinburgh.

Doreen Nightingale was the consultant thoracic surgeon at University College Hospital, UCH. She was a technically excellent and speedy surgeon. She trained at University College London, UCL, and University College Hospital, UCH, and qualified MB BS in 1940 when she was the McGrath scholar in medicine. She went on to take the FRCS and the MS in the same year 1945 at the end of the war. After the war, she went to Harvard Medical School, Boston, to learn her thoracic surgery and where she was Dorothy Temple Gross research fellow in tuberculosis. On her return she was appointed at age thirty-nine first assistant and deputy director of the professorial surgical unit at UCH. UCH however never did support the formation of a cardiac unit with the expense and staff needed for pump bypass work though a tentative foray was carried out.

In 1955 she was appointed to the National Temperance Hospital and consultant thoracic surgeon to UCH, the first thoracic surgeon that UCH had had on the staff. As a thoracic surgeon she operated mainly on tuberculosis of the lung and contracted TB herself (and was treated successfully) and also carcinoma of lung and oesophagus and continued to do some general surgery. She married her long-standing friend, a colleague Hugh Burt relatively late in life, perhaps feeling that an earlier marriage would not have been looked on kindly by the hospital.

Betty Slesser was consultant thoracic surgeon at the Groby Road Hospital, Leicester. She graduated from Edinburgh MB ChB in 1941 and took the Edinburgh FRCS in 1945. (She was granted the FRCS England twenty-seven years later). She got good surgical experience as surgical registrar in Plymouth and as first assistant on the professorial surgical unit at Sheffield.

She was appointed consultant thoracic surgeon at Groby Road Hospital Leicester where she pioneered open heart surgery. One small patient whose hole-in-the-heart Miss Slesser closed, with Philip Slade her registrar ably assisting, related her story to me years later when she was in her forties and I had asked about the provenance of her sternal scar. She told me that when she was a child, Miss Slessor had sat up all night with her on the intensive care unit as it was the first such operation that they had done at Leicester and she showed me photographs of herself as an eight-year-old with Miss Slessor on the ward on Christmas Day. Numbers of cardiac surgeons around the country were grateful to her for the training and experience they got with her as registrars.

Betty Slesser married JA Chatterton and retired to Thurcaston, Leicester.

Of the fourteen women surgeons who became FRCS during the years of World War II, six went into obstetrics and gynaecology, two into thoracic surgery, two into ENT – of whom one was a pioneering influence on treatment of the deaf child, one into neuro-otology research after grievous war injuries, two only in general surgery, and one of these having spent the war operating on general and neurosurgical and orthopaedic casualties with great distinction, went into radiotherapy where she also made a distinctive impact in a London teaching hospital. One who came from Bombay returned there to work as surgeon and director of a paediatric orthopaedic hospital. One only stayed a general surgeon returning to Edinburgh and working in a small women's hospital founded by the early pioneer doctors. Half of the Fellows married; two had children, one had four and one three, and one who was single adopted a daughter.

Women Fellows in World War II – FRCS 1940 to 1945

Eleanor Mary Mills FRCS 1940
Katharine Marian Robinson 1911-1998 FRCS 1940
Janet Elizabeth Bottomley (Janet Ritchie) 1915-1995 FRCS 1940 MD 1943 FRCOG
Dorothy Margaret Knott (Mrs Dorothy Barclay) 1914-1964 FRCS 1941 MS 1944
Katharine Isabel Liebert 1912-1965 FRCS 1941 MB ChB Manchester FRCOG
Eileen Mary Whapham 1907-2002 FRCS 1941 FRCOG 1954
Kathleen Mildred Harold Branson 1912-2001 FRCS 1941 MS 1946 FRCS Ed 1956
Margaret Dorothy Snelling 1914-1997 FRCS 1944 MRCP 1941 DMR 1942 FFR 1952 FRCP 1968
Miss Perin Kavasji Mullaferoze FRCS 1940
Carolina Mathilda van Dorp (Mrs Lessington-Smith) FRCS 1941
Margaret Ruth Dix 1902-1991 FRCS 1943 MD 1957
Edith Aileen Maude Whetnall 1910-1965 FRCS 1940 MS 1944
Doreen Nightingale 1916-2002 FRCS 1945 MS 1945
Betty Vivian Slesser FRCS Ed 1945 FRCS Eng 1972 MB ChB Ed

CHAPTER 6

Women Fellows in the Years of Austerity – FRCS 1946 to 1953

THE immediate post-war years were experienced as a time of continuing austerity.

Thirty-three women attained the FRCS in the eight years from 1946 to 1953. There were two taking the Fellowship in 1946, four in 1947, two in 1948, five in 1949 and one only in 1950. There were four in 1951, six in 1952, and eight in 1953.

A different battle was being enacted on behalf of women doctors at that time, different from the resistance put up by the Royal College of Surgeons forty years before against accepting women into their Fellowship. This was the pressure put on the great London teaching hospitals, all-male bastions of long heritage, to accept women as students. True, some had briefly accepted a few girls, hand-picked for intelligence and decorum, during World War I when the number of men medical students had fallen and the tuition fees that the girls brought were necessary to keep the medical schools going, but the benevolence of St Mary's and the London and St George's proved only temporary. Once the men came back in sufficient numbers after the war and the medical student places filled up, they ceased to accept girl students, St George's directly the war was over, the London two years later, St Mary's in 1924 and Charing Cross and Westminster in 1928.

Sir William Goodenough exerted the pressure: a grant from the UGC, the University Grants Committee, would only be forth-coming to those medical schools that accepted women as well as men. It was necessary also to say, 'men' as well as women, for the London (Royal Free Hospital) School of Medicine for Women had to drop half their title and accept a handful of lads, who later formed a successful rugger team. All the medical schools capitulated, some more grudgingly than others, and for a long time exerting a quota against the number of girls. Some like UCH, University College Hospital, had always exercised a quota against the girls from UCL, University College, taking the top six women on the class list and all the men who passed, leaving the other women to seek their clinical training elsewhere. St Bartholomew's, pleading a lack of facilities for women, made a doomed attempt to do a bargain with the Royal Free - they would take the Royal Free men if the Free would take the number of women allotted to Barts, a ruse that was stepped on very promptly.

As the ancient endowed all-male medical schools bowed to the inevitable and admitted their handful of women undergraduates in order to obtain the financial support from the University Grants Committee, it was still to be a long time before the famous, privileged and heavily endowed colleges of Oxford and Cambridge would slowly follow suit. They tumbled to the inevitable one by one. It was a matter of time. And patience. The much smaller in number and less well-endowed women's colleges, Girton and Newnham at Cambridge, and later New College, and at Oxford, Somerville, Lady Margaret Hall, St Hilda's, St Hugh's, and St Anne's, with varying degrees of enthusiasm and reluctance would also become co-educational.

Our thirty-three Fellows from 1946 to 1954 are listed on page 137. Four of them came from India and returned there; of these, two from the Lady Hardinge College New Delhi came to take the Fellowship and returned to professorships in their medical school. There were two from New Zealand. Three came from Australia. One came from and returned to Cyprus. One worked in Tanzania. Four went into eye surgery, two into ENT, one into radiotherapy, one into orthopaedics, one into pathology research, six into gynaecology – not all of whom became consultants – and finally, five planned to do general surgery – again, not all becoming consultants.

Women Fellows in the Years of Austerity – FRCS 1946 to 1953
Women of the Fellowship into General Surgery

The five women surgical Fellows who were intent on a career in general surgery and who attained the FRCS in the post-war years of austerity can justly be celebrated. Four of the five became consultant surgeons, one within the circle of women for women's hospitals, but one to a busy district general hospital, and one, while appointed to her own teaching hospital was subsequently voted on to the Council - the first women to be elected to the Council of the Royal College of Surgeons. One further, having put herself through medical school and surgical training after a first class degree at Oxford was taken under the wing of the Department of Overseas Development and worked as a consultant surgeon in Bahrain and in the West Indies, and on returning to England found locum consultant posts in retirement. The fifth having held the fort surgically in a district general hospital during the war years did not manage to stay in hospital surgical practice after the war and found her future in general practice.

Muriel Crouch was a consultant in general surgery, one of the few. She would like to have studied music but moved from music to medicine as a schoolgirl at High Wycombe Girls Grammar School. She did not come from a medical background, her father was a stockbroker in the City, but to her medicine was a calling. She trained at the London (Royal Free Hospital) School of Medicine and, graduating MB BS in 1940, held house posts there and at the Elizabeth Garrett Anderson, accompanying the students out to Oster House in Hertfordshire during the War, working as a lecturer in anatomy in the Royal Free, teaching the students. She took the FRCS in 1946 at the end of the war and was appointed as consultant to the Elizabeth Garrett Anderson Hospital, the Marie Curie Unit at the Mount Vernon Hospital in Northwood and the South London Hospital for Women and Children where she spent all her working life, living in Camberwell, and was renowned as a skilful surgeon, a good opinion, kindly, but withal a firm and strong-minded character.

Muriel Crouch was a single lady and in retirement she and her sister Beryl bought a house in Hunstanton and were never without their binoculars on their walks or in the car observing the rich birdlife of the Norfolk coast. Edna Wearn, a nursing sister and matron who had done work for the WHO, and Mary Fagg who had been highly respected for her work as a missionary nurse and midwife in Yakusi in the Belgian Congo, completed the household. Muriel was not interested in domestic and cooking skills. She was a member of the Christian Medical Fellowship and took her ethics to her work. She lectured extensively on Christian and moral problems in medicine, travelling to Finland, Rumania, Bangladesh, the USA and Australia. The titles of some of her publications give an indication of her concerns: 'A basis for medical ethics', 'Suffering, does God care?', 'Lying to patients – to lie or not to lie – a perennial problem', 'Christian doctor in the making', '. Imparting ethics to medical students', 'Coming to terms with suffering and death'.

Muriel Waterfall was an outstanding surgeon, trained in the classical manner to be able to tackle the full range of general surgery, including thoracic, in a district general hospital. She came from a large family, a brother and three sisters; one sister, like her, studied medicine, and became a consultant anaesthetist. Her father was the director of Post Office Savings and her mother was a teacher.

Educated at Tollington Preparatory School in Muswell Hill, and then at St George's Harpenden, and Manchester University, Muriel Waterfall did her clinical studies at the Royal Free Hospital where she qualified MB BS London in 1944. She did house jobs and her surgical training at Colchester, Winchester, and the Hammersmith Hospital/Royal Postgraduate Medical School, was senior surgical registrar at the Brompton Hospital and spent time both at Johns Hopkins in Baltimore and the Lahey Clinic in Boston. She learned her surgical skills with Sir Heneage Ogilvie, Russell Brock and Harry Platt.

Muriel Waterfall was appointed consultant surgeon at Kingston Hospital at a time when women were seldom able to get appointments outside the small circle of women's hospitals, and rapidly made a formidable reputation as a skilful and indefatigable operative surgeon. No-one told Muriel Waterfall in the operating theatre that it was too late to send for the next patient nor complain that the list might not finish on time. She was a powerhouse in the hospital, respected by all. She also worked at the New Victoria Hospital Richmond and the Royal Hospital Richmond.

In 1980, at age sixty, she began to spend her annual leave as a locum surgeon in Nepal and when she retired at sixty-five she went back to work in Nepal and also in the Ascension Islands and in Zambia. She died early at age sixty-nine.

Marjorie Powys was the resident surgical officer at St Charles' Hospital, in Ladbroke Grove, west London, then a busy district general hospital, throughout World War II.

Educated at The Mount in Leamington Spa, at St Margaret's Bushey, and the Royal Free Hospital, qualifying MB BS London 1935 Marjorie Powys went on the district delivering babies in the community as obstetric assistant, taking the DRCOG in 1940. She had planned to be a medical missionary but in the event, the war and her health conspired against this. She practised surgery as assistant medical officer 1, from 1940 to 1947 at

St Charles' Hospital, Ladbroke Grove, North Kensington during the war when it was an LCC Hospital and took the FRCS in 1949 and attempted the MS by examination. After the war, a definitive surgical post was not forthcoming and she went to work in the Brook Lane Medical Mission in South London and was in general practice for twenty-eight years. She retired at age sixty-six in 1977 and did various locums afterwards and died age seventy-one. She never felt that she was discriminated against as a woman in surgery and felt that part-time training would encourage more women to persist in a career in surgery. She is remembered with respect in the Ladbroke Grove area of North Kensington because of her surgical work at St Charles' during the war years.

Phyllis George was appointed consultant surgeon at the Royal Free Hospital and became the surgeon for the liver unit of Professor Sheila Sherlock, the famed professor of medicine, who persuaded her to undertake the demanding practice of hepato-biliary surgery for her patients with cirrhosis, hepato-portal shunts, which Phyllis performed with great technical skill but without becoming as interested in the liver as Dame Sheila Sherlock. She also had a thyroid surgery practice and started the breast unit and was on the emergency surgical rota.

Phyllis was the elder of two girls, daughters of a father with a PhD in statistics, who worked for a large distillery in Bromley-by-Bow, a man who would like to have done medicine and become a surgeon himself. The two girls went to the City of London School for Girls and were evacuated in the war to Keighley, a happy time, and where Phyllis took an interest in the history of the Bronte sisters and their writing. Her father, Pop, decided Phyllis should become a doctor and she saw no reason to disagree. Her sister became a Guy's nurse and married and had two children. Phyllis was a quiet conventional person, with gentle manners, who ruffled no feathers.

After house appointments, she was Senior Casualty Officer at the Royal Free, and was house surgeon and registrar to both Geraldine Barry and George Quist. She is unaware what drew her to surgery, certainly no macho desire to lead or dominate, rather a quiet conviction that she was good with her hands, and could operate efficiently. Doubtless, Geraldine Barry, doyen of the women surgeons at the Royal Free, would have cast around among the medical students for one who might succeed her, and Phyllis was the choice.

Phyllis George went to America where she spent two years in Memorial Hospital in New York, a cancer hospital where she did get quite a lot of operating and they would have liked her to stay. She said that she felt flattered but also felt that what talents she had should be devoted to her home country.

Although appointed consultant surgeon to the Royal Free at a time when it still cherished its past history as the London School of Medicine for Women, Phyllis was no feminist. She would not meet a woman candidate for the newly proposed Chair of Surgery at the Free although it was a tradition that candidates for a post on the staff should do the rounds of introducing themselves to the present surgeons of the hospital, though this may have been as much as not wishing to be involved in the whole process of king-making as any lack of fellow-feeling for women.

Phyllis George was the first woman FRCS to be elected to the Council of the Royal College of Surgeons, 1979. She was mindful of the honour and said that her heart beat fiercely as she first took her seat on the Council. As she said, she was not very tall, and felt small by the men. She was concerned that she did not do anything that would make it more difficult for women who came after and on reflection wondered if she could have done more. It was certainly not a position that she had pushed for and felt that it must have been organised behind the scenes. To the fury of feminists, it was reported that she brought honey cakes that she had baked herself for the men at tea-time at the meeting of Council, a feature said to be perpetuated by the second woman on the Council, Averil Mansfield, and akin to the tyranny for the wives of American Presidents having to bake the best brownies. Nor would she protest when meetings in College were addressed by the President as 'Gentlemen' and Fellows responded to the Chair with 'Mr President, Gentlemen'.... She was a single lady who continued to live opposite the Royal Free at its new Hampstead site in her retirement.

Betty Underhill had a remarkable career, putting herself through medical school after a research career and teaching. She became a surgeon, practising all over the world.

Educated at the North London Collegiate School she went up to Somerville College Oxford where she took first class Honours in her BA Oxon. Her parents who were teachers were unwilling for her to read medicine. She went on to do studies in genetic cytology for a science degree and then taught at Kings Norton Grammar School, Birmingham and the County School for Girls, Ealing, saving enough money to put herself through medical training. She entered the Royal Free in 1943 as a mature student age thirty-five and was a prize winner in anatomy, paediatrics, and public health and qualified in 1947, MB BS London, at age thirty-nine. She had posts at the Royal Free, Leicester Royal Infirmary, Chase Farm Hospital, Whipps Cross, and the Central Middlesex, gaining good experience and taking the FRCS in 1953 at age forty-five. She had further training at the Frenchay Hospital, Bristol and the Royal Marsden Hospital.

In 1956 Betty Underhill was appointed by the Ministry of Overseas Development to work at first in Bahrain, then in the West Indies where she was lecturer in surgery in Barbados in the University of the West Indies. In 1957, when first appointed consultant surgeon to the Government Hospital in Bahrain, her letter to her old school gives a vivid account of the medical and social life as an expatriate surgeon, reflecting life in a former age. She wrote Founders' Day Greetings to the North London Collegiate School where Dr (later Dame) Kitty Anderson was then the headmistress and had formerly been the head at Kings Norton Grammar School Birmingham where Betty had taught before embarking on medical training.

The text of Betty Underhill's letter from 'The Government Hospital, Bahrain. Persian Gulf. 12 03 1957' was as follows:

> Dear Dr Anderson, Millie Hancock tells me that she gave you some news of me when she met you recently and I thought perhaps I might combine my Founders Day greetings with a little first-hand account of life out here.
>
> It was nearly a year ago that I was asked if I would come out as consultant surgeon to the government hospital which is shortly to be greatly extended by the addition of a huge new building. The political situation made arrangements difficult, however, and it was not till the beginning of January that I arrived to take up my post. Bahrain is an island of contrasts. The native population is predominantly Arab, but there are many Persians and Indians, all adding to the difficulty of the language problem. Many

of the merchants and Shaikhs (this is one of the few remaining independent Shaikhates) are fabulously rich with an income running into millions of pounds sterling a year. They have however very little idea how to spend this immense wealth. The men go to Europe on elaborate journeys and unfortunately fall a prey to money-grabbers everywhere. They are persuaded to buy expensive toys, useless here. One arrived with a vast television set and was furious to find that the pictures were not included! One has, thus, the state banquet, served in a vast palace under wonderful pendants imported from Venice, with the meal served on the coarsest of kitchen china and eaten of course only with the right hand. In deference to European guests, cutlery is usually provided and I am cowardly enough to use it as the thought of grabbing a handful of sheep roasted whole is more than I can bear.

There is a very large American and European colony working the oilfield and running many of the government enterprises. Purdah is very strict indeed and all women from the ages of about ten years are entirely enveloped in a black garment. This covers them quite literally from top to toe without hole for nose or eyes and the direction of their travel is the only indication of the position of their face. They usually have a child a year and as they eat only the scraps which are left by the men folk, they are usually undernourished and anaemic. Even the ladies of the royal household are badly fed, though hugely fat as they stuff themselves with chocolates and other unsuitable foods. The women are almost all completely illiterate and the level of intelligence is very poor, possibly because the anaemia makes the brain chronically short of oxygen. Haemoglobin levels of 10-20% are common - and yet they make astonishing recoveries from severe illnesses and injuries. Medical problems among the women and children are very largely those of ignorance and a very primitive social system. Road accidents are devastating as the Arab loves a vast fast Cadillac and burns are commonly fatal. The people cook on a Primus stove which is always being lurched over and their loose garments become a sheet of flame. Surgery amongst the men is much more like that at home. Their nutrition is generally much better than that of the women.

The climate is difficult – at present the temperature is perfect, daily sun with breeze and cloud, but for the three summer months I am told that the heat and humidity are shattering but our rooms are very huge and air-conditioned. Social life is quite different here from what it is at home. There is so much more of it and it is on a more elaborate scale. One reckons to be in full evening dress two or three times each week and a party in an ordinary flat will consist of eighty to a hundred people. The cost of living is very high and food largely tinned or frozen but catering is very elaborate.

Salaries are enormous in comparison with England and there is no Income tax whatever so most people manage to save £1000 to £2000 a year. Up to the present, I have found life much more fun than at home – very Arabian Nights entertainment.

Yours very sincerely,
Betty Underhill (NLCS 1918-27).

After Bahrain, Betty Underhill was surgeon in Barbados and lecturer in the University of the West Indies. She retired age sixty-five in 1973 and continued working as a locum consultant in Worthing and in Chichester. She was single. She had done much travelling, circumnavigating the globe once by the northern route and once in the southern hemisphere. She was expert in photography, and had shown her work at many major international exhibitions. She enjoyed gardening and cookery. She was a keen member of the Medical Women's Federation and an active member of the Royal Society of Medicine.

Kathleen Frith graduated MB BS London in 1946 and was surgical registrar at Leicester Royal Infirmary, taking the FRCS in 1952, and senior surgical registrar at the Hospital for Sick Children, Great Ormond Street. She married M Barton and they lived in Kingussie, Invernesshire, and they had a daughter Susan. Kathleen Frith retired in 1974 because of aortic valve incompetence and bacterial endocarditis.

Agnes Robertson Donald Bartels was an officer in the RAF during World War II. She was in Changi, Singapore. After the war she trained at the West London and qualified MB BS London with honours in 1951 and took the FRCS in 1953. As a squadron leader in 1956 in an RAF Sunderland flying boat, she saved the life of a ship's captain, the master of the Fort Charlotte, by operating on him for acute appendicitis.

Women Fellows in the Years of Austerity – FRCS 1946 to 1953
Women of the Fellowship into Gynaecology

Six women went into gynaecology, three of them becoming consultants, Wendy Lewington at the South London Hospital for Women and Children who, together with Margaret Louden in general surgery, maintained that hospital in high esteem over many years, and Marjorie Dunster and Jean Burton Brown who became established in general hospitals outside the inner circle of women for women's hospitals. The three who went eventually into general practice, Dorothy Ridout, Elaine Rankin (nee Lister), and Daphne Scott, were able to utilise their particular skills for their patients, such is the nature of their speciality.

Wendy Lewington became the consultant obstetrician and gynaecologist to the South London Hospital for Women and Children and to the Royal Homeopathic Hospital, following in the footsteps of the founders Eleanor Davies-Colley and Maud Mary Chadburn, when her immediate predecessor Edith Hall had been in poor health and retired. The work she did and her eminence there was important

Wendy Lewington was educated at the Notting Hill and Ealing High School, a GPDST (Girls' Public Day School Trust) school, where she and another girl both destined for medical school were taught in a class of two and allowed to take the first MB from school instead of, with a group of other girls, taking the higher school certificate in science subjects. They both passed, the other girl went on to Scotland and Wendy Lewington to the London (Royal Free Hospital) School of Medicine when her training was all through the war years. She qualified MB BS London in 1946.

The war was barely over and her house doctor posts were to be at the Arlesley Hospital which had been part of the Emergency Medical Service, but when she got there, there had been confusion (a situation not unknown in recent times) and the posts had been allotted to others and, trying to be accommodating, they offered her work in pathology. She was naturally keen to get started in clinical work and turned down the pathology and she found and applied for Taunton, where she did first the house physician post and then a house surgeon which included both general surgery and gynaecology which she thoroughly enjoyed and was encouraged by her consultants to go for a surgical future and advised that she should take the Fellowship whichever route she chose. She went on therefore to a senior house officer post at the Hammersmith Hospital in gynaecology and a number of locums in general surgery while she took both the primary and then the final Fellowship. At the West Middlesex Hospital, David Stern was her mentor before she went on to work for John Howkins at the Hampstead General and Dame Josephine Barnes at the Elizabeth Garrett Anderson Hospital, all of whom were impressed with her surgical skills and supported her. After a locum as senior registrar at the West Middlesex, she was ready to apply for consultant posts but it was not easy to break into a suitable post. She had the FRCS in 1950 and the MRCOG in 1955.

At the South London Hospital for Women and Children, the gynaecologist Edith Hall had suffered ill health and retired early, subsequently dying at age sixty-one, and Wendy Lewington was appointed in her place. The post was only four sessions at first but there were also a further two sessions at the Royal Homeopathic Hospital and she spent her working life at the two hospitals. Her anaesthetist, originally Christine John, was also with her at the Homeopathic, and later Marjorie Davies. On the general surgical side, Gwen Smith was followed by Margaret Louden and Muriel Crouch, and later came Betty Gordon.

Wendy became FRCOG in 1971. She remained single. She had not felt prejudice against her as a woman in medicine and indeed had had good encouragement and support from her colleagues and her seniors. She valued her friendships from Royal Free days, Kate Fussell who went to Wigan and Elaine Lister, later Rankin, to Carlisle. While she expressed herself in favour of part-time posts and training for those who needed it, she herself had always worked full-time.

Marjorie Dunster became consultant gynaecologist at Southmeads Hospital, Bristol. She was educated at Newport High School, both parents were head teachers. She did her medical training both in Bristol and in London, graduating with MB ChB Bristol and MB BS London in 1939, took the MD London and the ChM Bristol and the MRCOG in

1943, and the FRCS in 1947. She later took the DMRT in 1953 and became FRCOG in 1960. She married Douglas Bennett FRCS in 1950 at age thirty-five and they had a daughter. She was a clinical teacher in the University as well as being consultant in obstetrics and gynaecology at Southmead Hospital, Bristol. She lived to a good age, dying at eighty-four in 2000.

Jean Burton-Brown became consultant in obstetrics and gynaecology to Canterbury Hospital in Kent. She trained at the Royal Free Hospital graduating MB BS London 1940. She was registrar at the Samaritan Hospital for Women and took the MRCOG in 1944 and the FRCS in 1948. She was first assistant in the Nuffield Department of Obstetrics and Gynaecology at Oxford under Professor Chassar Moir and won the gold medal in the MD examination in December 1946 for her work on placental research. She became consultant to the Canterbury and Thanet Hospital in East Kent in 1950 where she spent her working life over the next twenty-three years. She was elected FRCOG in 1963, and retired in 1973.

Dorothy Ridout was the fifth of eight children of Charles Ridout FRCS, consultant surgeon at the Royal Portsmouth Hospital; her father was among the first surgeons to specialise in ENT and was senior surgeon at the hospital and at the Portsmouth Southern counties Eye and Ear Hospital, Gosport War Memorial Hospital and Midhurst Cottage Hospital. He was commissioned as major in World War I and served in Salonika and Italy. He organised meetings both locally and in the Royal Society of Medicine and published in his field. As World War II broke out he was responsible for organising cover for those who went off to fight. He was a man of great physical powers and a clever and industrious man.

His daughter Dorothy went to Cheltenham Ladies' College on a scholarship and she and best friend Dorothy Chapman there, later Symons, both went on to enter medical school. She trained at the London (Royal Free Hospital) School of Medicine and qualified MB BS London in 1943 and it was her intention to become a gynaecologist. Her father had died age sixty-six in 1941 and two of her brothers were fighting in the war, one went through Flanders and Dunkirk, one – a doctor – serving in naval engagement in Narvik on the Norwegian coast. It was in the early years of the war and life was somewhat disorganised. She did her early posts in Northampton and later felt that not having done a house job at her own hospital told against her advancement. She did various training posts and took the MRCOG in 1951 and the FRCS in 1952. Unfortunately she did not then get support from the gynaecology department from her own teaching hospital. She contracted pulmonary tuberculosis and had part of one lung removed but made a complete recovery. She obtained an appointment to work with an older woman doctor in a practice in Harrogate and took over when her colleague retired. She enjoyed general practice and was able to use her specialised training in family planning clinics and in teaching which work was recognised by the awarding of the FRCOG in 1986 by the college. Her husband was a PhD and worked in the tanning business in leather manufacture. Her married name was Shortridge. She was forty-three when their son was born. He is an accountant and did not follow her into the medical profession. She continued working until retirement age, still working part-time, four sessions a week, forty years after she initially qualified.

Elaine Rankin, Elaine Lister as she was then, was surgical registrar with her Fellowship working in obstetrics and gynaecology in the City Hospital Carlisle for Josephine Williamson. She had been registrar formerly to Josephine Barnes in London and had the FRCS but as yet there was no clear path to a consultant vacancy and Dame Barnes had responded to a plea from her friend and colleague in Carlisle to provide her with a competent registrar. As Elaine gave a lecture on her subject to the local general practitioners, the course of her working life changed as she met Dr Archibald MacPherson Rankin who was in a family practice with his father. Marriage and two children followed and Elaine Rankin eventually joined the partnership full-time and she thrived and enjoyed her work, though Dame Josephine Barnes was said to be not best pleased at the loss of Elaine from the ranks of consultant gynaecologists.

Elaine Lister's brother and father were in the army. Her father was Major Charles Martin Lister MC Royal Artillery who had fought in Gallipolli. Elaine's horsemanship came from her early family environment. She was educated at Babbington High School in Eltham, in Hillingdon School, and in Cheltenham, and trained at the Royal Free where she qualified MB BS London in 1946. She was prosector in anatomy at the College with Professor Raymond Last while she studied for the primary and took the final Fellowship while working as surgical registrar to Dame Josephine Barnes at the Elizabeth Garrett Anderson Hospital, and then moved to work at the City Maternity Hospital, Carlisle under Josephine Williamson.

Having trained under two such powerful women it was not surprising that she spoke with authority and she had a phrase that would cap and deal with a long peroration of woes from a patient, 'And what of it?' she would succinctly ask. As though to say, 'Your point is?'

Elaine kept her interest in gynaecology and wrote *The Problem of Birth Control* in 1972. She made and kept many good friends from her Royal Free and training days and was area secretary in the Medical Women's Federation.

Elaine Rankin was a JP for over thirty years, vice-chairman of the local board, a governor of the Nelson-Thomlinson School in Wigton, and on the management committee of a nursing home in Silloth. In her sixties she was working whole-time, and did not feel that she had experienced prejudice as a woman in medicine, but she did feel that part-time work would help to keep women at work in medicine and, broad-mindedly, also viewed part-time training as an acceptable initiative. Working full-time, she had daily help in the home. Her son and daughter were grown-up and her daughter has followed her parents into medicine and is a consultant rheumatologist in Birmingham. She was near eighty when she died and a woman patient, waiting to enter the packed church at her funeral, said to Elaine's husband, 'I was frightened of her – but I did like her.' Many of Dame Jo's patients might have said the same.

Daphne Scott trained at St Andrews, qualifying MB ChB in 1943, and took the MRCP in 1948 and the FRCS in 1953. She went into family planning being clinical assistant at University College Hospital and medical officer to the Croydon and Oxted Clinics. She worked part-time, about six sessions a week and she stated that, for her, managing children precluded training in full-time hospital work. She had daily help, about twenty-five hours a week..

On the question of prejudice against women, she wrote that she had met many men who would never have made the appointment of a woman their first choice especially in general practice and in consultant hospital work. However she did not feel that she personally had been discriminated against for, as she said, she had exceptional qualifications with both the MRCP and the FRCS. She had a medical marriage and children and the choice was hers.

Women Fellows in the Years of Austerity – FRCS 1946 to 1953
Women of the Fellowship who worked abroad: Tanzania

Marion Phillips with the FRCS in 1948, worked as a surgeon in Tanzania all her working life. She was full-time as a surgeon, had daily domestic help – seven hours a day for five and a half days a week, never felt prejudiced against as a woman in medicine. Her married name was Marion Bartlett – her husband was not medical.

Qualifying MB BS in 1944 she was house surgeon at the Norfolk and Norwich Hospital. She worked first at UMCA, St Andrews's College, Minaki, Dar-es-Salaam, then at St Luke's Medical Training School, Minaki, and then in 1965 was the medical officer in charge of the Lulindi Hospital, Lulindi, Masasi, Mtwara Region.

Women Fellows in the Years of Austerity – FRCS 1946 to 1953
Women of the Fellowship from New Zealand and Australia

Jean Sandel came from New Zealand and is one of only two New Zealander women with the FRCS in the years from 1911 to 1970. Rose Fordyce-Brown followed her with the FRCS in 1953.

In New Zealand, in spite of the apparent early and liberal access for women to a medical training and university degrees in New Zealand, misogyny had made the ability to work and earn a living as a medical practitioner for a woman extremely difficult. The men formed Lodges that were not accessible to women.

New Zealand women had been saved the long and bitter battle campaign that had characterized the British fight for entry into the medical profession. In 1885, as the Otago medical school was being established, the university council affirmed that entry would be equal to women as to men. The early women were subjected to some harassment by male students, one hounded out, one pelted with human flesh, some asked to leave at certain times in a lecture where the subject was considered indelicate, but in general the situation settled down.

However, once qualified, the system conspired against the women. Hospital appointments which alone gave access to higher training were honorary and the posts all went to the men. Private practices were bought and sold within the men's Lodges and few women had family financial back-up to buy into a practice that would provide a living wage. Perhaps the population was not large enough to sustain the formation of women for women hospitals as took place in Melbourne, and later in Sydney, and in England.

By the 1920s however, specialization began to increase allowing some salaried posts within the hospital, notably in anaesthetics and radiotherapy, not as attractive to the men, and allowing some women to forge a useful career. But most women were forced into marginal positions, back-country doctors, or working in the school medical service. The formation of the New-Zealand Medical Women's Association in 1921 was a great supporting network for women.

In fact, the position of women with the FRCS in Britain was not so very different. Many of the women surgeons circulated into jobs in the women's hospitals, went abroad to the mission field, or transferred into specialties, predominantly obstetrics and gynaecology, but also into eyes, ENT, radiotherapy, even thoracic or neurosurgery where competition was not so fierce. The number who obtained consultant posts in general surgery in district general hospitals was small and even fewer within the teaching hospitals.

Jean Sandel had had a brilliant career in Otago winning most of the prizes and awards including the travelling scholarship. Like many of the men, and some of the women in other specialties, for example child psychology, she went abroad for her higher training and qualifications.

Jean Sandel was educated at the Girls' High School, New Plymouth and Otago University, Dunedin, where she won scholarships and prizes. Like her English opposite numbers, World War II threw up opportunities that she might not have had otherwise. New Zealand men, including NZ doctors, motivated by a historic allegiance came to fight as ANZACS alongside the British in Europe. Jean Sandel was therefore able to get considerable surgical experience from 1940 to 1946 and came to England to take the FRCS in 1947. On her return, she was appointed consultant surgeon to the New Plymouth Hospital. She later took the FRACS in 1957. She was respected and admired for her surgical skills and clinical judgement, as well as for her Presbyterian values, and made a name for herself with her historic house and garden, her hospitality, and enjoying golf and bridge.

In spite of all her success in treating others, she was not immune to disease herself and fell ill and, in spite of treatment and radiotherapy, died too early at age fifty-seven in 1974.

Rose Fordyce Burton was also a New Zealander who passed the FRCS six years after Jean Sandel in 1953.

Doris Clifton Gordon, also from Otago Medical School, MB ChB 1916, was a likely inspiration to both Jean Sandel and Rose Fordyce Brown. Born Doris Jolly in 1891 in Australia, the daughter of a bank manager, the family came to New Zealand in 1894. She was a medical student in Otago during World War I, graduating 1916, and came with her husband, also a doctor, to Britain to take the Edinburgh FRCS in 1925. In New Zealand they settled in rural Stratford, Taranaki. From there she helped to found the Obstetrical Society of New Zealand and was their honorary secretary, an important force in improving maternity services from specialists and general practitioners, and organised the campaign for professorial chairs in Otago. She was the first medical woman to be awarded an honorary FRCOG, 1937, having become MRCOG in 1929. She died age sixty-five in 1956.

Rosahun Rodriguez came from Australia to take the FRCS in 1949 and returned to work in Bellevue Hill, New South Wales.

Joyce Daws came from the state of Victoria to take the FRCS in 1952 and returned to Melbourne to practise. Thirty years later she was working full-time as a surgeon. She was single. She had a little domestic help twice a week. While she felt that access to part time training would help to keep women working in medicine, she did not feel that it was practical in surgery. She has not felt herself the subject of any prejudice as a woman in surgery.

Margery Scott-Young was consultant surgeon at the Rachel Forster Hospital in Sydney.

She was born in north Sydney, went to school at the Monte Sant'Angelo College and on to the University of Sydney, graduating MB BS in 1936. She was resident medical officer, at Sydney Hospital, medical superintendent of the Rachel Forster Hospital, and resident medical officer of the Royal Hospital for Women.

During World War II Margery Scott-Young joined the Royal Australian Army Medical Corps, where she was deputy assistant director of NSW lines of communication with the rank of major. After the war she took the MS in 1946 and the FRCS and the FRACS in 1953 when she was at first assistant surgeon, then full surgeon, at the Rachel Forster Hospital.

She was a life governor of the Australian Postgraduate Federation in Medicine, a councillor of the NSW branch of the Australian Medical Association and its honorary librarian, and President of the Australian Drug and Medical Information Group. She wrote a history of the Medical Benevolent Association of NSW, and was appointed CBE for services to medicine.

Women Fellows in the Years of Austerity – FRCS 1946 to 1953
Women of the Fellowship to Cyprus

Helen Mellor took the FRCS in 1952 and practised surgery under her maiden name in Cyprus. Thirty years later, in 1981, she was working part-time, four sessions a week, for the Cyprus Government and described herself as a refugee. She has not felt prejudiced herself as a woman in medicine.

Women Fellows in the Years of Austerity – FRCS 1946 to 1953
Women of the Fellowship to Radiotherapy

Irene Cade was the daughter of the renowned surgeon Sir Stanford Cade and she became a consultant radiotherapist in Portsmouth. She was educated at Queen's College, Harley Street, Aylesbury College, and the Malvern Girls' College and at the Royal Free Hospital where she won the Gwendolynne Lynn prize in surgery and graduated MB BS London in 1947. She had posts at the Royal Free, East Ham Memorial Hospital, the Royal Sussex, and The Hospital for Sick Children, Great Ormond Street and took the FRCS in 1952.

She presented her MS in 1959 with a thesis on hypophysectomy for carcinoma of the breast and prostate and took the DMRT the same year. She was appointed consultant radiotherapist in Portsmouth in 1962 at age twenty-seven and did work on megavoltage radiotherapy and also on hyperbaric oxygen. She continued to attend the combined clinic at the Westminster Hospital every Wednesday for many years bringing her more complicated cases and giving an opinion on the patients who attended that clinic, especially those that attended from the Army and the Royal Air Force.

Her married name was McEwen. Her hobbies were photography and sailing and she excelled in both. She died in year 2000 at the age of seventy-five.

Women Fellows in the Years of Austerity – FRCS 1946 to 1953
Women of the Fellowship into Orthopaedics

Cicely Pepler graduated MB BS London in 1944 from the Royal Free Hospital and taught there as lecturer in anatomy. She was a Nuffield scholar senior registrar in orthopaedics at Oxford and took the FRCS in 1952. She was appointed consultant orthopaedic surgeon at Great Yarmouth, Gorleston and Lowestoft Hospitals where she spent her working life. She was a member of the Girdlestone Society. She died in 1977.

Women Fellows in the Years of Austerity – FRCS 1946 to 1953
Women of the Fellowship into Eye Surgery

Four of the Women Fellows gaining the FRCS in the years from 1946 to 1954 went into the field of eye surgery and all obtained established consultant posts.

Mary Savory was consultant eye surgeon at the Royal Eye Hospital London, St James' Hospital Balham and the South London Hospital for Women, and practised from Devonshire Place.

She went up to Cambridge and did her clinical studies at University College Hospital London and qualified MB BChir Cambridge in 1939. She was a BMA Research Scholar in 1946-7 and took the DOMS in 1946 and the FRCS in 1949. She was a member of the Oxford Ophthalmic Congress and Ophthalmic Society. This Society was founded in 1909 by Robert W Doyne and holds an annual academic and social meeting which extends an invitation to a few overseas doctors who would benefit from interaction with colleagues, and funds them. The laudable stated aims of the society are: 'For the cultivation of the spirit of good fellowship and of unconventionality, the right of our youngest member to rank with his oldest colleague and last, but assuredly not least, the frank, free and tolerant discussion of scientific matters brought before it felt any prejudice in its gathering.'

Mary Savory became Consultant at the Royal Eye Hospital, St James' Balham and the South London Hospital for Women where she spent her working life, retiring at age sixty-seven. She had not felt any prejudice in her career as a woman in medicine and, though not against part-time posts in principle, felt that they should be available to men as well as to women.

Iris Kane became a consultant eye surgeon at the Victoria Hospital, Woking, in Surrey. She did important work under the MRC on retrolental fibroplasia.

Both her parents were doctors in Bulawayo, Southern Rhodesia and she was sent to school in the Roedean School of Johannesburg and then home to Benendon before going up to Newnham College Cambridge on a scholarship, doing her clinical studied at King's College Hospital, London where she won the Legge prize in surgery, and graduating MB BCh Cambridge in 1947. She took the DOMS in 1950, the FRCS in 1951, and the MD in 1955.

She was house surgeon at KCH and Dulwich, and held posts at the Royal Free and senior registrar at KCH under Keith Lyle. Then followed her research on retrolental fibroplasia with the MRC, before being appointed consultant eye surgeon at the Victoria Hospital, Woking where her skills were well respected.

Iris Kane married Philip Steer-Watkins, a farmer, in 1955 at age thirty-two and they had a son Martin. She retired at age sixty-three and went to live in Portugal for a while before returning to Woking where she died age seventy.

Elizabeth Simpson was consultant eye Surgeon to St James' Balham, St George's Tooting and the South London Hospital for Women. She was also ophthalmic surgeon to Queen Mary's Hospital for Children,

Carshalton and earlier at St John's Hospital, Battersea. She had a private practice from Harley Street.

She trained in Dublin, qualifying MB BCh BAO in 1941 and took the DOMS England in 1944. Elizabeth Simpson was chief clinical assistant at Moorfields Eye Hospital and chief assistant at the Hospital for Sick Children, Great Ormond Street. During the War she was a squadron leader in the RAF. She took the FRCS in 1952.

Irene Gregory trained in Bristol qualifying MB ChB Bristol 1944. She was house surgeon at Bristol Royal Infirmary and the Bristol Eye Hospital and took the DOMS in 1946. She was senior registrar at Guy's and took the FRCS in 1953. She was consultant eye surgeon to Sidcup Hospital and to the Greater London Council Inner London Educational Authority.

Women Fellows in the Years of Austerity – FRCS 1946 to 1953
Women of the Fellowship into ENT Surgery

Two women Fellows who gained the FRCS in the years from 1946 to 1954 went into ENT surgery, Margaret Mason and Esme Hadfield who made the discovery of the link between nasal carcinoma and the woodworkers of High Wycombe, an industrial disease.

Margaret Mason became consultant ENT surgeon at King George Hospital, Ilford and consultant in the Department of Audiology at St Mary Abbots Hospital, Kensington.

She went up to Newnham College, Cambridge and did her clinical training at King's College Hospital in London, graduating MB BChir Cambridge in 1945. She was house surgeon and Clinical Assistant at King's and first assistant at the Institute of Laryngology and Otology, and had training at the Princess Beatrice Hospital, and Sutton General Hospital, and took the FRCS in 1948. She was appointed consultant ENT Surgeon at King George Hospital Ilford and at St Mary Abbots where she spent her working life. She retired in 1984 and died the following year in St Christopher's Hospice, Sydenham.

Esmé Hadfield made a benchmark contribution linking nasal carcinoma with the sawdust of woodworkers in High Wycombe.

Having made the original connection, she shared her discovery with R G Macbeth at Oxford and went on to original experimental work on the initial squamous metaplasia, the incubation period – 39 years, the site of incidence – the mucosa of the middle turbinate of the ethmoid sinus, and the effect of the sawdust on the cilia. Her work is further described in the chapter on Surgeons who went into Ear, Nose and Throat, together with a description of the working practices of bodgers, under-dogs and top-dogs.

She was part of a famous medical family. Her father was a professor of pathology at Barts and at the Institute of Basic Sciences at the Royal College of Surgeons and her two brothers became consultant general surgeons at Stoke Mandeville and at Bedford. She was educated at Clifton High School, and went up to St Hugh's College, Oxford, and completed her clinical studies at the Radcliffe Infirmary Oxford, graduating BM BCh Oxford in 1945. She was house surgeon and first assistant in ENT at the Radcliffe working under R G Macbeth and G H Livingstone. She travelled to visit clinics in Zurich, Vancouver and Toronto as a BECC (British Empire Cancer Campaign) Exchange Fellow.

Esmé Hadfield became consultant ENT surgeon to High Wycombe and Amersham Hospital. She was a strong-minded lady, changing for theatres in the room marked 'surgeons' as she was one. She was a Hunterian professor at the Royal College presenting her landmark work on tumours of the nasal sinuses in the woodworkers of High Wycombe in a lecture entitled 'A study of adenocarcinoma of the paranasal sinuses in woodworkers in the furniture industry'. She was an inveterate smoker and was known to deposit her lighted cigarette into her desk drawer and close it during a clinic, the while exhorting her patients not to smoke. She spent her working life there retiring at age sixty-five. She enjoyed foreign travel particularly to Italy and was a keen fisherman. She died age eighty-one.

Women Fellows in the Years of Austerity – FRCS 1946 to 1953
Women of the Fellowship into Research

Barbara Smith trained in Bristol and took her MB ChB in 1944 and her FRCS in 1949. She was awarded a fellowship in Clinical Research by the MRC, the Medical Research Council, taking her PhD in 1965 and her MD in 1968, and becoming senior lecturer in pathology at Barts, St

Bartholomew's Hospital. She was a member of the Pathological Society and a Fellow of the Royal Society of Medicine. She felt that women in medicine did experience some prejudice. She published her work in scientific papers and in a book *The Neuropathology of the Alimentary Tract* in 1972.

Women Fellows in the Years of Austerity – FRCS 1946 to 1953
Women of the Fellowship in India

Four women returned to India with their FRCS, three to take up positions in the Lady Hardinge medical school and hospital in Delhi.

Sita Achaya became the professor of anatomy at the Lady Hardinge Medical College in New Delhi where she was also the principal and superintendent of the Hospital, and dean of the medical faculty of Delhi University.

She was educated at an Indian government school and came from Madras where she graduated MB BS in 1940, and receiving the MS, winning 19 Gold Medals. She came to Britain and was surgical registrar in Edinburgh and took her FRCS in 1947.

Sita Achaya's leadership at Lady Hardinge was legendary and is described more fully in the chapter on India. She was president of the Anatomy Society of India and Deputy Director-General of Health and of Medical Education in the Ministry of Health in India. She married Lt. General AC Iyappa, the chairman of India's largest electronic production industry. She died in 1993.

Miss Maitreyes Chaudhuri was appointed Professor of Surgery on 1 April 1948, the first alumnus of the Lady Hardinge College to attain the FRCS. She was notable for her dedication to obtain all the surgical experience that she could while still a house surgeon in Lady Hardinge and became an accomplished surgeon and research academic. She was principal and medical superintendent to the Lady Hardinge Medical College and Hospital. She was professor and head of the department of surgery. She was Dean of the Faculty of Medical Sciences in the University of Delhi.

Over thirty years later, she was still working part-time in academic research. On being asked, she did feel that there was prejudice against women in medicine and she felt part-time positions would help women doctors at work though in limited specialties and, like many of her generation, she thought that part-time during the training years seemed to her to be a step too far. Her mother had been a working woman also. Living and working in India she had both resident and daily domestic help.

In 1954-1956 there was re-organisation and expansion in the Lady Hardinge Medical College and Hospital. Dr P Mukerjee, who as Prem Virmani got the FRCS in 1957, her husband Dr S Mukerjee, and Dr S Samtakay were appointed Associate Professors of Surgery, all with the FRCS.

Grace Lukose took the BSc in Madras where her mother Dr Mary Pooner-Lukose was Surgeon-General to the Government of Travancore. She came to London to the Royal Free Hospital and qualified there MB BS London in 1946. She returned to Lady Hardinge College and Hospital from 1947-1949 where she was assistant to Dr H E Reid, the reader in Orthopaedic Surgery, and they treated casualties in the riots of 1947. She returned to London, living in the Canterbury hall of residence, and took the FRCS in 1951. After she returned to India, she was unwell with rheumatic fever and died age thirty-six on a visit to her mother in an accident with an overhead fan.

Miss Sehar Panchalingan FRCS 1951 came from India for the FRCS and returned to work there.

Thirty-three women attained the FRCS in the eight post-war years, 'the years of austerity', from 1946 to 1953.

Three general surgeons were appointed consultants in the home country. Phyllis George, appointed at her own teaching hospital of the Royal Free, provided the renowned liver unit of Professor Dame Sheila Sherlock with hepato-biliary surgery. Two years at Memorial Hospital New York had contributed to her expertise. She also had a thyroid and a breast practice and played her part in the emergency rota. Her election to the Council of the Royal College of Surgeons, the first woman on the Council, was accomplished characteristically quietly, without fanfare. Muriel Waterfall achieved and filled a consultant surgeon post at a busy district general hospital, a barrier that was extremely difficult to break into. She was a powerhouse at Kingston with surgical skills that derived from her mentors Heneage Ogilvie, Russell Brock and Harry Platt, covering all general and emergency surgery. Muriel Crouch at the South London Hospital for Women and the Elizabeth Garrett Anderson gave a lifetime of surgical competence to these women's hospitals. Marjorie Powys, having held the fort at St Charles' Hospital in London's Ladbroke Grove during the war years, did not secure a consultant appointment once the returning soldiers came home to seek jobs at the end of the war; she had intended missionary work abroad but settled instead into a mission general practice in south London. Betty Underhill, who put herself through both medical and surgical training after a first class honours science degree at Cambridge, and after research and teaching, found employment with the Ministry of Overseas Development working as a surgeon in Bahrain and in the West Indies. Irene Cade opted for a career in radiotherapy having initially trained in surgery.

Of those who went into gynaecology, Wendy Lewington at the South London, Marjorie Dunstan at Bristol and Jean Burton-Brown at Canterbury were accomplished and busy consultants. Three others who spent their careers in general practice, nonetheless used their obstetric and gynaecological expertise as a valuable asset to their women patients, acknowledged by the FRCOG bestowed on one, and useful publications from another; for them marriage and children were an added occupation. Marjorie Dunstan was married with a daughter, Dorothy Ridout was married with a son and Elaine Rankin married with a son and daughter, her daughter a consultant in rheumatology, and Daphne Scott married with children.

Those who chose the specialties found the attainment of a consultant post easier. The eye surgeons, orthopaedic, and ENT surgeons were all appointed to district general hospitals where they could give a life-time of service – and one in particular, Esme Hadfield, produced a contribution of seminal importance, describing the industrial disease of nasal carcinoma in the wood-workers of High Wycombe. The eye surgeons were appointed to the Royal Eye, St James' Balham, Woking, Bristol, the South London and St George's Tooting, the orthopaedic surgeon to Great Yarmouth, the ENT to King George Ilford and High Wycombe.

The India contingent came for the Fellowship and returned, two to the Lady Hardinge College in Delhi to be surgeons, faculty dean, professors and head of the surgical department there in the women's medical school.

Jean Sandel lays claim to a special place in New Zealand, the first established woman consultant general surgeon there. Margery Scott-Young holds a formidable record in Australia, as does Marion Phillips in Tanzania, and Barbara Furnell Smith working away on the autonomic nervous system in the bowel in a life-time of research.

The analysis seems to show that the battle to be appointed consultants in general surgery in hospitals in the wider sphere of surgical practice was perhaps beginning to yield results but it was still hard to combine the surgical life with husband and children. An extraordinary and welcome advance in Royal College of Surgeons' history was the election of the first woman to a seat on the Council.

These were the difficult post-war years, the 'years of austerity'. Most of the women surgeons in this group remained single.

Women Fellows in the Years of Austerity – FRCS 1946 to 1953

Muriel Crouch died 2010 FRCS 1946
Muriel Cornish Waterfall FRCS 1946
Sita Achaya FRCS 1947 MS Madras
Professor Miss Maitreyes Chaudhuri FRCS 1947
Marjorie Olive Dunster 1915-2000 FRCS 1947 DMRT MD FRCOG
Jean Mary Sandel 1916-1974 FRCS 1947 Otago NZ
Jean Rosemary Campbell Burton-Brown died 2009 FRCS 1948
Margaret Mary Mason died 1985 FRCS 1948
Marion Phillips (Mrs Bartlett) FRCS 1948
Marjorie Agnes Powys 1911-1983 FRCS 1949 DRCOG
Mrs Rosahun Rodriguez FRCS 1949
Mary Savory 1911-1999 FRCS 1949
Barbara Furnell Smith FRCS 1949
Wendy Ellen Lewington FRCS 1950
Esmé Havelock Hadfield 1921-1992 FRCS 1951
Iris Kane 1923-1993 FRCS 1951 DOMS 1950 MD 1955
Grace Mary Lukose 1918-1954 FRCS 1951
Miss Sehar Panchalingan FRCS 1951
Irene Margaret Stanford Cade (Mrs Irene McEwen) 1925-2000 FRCS 1952
Joyce Margretta Daws FRCS 1952
Helen Margaret Mellor FRCS 1952
Kathleen Alice Maud Frith FRCS 1952

Cicely Pepler died 1977 FRCS 1952
Dorothy Mary Ridout FRCS 1952 FRCOG
Elisabeth Davis Liken Simpson FRCS 1952
Agnes Robertson Donald Bartels FRCS 1953
Rose Fordyce Burton FRCS 1953
Phyllis Ann George FRCS 1953
Irene Dorothy Rosalie Gregory FRCS 1953
Elaine Rankin (née Joan Frances Elaine Lister) 1920-2000 FRCS 1953
Daphne Mary Scott FRCS 1953
Margery Scott-Young 1912-1997 FRCS 1953
Betty Margaret Lois Underhill 1908-1983 FRCS 1953

CHAPTER 7

Women Fellows in the Fifties – FRCS 1954 to 1959

THIRTY-SEVEN women were given the Fellowship in the six years from 1954 to 1959.

Four of the new Fellows elected were those who had achieved more than twenty years of distinguished work as consultants and were therefore not part of the cohort of new young surgeons taking the examination, but it does perhaps indicate a readiness on the part of the College to open their doors to senior women doctors who had not taken their Fellowship earlier.

Nine came from India and all but one of these returned home to practise, and one came from Australia and returned home. This leaves a less impressive twenty-three new Fellows in the six years, on average four a year.

Once again, those young doctors attaining the FRCS in these years achieved consultant status in the specialties: three in gynaecology, three in eye surgery, three in ENT, two in orthopaedics, two in accident & emergency, one in paediatric surgery, one in radiotherapy, and one in plastic surgery. One established her career in the Ministry of Health. The pathway to a consultant post in general surgery was still hard to achieve, one only of the three who hoped to stay in general surgery achieving a consultant post.

Of the Indian women surgical Fellows, amongst those who returned to India were those who attained exceptional positions in their medical schools and hospitals. The destinations of all the returnees are not known however. One who stayed in England working in orthopaedics felt that she had not been able to achieve her potential.

Women Fellows in the Fifties – FRCS 1954 to 1959
The Fellowship Bestowed on those of Twenty Years Standing

One was an eye surgeon, Dorothy (Adams) Campbell, one the radiotherapist Gwen Hill (Elfrida Lilian Gwendoline Hilton) who had pioneered and founded oncology at UCH, and the third was that singular woman, the first woman professor of anatomy, who was also the first woman to be an examiner for the Royal College of Surgeons, Mary Keene, to be followed later by her successor Professor Ruth Bowden. Dame Lilian Penson of the University of London, who had been active in the recognition of the Institute of Basic Sciences at the College had an honorary Fellowship bestowed on her.

Dorothy Adams Campbell (Dorothy Rose Adams) 1902-1982 was made an FRCS in 1954 by election as a distinguished surgeon of twenty years standing, so she belongs in fact to the mid-1930s group of women Fellows. She was a consultant eye surgeon and director of the research department of the Birmingham & Midland Eye Hospital. As a Cambridge University student she made a land-mark contribution to the understanding of the causation of cataract in glass-workers, and her academic commitment continued right through to her founding of the research unit that helped to make the Birmingham Eye Hospital outstanding. Her sphere of interest included the biochemistry of the lens, retinitis pigmentosa, and vitamin A and the eye.

Dorothy Adams was educated at the North London Collegiate School after Claire House Preparatory School and then won an entrance exhibition to Girton College Cambridge where she took a double first in 1923. She had a brilliant university career winning many medals and prizes and was awarded the Scientific and Industrial Research Studentship for a piece of work entitled *The metabolism of the Crystalline lens* for the Glassblowers' Cataract Committee of the Royal Society. The government had funded research on Glassworker's Cataract after the Workman's Compensation Acts was passed in 1896 and 1906. Sir William Crookes, an analytical chemist, President of the Royal Society and discoverer of the element thallium, had worked on the premise that infra-red and ultraviolet radiation in the extreme conditions where the glassblowers worked was responsible for clouding of the lens and this had led him to the inclusion of rare earth metals into glass and the development of tinted glass spectacles for industrial protection and indeed against strong sunlight and glare for leisure use. Although the glassworkers, puddlers and tin-platers did not take to the wearing of industrial protective glasses, the innovation did found the sun-glasses industry. After the end of World War I, the research was re-started supported by the Gilchrist fund and was handed to Dorothy Adams by Gowland Hopkins of vitamin and trace element fame. Using fresh ox and sheep eyes, she brilliantly showed that opacification of the lens was due to an autooxidation process reminiscent of that described in muscle by Gowland Hopkins and that reduced the amount of glutathione leading to clouding of the lens.

Dorothy Adams' clinical training followed at University College Hospital in London and she qualified MB BS London in 1927. She had early posts at the Royal London Ophthalmic Hospital and the Central London Ophthalmic Hospital, and took the DOMS in 1930. The stimulus for academic biochemical research had come while she was still at Cambridge. In the first three years after qualifying she carried out further research on the biochemistry of the lens for the Medical Research Council. She went on to training posts to qualify as an ophthalmic surgeon. Her first appointment was as consultant to the New Cross Hospital, Rugby and the Birmingham Midland and Eye Hospital where she worked from 1934 to 1940.

Dorothy Adams married Dr George Campbell MA BM BCh Oxford, in 1938, at the age of thirty-six and they had a son and a daughter. She was a consultant for thirty-five years in the Coventry area, and in the war years she joined the Emergency Medical Service, and covered Coventry, Warwick, Leamington and Nuneaton. Her husband, who was a GP, served in the war as a lieutenant commander in the RNVR and was a support to her in her work. She had a good woman friend who was Froebel-trained who looked to the care of her children. Dorothy makes the point that it was realized from the start that she had to earn enough to help cover the extra domestic expenses of her working. It was essential for her to have her consulting rooms away from the home as her husband's practice was there.

After the war, she went on to found the Research Department of the Birmingham & Midland Eye Hospital from 1947 to 1965, which helped to make the Birmingham Eye a beacon in the Midlands. She felt fortunate in working with many distinguished ophthalmologists.

Dorothy Adams won the Nettleship Medal in 1940, gave the Middlemore Lecture in 1946 and again in 1960, gave the Doyne Memorial Lecture and gained the Medal in 1952, and gave the Percival Hay Memorial Lecture in 1962. Her research was supported by the Medical Research Council. She was a member and vice-president of the Ophthalmic Society of the UK and a member and deputy-master of the

Oxford Ophthalmic Congress, belonged to the Ophthalmic Section of the Royal Society of Medicine, was an examiner for the DOMS, and gave lectures and presentations to many universities and congresses.

She wrote, when asked about women and surgery and the consideration of part-time work: 'Medicine is such a rewarding occupation but the choice of part-time work is important. Ophthalmology is one of the best possible for women. In part-time work, medical women would be well advised to choose a speciality rather than general practice – to avoid the mix-up between professional and domestic duties.' Then she adds (like most women of her generation): 'I feel that specialist training must be a whole-time commitment.'

Dorothy Adams and her husband were enthusiasts for small-boat sailing, chiefly in the Royal Corinthian I design class in Burnham-on-Crouch. She was also a keen horse rider.

Gwen Hilton (Elfrida Lilian Gwendolen Hill, Mrs Hilton) 1898-1971 was elected FRCS, as one of 20 years standing, in 1955. She belongs in fact to the 1938 Fellowship group.

Gwen Hill was educated at Roedean School. Her father was a professor of mathematics and a Fellow of the Royal Society and there were a number of distinguished scientists in the family. She studied at University College London where she took first class honours in her BSc won the gold medal in physiology, and went on to University College Hospital, UCH for her clinical studies, qualifying MB BS in 1924. She married Dr Reginald Hilton the following year, 1925, at the age of twenty-seven. Their daughter, Clare Terrall, followed her parents into medicine, and her mother in becoming a radiotherapist. Her father was a consultant physician at St Thomas's.

In 1938 Gwen became the first radiotherapist at UCH, and afterwards director in 1948. She had joined the radiology department at UCH in 1931 as assistant to Dr RWA Salmond and was soon especially attracted to radiotherapy. When diagnostic radiology moved to form a new department in 1938, Gwen Hilton remained in the old area, adapting it for radiotherapy, and became the radiotherapist to the hospital. She made important advances in radiotherapy, developing the technique of fractionated dose irradiation, reducing skin reaction. She was prescient in recognizing the importance of drugs, the harbinger of chemotherapy, alongside radiotherapy, particularly for treatment of the reticuloses, lymphoma and leukaemia, and bone tumours, and collaborated with physicians in this therapy. She was one of the first to apply radiotherapy in an oxygen chamber. She gave the Mackenzie Davidson Memorial Lecture, speaking on the role of radioiodine in the treatment of carcinoma of the thyroid.

Gwen Hilton attracted funds to the department which was re-built and it became an important training centre for future generations of radiotherapists. Above all, she was not only a superb clinician, but she retained human warmth in her relationships with her patients.

Mary Keene (Mary Frances Lucas) 1885-1971, FRCS 1956 was the first woman to become a professor of anatomy, appointed in 1924, and the first woman to be appointed on to the Court of Examiners of the Royal College of Surgeons. She was the first woman to be on the Council of the Anatomical Society and she became its president from 1949 to 1951.

Mary Lucas was educated at the Rochester Grammar School for Girls and Eversley School, Folkestone. Her father was a dental surgeon. She entered the London School of Medicine for Women in 1904 and qualified MB BS London in 1911. She taught anatomy under Professor Frederic Wood Jones who was the first full-time professor of anatomy at the Royal Free but he was much involved as an RAMC Officer at the Shepherds Bush Hospital and went to Manchester at the end of the war. As the first woman professor of anatomy at the London School of Medicine she taught generations of women medical students.

During World War II she was vice-dean at the Royal Free Hospital from 1939 to 1943 and then became acting dean. The medical school was evacuated in part to Aberdeen, in part to Exeter. The anatomy department sustained a direct hit with a V2 rocket toward the end of the war and students were taught temporarily at St Mary's and at Guy's and she was much involved with rebuilding. She became emeritus professor, part-time teacher and researcher on the intrinsic muscles of the larynx. She wrote two textbooks in addition to papers, *Manual of Practical Dissection by Six Teachers* with Dr Evelyn Hewer and *Anatomy for Dental Students* with James Willis.

She married Richard Keene, a farmer, in 1916 at age thirty-one and was down on the farm each weekend in Kent.

Ruth (Elizabeth Mary) Bowden 1915-2001 followed Professor Mary Keene as professor of anatomy at the London School of Medicine for Women and the Royal Free Hospital. She was made FRCS by election in 1973.

Ruth Bowden was the daughter of an India missionary and her aunt had founded the Christian medical college in Ludhiana, Punjab. She was educated at St Paul's Girls' School and the Royal Free and graduated MB BS in 1938. She did house posts at the Elizabeth Garrett Anderson, and then joined Professor Seddon at Oxford working on nerve damage and repair, neuropraxia, axonotmesis, neurotmesis. She presented the research work as a Hunterian professorship lecture in 1969 at the Royal College of Surgeons with the title 'The factors influencing functional recovery of peripheral nerve injuries in man'. She went on to study at Johns Hopkins on a Rockefeller Fellowship.

She succeeded Mary Keene as Professor of Anatomy at the Royal Free in 1950 at the age of thirty-five and taught generations of medical students being an important role model. She never retired from work, going on after retirement age as lecturer in anatomy at St Thomas's and also made great efforts on the Archives of the Royal Free Hospital and Medical School.

Ruth Bowden was a member of the Grand Priory order of St Lazarus of Jerusalem. She equipped hospitals in St Petersburg in Russia. She was concerned with charities in Poland, Rumania, and with leprosy in the colonies, particularly in India. She was a supporter of Riding for the Disabled.

Dame Lillian (Margery) Penson 1896-1963 was professor of modern history (modern implying 'as opposed to ancient' history, rather than recent times) at Bedford College, University of London. The reason she was given the honorary FRCS in 1959 was for her role in negotiating the relationship between the Institute of Basic Medical Sciences at the Royal College of Surgeons with the University of London, in 1952. She was a member of the senate of the University of London and its first woman vice-chancellor in 1948.

She had been educated privately and at Birkbeck and University College London, becoming BA London in 1917. Her historical research interests were in colonial history and the origins of wars of the nineteenth and twentieth centuries, and she gained her PhD in 1921. She became professor of Modern History in 1930. In World War II she worked in the Ministry of National Service and the War Trade Intelligence Service, and became DBE. The bestowal of the honorary FRCS was in gratitude to her skilled help in establishing professorships in the College and easing the relationship between the Institute of Basic Medical Sciences and the University of London.

Women Fellows in the Fifties – FRCS 1954 to 1959
Women of the Fellowship into General Surgery

Of the four women surgical Fellows who worked in general surgery, Kate Fussell achieved the consultant post in general surgery in a district general hospital that is so desired. Mary Richardson, who had had excellent surgical training posts and had held down a busy and successful surgical hospital life in Assam, would be one of many who found it difficult to break into a consultant post on return from overseas. Nonetheless she worked for thirteen years as a clinical assistant in casualty in Hereford until retirement, as did Jean Green and Jean Fowler-Wright in surgery.

Katharine Mary Fussell (Kate Fussell) became a consultant surgeon at the Royal Albert Edward Hospital, Wigan. She was educated at Headington School, Oxford and moved to the Dudley High School for Girls because Headington could not provide the science teaching needed for entry to medical school. In fact at Dudley High, arrangements had to be made for her to study science in the sixth form of the boys' school, fortunately alongside two other girls. The teaching was excellent and she won a state scholarship and applied to medical schools, though still rather young for entry, and intending perhaps to take Cambridge entrance a year later. However the medical school at Birmingham, offering her a place for the following year, asked her to sign a note saying that she agreed not to apply elsewhere. Her father was the chief education officer of Birmingham and protested at their attempt to secure and confine the ambitions of a bright student and at once they replied that they had two unexpected vacancies and if his daughter would like to start right away, they had a place for her, which she took up two weeks later.

So she went to Birmingham University to study medicine, graduating MB ChB in 1951, and getting a house surgeon's post at the Queen

Elizabeth Hospital Birmingham and various other training posts, taking the FRCS in 1957. She then decided to gain further experience in the States, a 'BTA' (been to America), and was in New York in Stuyvescent Square and then at Memorial Hospital, where she broke her leg skiing, and then on to Lennox Hill Hospital where she spent eighteen months and contracted hepatitis, then on to do orthopaedics. She was in the States five and a half years and would have stayed and completed her Boards specialist training, but she was on an exchange visitor visa and in spite of strenuous efforts she could not get that changed. Coming back from America she stopped off at Jamaica and had her photograph taken in the market-place trying on hats which got into the local paper, the Kingston Gleaner, and Kate got a letter from a former fellow Birmingham medical student Pamela Moody (Pamela Ball) who came from Jamaica.

When Kate came back to England she was now an experienced surgeon. Alfreda Baker was just retiring from the Elizabeth Garrett Anderson Hospital and Kate was appointed. But this was only three sessions, later made up to four, and Muriel Crouch helped her to get a few sessions at the Florence Nightingale Hospital, and she taught anatomy to speech therapists and orthopaedics to occupational therapists while she applied for full-time posts with a living wage. She spoke to Elizabeth Shore at the Department of Health who was helpful and wondered whether Kate would be advised to pick a minor speciality such as ENT, or whether she would come and work in the Ministry. She continued to apply around.

Appointed as consultant surgeon to the Royal Albert Edward Infirmary at Wigan, she did the full range of general surgery and published on a follow-up for Peter Lord's procedure on haemorrhoidectomy, and on problems with colostomy and ileostomies. She founded the specialised breast clinic at Wigan. She was an active member of the Association of Surgeons, the Royal Society of Medicine and was a Soroptimist rising to be president. Katherine Branson, a fellow Soroptimist, asked her whether she would be willing to take over her post in Edinburgh when she retired from Bruntsfield Hospital, founded by Sophia Jex-Blake and where Elsie Inglis had worked, but Kate was well settled by then in Wigan. She was a great traveller, bringing back a mink of different hues from many visits. She was a sociable woman. If she were ever delayed for an afternoon session theatre list, her anaesthetist would observe wryly a special hair-do under her theatre cap. She was a great golfer and a sports car driver. She trekked in Nepal and as medical officer on one arduous journey at high altitude she needed to be transported on a mule. She visited Africa, supporting medical work abroad. She offered to sponsor a child and instead of an expected African girl baby, she was allotted a six year old boy refugee from Tibet. He was brought up in a children's village in northern India and Kate visited there several times, sponsoring him over sixteen years through time and currently he has a Master's degree and is a librarian.

In her time at Wigan, Kate had been chairman of the medical executive committee and in retirement she stood on the Community Health Council, as a non-executive director of the hospital and now a governor of the trust. She continued to travel into her eighties including a strenuous visit to Greenland and the Arctic.

Mary Richardson was educated at Hereford High School for Girls and the Godolphin School, Salisbury and went up to St Hugh's College Oxford where she was a rowing blue and president of the women's boat crew. She graduated BM BCh Oxford in 1942 and had a house surgeon post in obstetrics and gynaecology at the Radcliffe Infirmary, and at the Parkswood Hospital, Worcester. In the war she worked, 1944-1947, in anti-aircraft command as a captain in the RAMC. She was two years in India doing orthopaedic and maxillofacial surgery and contracted TB and was sent home to England.

She was surgical registrar at Crewe and senior registrar at the mid-Ulster Hospital in Magherafelt County Derry and took the FRCS in 1956. In 1959 she returned to India for eleven years and worked as a surgeon at the Johar General Hospital in Assam. From 1963 to 1970 she was chief medical officer, PMO, at the Jorehaut Tea Company Limited in Johar, Assam, a hospital of one hundred and twenty beds, looking after a population of fifty thousand.

Mary Richardson returned to England in 1970 and for the next thirteen years to 1983 was clinical assistant in casualty at Hereford County Hospital where she worked full-time, nine sessions. She had a daily in England nine hours a week; presumably in India she had servants. She married Richard (Dick) Clifford whom she had met in Assam and she had step-sons.

Jean Anne Evans (Mrs Jean Green) studied at University College and University College Hospital qualifying MB BS London in 1953. She did house surgeon and house physician jobs at UCH and took the DCH in 1956, and went on to be surgical registrar at the Royal South Liverpool Hospital taking the FRCS in 1957. She was medical assistant in surgery at Clwyd and Deeside Hospitals and was working part-time eight sessions a week more than twenty years after getting the Fellowship. Her husband Dr Rodney Irwin Green was a consultant radiologist, also at Clwyd, and trained at Liverpool.

Jean Fowler-Wright graduated MB BS in 1947 at the Royal Free Hospital. She took the FRCS in 1958 and was surgical assistant at the Kent and Sussex Hospital, Tunbridge Wells, where she worked full-time for many years. She did feel that there was prejudice against women in medicine and felt that part-time work and training might be helpful to women. She retired at age sixty-five in 1989 dying in 1995.

Women Fellows in the Fifties – FRCS 1954 to 1959
Women of the Fellowship into Gynaecology

Two women Fellows went into gynaecology and made a very successful and rewarding career: Pamela Spencer at the Whittington and the Elizabeth Garrett Anderson Hospitals, and Valerie Thompson at the Royal Free. Both were married with children.

Pamela Spencer became consultant at the busy unit of obstetrics and gynaecology at the Whittington Hospital and at the Elizabeth Garrett Anderson Hospital. She was a highly competent and much appreciated colleague with a sunny nature.

She trained at University College Hospital, as Pamela Bacon, qualifying with the MB BS London in 1950. She took the DRCOG in 1952 and the FRCS in 1957. She did jobs at Queen Charlottes and the Chelsea Women's Hospital before becoming First Assistant at University College Hospital. She was FRCOG in 1973. She published a paper of seminal importance on delivery of the placenta by cord traction – a paper that was much quoted and acted on. She married Dr Alfred George 'Spike' Spencer GM, reader in medicine at Barts, St Bartholomew's

Hospital, and they had a son Charles who became an anaesthetist. She died in 2011.

Valerie Mary Thompson (Mrs S C B Yorke) was consultant gynaecologist at the Royal Free Hospital and was an inspirational teacher of gynaecology to the Royal Free students and to the junior doctors who worked for her.

Valerie was born in Canada and came back to England in her childhood. Her father was an engineer and moved to find work in the economic depression. She was educated at Huddersfield Grammar School. At the age of ten or eleven when she came top of biology someone remarked that perhaps she would be a teacher which she vehemently refuted and they went on to say, well, perhaps a lady doctor then. So the seed was sown.

She trained at the Royal Free qualifying MB BS London in 1948 and took the MRCOG in 1953 followed by the FRCS in 1958 and the FRCOG in 1969 and was the recipient of many awards. She had two children, a son and a daughter, and a nanny who was with her for sixteen years and a daily for ten hours a day. When she drove from her home in Barnes to the Royal Free each day, the first half of the journey she was thinking about the myriad difficulties at home, then halfway to work her attention would switch to the problems she would encounter in the hospital.

Her husband was Dr Sydney Clifford Brookfield Yorke MRCPsych and DPM, a psychiatrist who was a consultant psychotherapist at Napsbury Hospital and medical director of the Hampstead Child Therapy Clinic. She herself was a member of the Institute of Psychosexual medicine.

Women Fellows in the Fifties – FRCS 1954 to 1959
Women of the Fellowship into Eye Surgery

Three of the women Fellows of the fifties chose to be eye surgeons, Kate Goddard at Hull, Mary Jones in Sheffield and Mary Starbuck in Canterbury. All became consultants.

Kate Goddard (Una Kathleen Merrill) became a consultant ophthalmic surgeon at Hull Royal Infirmary. She trained at Sheffield qualifying MB

ChB in 1955, served as house surgeon at the Central Middlesex Hospital, went on to Sunderland Eye Infirmary as senior house surgeon, and took the DO and the FRCS in 1959. She was senior ophthalmic registrar at the United Sheffield Hospitals, before being appointed to her consultant post at Hull Royal Infirmary. She took the LlB in 1985 and the FCOphth in 1988.

Like many other surgeons of her generation, she thought that the availability of part-time work might well help women to stay in medical practice, but also like nearly all, felt that *training* part-time in the surgical specialties was unacceptable. She had not felt prejudice against her as a woman in medicine. However she had an insightful and penetrating response to the question in the survey as to whether her own mother had worked – the attempt was being made to try to correlate whether a working mother helped encourage the daughter to persevere with a working lifetime. She pointed out that, since the husband's attitudes are so crucial to a working woman, a factor of at least equal, or she suspected more importance, would be whether one's *husband's mother* had been a working woman. She added that she hoped that she had brought up her own son to give support to a working wife in due course.

Mary Allan Craig Jones became consultant ophthalmic surgeon at the Royal Hallamshire Hospital, Sheffield. She trained in Birmingham graduating MB ChB in 1948 and went on to take the FRCS in 1959. Her consultant appointment was to the Royal Hallamshire Hospital, Sheffield. She worked full-time and with some private practice and she had domestic help by two people covering every weekday from 8.30 am to 4 pm. She had not been aware of any prejudice against her in medicine because she was a woman. Like her fellows, she felt that part-time work might help women but was not in favour of it during surgical training.

Mary Starbuck became consultant ophthalmic surgeon at Canterbury and Thanet and the South-East Hospitals. Mary trained at King's College Hospital qualifying MB BS London in 1952 and where she did house officer jobs. She sat the DRCOG in 1954. She was house officer in the eye department and took the DO in 1956. She took the FRCS in 1959. She became senior ophthalmic registrar at King's and also clinical assistant at Moorfields Eye Hospital. Her consultant appointment was to Canterbury Hospital where she spent her working life. She was a member of the

Ophthalmological Society of the UK. In Canterbury, she was a colleague of Maud Burton Brown and wrote her obituary in the BMJ.

Women Fellows in the Fifties – FRCS 1954 to 1959
Women of the Fellowship into ENT Surgery

Three of the women Fellows in the fifties chose ENT as a speciality, Betsy Brown in Bradford, Peggy Orton at Queen Mary's Hospital for Children and St Helier, the South London and the Elizabeth Garrett Anderson Hospital, and Joselen Ransome at Charing Cross.

Betsy Brown was the consultant ENT Surgeon in Bradford Royal Infirmary. She trained in Glasgow qualifying with the MB ChB in 1945, taking the DPH in 1948, the DLO in1950, and the FRCS in 1955. She was a lecturer in otorhinolaryngology in Manchester before getting her consultant post in Bradford Royal Infirmary. She published on tumours of larynx and nose and their treatment.

She was married and her husband was medical. She had not felt any prejudice herself in her career pathway and, while she was in favour of part-time posts encouraging women to work, she herself worked full-time and did not think part-time practical during the training years.

Peggy Orton trained at the Royal Free Hospital and qualified with the conjoint diploma in 1943. After initial house posts including one at the Royal Cancer Hospital (the Marsden), she decided on ENT as a career and took the DLO in 1947. She was first assistant in the aural department at the London Hospital and senior registrar at the Royal Free, and took the FRCS in 1955. She was appointed consultant in otolaryngology at Queen Mary's Hospital for Children and the St Helier Hospital, Carshalton, the South London Hospital for Women and the Elizabeth Garrett Anderson Hospital where she spent her working life. She was a single lady and had some daily help thrice weekly. She herself always worked full-time and had reservations about part-time working or training, feeling that women should not have any preferential treatment over men and should not be treated differently.

Joselen Ransome (Mrs Heron) was Consultant Otolaryngologist at Charing Cross Hospital. She trained at the Royal Free Hospital qualifying

MB BS in 1949 and was house surgeon at the Radcliffe Infirmary Oxford where she decided on ENT surgery as a career. She was registrar at the Royal Throat, Nose and Ear Hospital taking the FRCS in 1958 and going on to be senior registrar at the Royal Free. Her first consultant posts were at the Metropolitan Ear Nose and Throat Hospital and St Stephen's Chelsea and she was appointed to the Charing Cross Hospital.

She wrote and edited books in the field of ENT surgery, including the *Recent Advances* series and the *Operative Surgery* volumes. She was hon sec of the British Association of Otolaryngologists.

Women Fellows in the Fifties – FRCS 1954 to 1959
Women of the Fellowship into Orthopaedics

Three women went into orthopaedics, one who had started out in general surgery and found an opportunity in orthopaedics and enjoyed a successful career alongside family life, one who became a consultant and specialised in hand surgery, and one from Calcutta who had worked at the Royal National Orthopaedic Hospital but who felt she had not achieved all she might.

Ruth Margaret Robinson (Mrs Ruth Hickson) was an associate specialist in orthopaedics in Stoke-on-Trent. She was educated at the Torquay Grammar School for Girls during the war years and went on to train at the London (Royal Free Hospital) School of Medicine for Women where she was a prize-winner and qualified MB BS London in 1951. She was house surgeon to Geraldine Barry at the Royal Free and to Alfreda Baker at the Elizabeth Garrett Anderson Hospital. She was awarded a training grant at the Royal Free and used it to take the primary FRCS course at the Royal College of Surgeons. She then went on to the surgical professorial unit at Bristol under Professor Milnes Walker where he gave her extremely pessimistic advice about the impossibility of a surgical future for a woman in England and suggested she think about service in the foreign field, India or Uganda.

Ruth Robinson took the FRCS in 1956 when she was registrar at Weston-super-Mare, where her future husband was her house surgeon. He had been an engineer before studying medicine. She came back to the Royal Free as surgical registrar to Dorothy Barclay and then married and went with her husband to Stoke-on-Trent where he had the offer of a good practice and she became a locum orthopaedic surgical registrar, her entry to orthopaedic surgery. Three children and family life was a discouragement to a further operative surgical career but together with Denys Wainwright whose special interest was children's orthopaedic problems, Perthes disease, CDH (congenital dysplasia of the hip), and physical handicap, she forged a rewarding career doing joint clinics in the hospital and in the special schools in Biddulph Grange.

She worked solidly all her life as associate specialist in orthopaedics in the West Midlands, doing about six sessions a week, telling her husband in the time-honoured way of women doctors when she had had one of her three children, to ring Denys at the hospital and tell him that she had had the baby and wouldn't be in to do the clinic the following morning. She retired at age sixty-five. She herself had no feeling that she had had prejudice against her as a woman in medicine.

Mary Shelswell studied at St Andrews and qualified MB ChB in 1948. She did her early training as Orthopaedic house surgeon at the Royal Portsmouth Hospital and the Royal Cancer Hospital (the Marsden) and was lecturer in anatomy at the Royal Free. She took the FRCS in 1956. She was appointed consultant orthopaedic surgeon to the Portsmouth group of hospitals. She was a Fellow of the British Orthopaedic Association and a member of the British Society of Hand Surgeons.

Mini Hoshang Mehta took her MB BS in Calcutta in 1951 and came to London for experience and teaching and to take the FRCS which she passed in 1959. She was working full-time as a senior lecturer in the clinical research unit at the Royal National Orthopaedic Hospital in London. She was a single lady. She felt that she had experienced prejudice against her as a woman in medicine and was in favour of part-time work and part-time training.

Women Fellows in the Fifties – FRCS 1954 to 1959
Women of the Fellowship into Accident & Emergency

Two women surgical Fellows became consultants in accident & emergency departments. Rosemary Adams had the intention of making her career in general surgery, and found progress hard combining a surgical life with husband and children. She was advised to consider ENT and did follow that pathway but in fact found the progression to senior registrar also daunting. She found her niche in an A & E department. As did Kit Taylor (Katherine Burkill).

Rosemary Adams (Mrs Campbell) was Consultant in the A & E department, accident and emergency, at the Norfolk and Norwich Hospital. She trained in Edinburgh and took the MB ChB Edinburgh in 1948. She won the Ettles Scholarship, and the Buchanan Scholarship in obstetrics and gynaecology. She had house posts at the Royal Hospital for Sick Children and at the Royal Infirmary, Edinburgh.

Although she had intended to pursue her career in general surgery, she increasingly felt that this was going to be difficult for a woman alongside the other commitments in life. Accordingly she was advised to consider ENT as a possibility. She was ENT registrar at the Royal Infirmary Hull and took first the Edinburgh Fellowship in 1952, then the England FRCS in 1955. She married and had two children, a son and a daughter. She had given up general surgery and started specializing in ENT. Even so, she was not able to do her senior registrar training in ENT because she was bringing up her family. However, after she became a consultant in accident & emergency at the Norfolk and Norwich Hospital she worked full-time.

She wrote, giving her opinion, as she found it: 'I do not think a career in general surgery is compatible with marriage and the rearing of a family. I gave up general surgery when I married and started specializing in ENT. I was not able to do my senior registrar training because I was bringing up my family. Later I became a consultant in accident and emergency.'

She went on to say and again, this is how she found it: 'Unless a woman is totally dedicated to surgery, has no family commitments, and is physically very strong, I do not think she is likely to stay the course in general surgery, nor do I think a woman would stand a chance of being appointed to a consultant post against good male opposition!'

Then she softens it a little: 'Specialist subjects are different, ENT, eyes, gynaecology'. (Presumably this is why she tried ENT).

Then (an important point): 'There are far too few women appointed as consultants in obstetrics and gynaecology. This distresses hundreds of patients who particularly want to have their gynaecological problems dealt with by a woman.' (This she has observed when working in casualty).

Now she makes a general point (and this is in 1981): 'In general, far more part-time appointments should be made available for fully qualified women and part-time training should be encouraged to the maximum. The Health Service is not utilizing the resources of trained practitioners because it is too inflexible.'

Well, she proved she was capable of full-time work as consultant in the accident & emergency department where she was still doing nine sessions in her sixties. She had a daily help for nine hours a week, presumably someone who came in to clean through twice a week. Her opinions are very valid and worth listening to. And she has done a rewarding and useful job. But is it what she wanted to do, and was there more she would like to have done? Were there any regrets?

Besides being a full-time consultant in A & E, she found time also to serve as a JP.

Katharine Mary Burkill (Mrs Kit Taylor). Kit Taylor became consultant in the accident and emergency department, A & E, at the Royal Hallamshire Hospital and the Northern General Hospital.

Katharine Burkill was educated at the Perse School Cambridge and went up to Newnham College Cambridge and did her clinical studies at University College Hospital, London where she was a prizewinner and graduated MB BCh Cambridge in 1955. Her father was a professor of mathematics.

She had a casualty post at Addenbrookes Hospital in Cambridge, house physician at the Cancer Hospital (the Marsden), SHO posts at Bromley and then surgical registrar at Addenbrookes where she worked for Philip Ghey and Brian Truscott, and went on to be registrar at Sheffield. She took the FRCS in 1958. She married Frank Whitehead Taylor, orthopaedic surgeon, in 1963 when she was thirty-four and they had two sons and three daughters.

Among her skills Katharine Burkill was renowned for her ability in organising celebrity events.

Women Fellows in the Fifties – FRCS 1954 to 1959
Women of the Fellowship into Paediatric Surgery

Irene Marion Irving (Mrs Irene Desmet) was paediatric surgeon at the Alder Hey Children's Hospital.

Irene was educated at Broughton Hall, a convent school in Liverpool where she received a good education and won a state scholarship to go on to medical school at Liverpool University. She took the BSc with honours in 1949. While she was a clinical student at Liverpool, the students went to Alder Hey Hospital as part of their training and it was seeing the babies on the neonatal unit that confirmed her in her decision to enter paediatric surgery. Irene qualified MB ChB with honours in 1952.

She did her house jobs at the Royal Infirmary, Liverpool and was surgical registrar and medical assistant at the Alder Hey Hospital for Children and the David Lewis North Hospital and took the FRCS in 1957 and the ChM in 1969. Isabella Forshall and Peter Rickham were colleagues and her professor was James Lister.

She became senior lecturer in the university and paediatric surgeon at the Alder Hey from 1975 to 1986. She published extensively, particularly in the field of neonatal surgery. She was co-editor with her professor, James Lister, of the textbook *Neonatal Surgery* when the author Peter Rickham moved to Zurich. Irene married becoming Irene Desmet; her husband was Belgian, and had a trout farm and a boarding house in Liverpool. Of their three children, one son became an engineer and her daughter an artist. A former registrar, now paediatric surgeon Nick Madden, wrote that she was a delight to work for and related that when he had to phone her at home to ask advice on a patient, and asked to speak to Miss Irving, the small child answering the phone would call out, 'Mum, it's the hospital', a form of words repeated later in his own home for his wife, the fellow paediatric surgeon, Miss Su-Anna Boddy. One other recollection was his pride and satisfaction that Miss Irving always left him to carry out the last operation on the morning list solo and he felt this to be a sign of her confidence in his ability until the theatre sister deflated him, pointing out that it was because the fearsome surgeon whose list followed, patrolled the operating rooms to ensure that the morning list would not over-run and he be kept waiting and Miss Irving made herself scarce before his shadow appeared at the door.

Women Fellows in the Fifties – FRCS 1954 to 1959
Women of the Fellowship into Oncology

Eileen Busby went into radiotherapy as a career. She became consultant in radiotherapy and oncology at Kingston Hospital. She trained at

Charing Cross and graduated MB BS with honours in surgery in 1955. She was surgical registrar at the Royal Marsden and took the FRCS in 1959 and was first assistant in surgery at St George's. She took the DMRT in 1966, the FFR in 1972, and the FRCR in 1975 during which time she was senior registrar, then first assistant and associate specialist in the radiotherapy department at the Royal Marsden before getting her consultant appointment at Kingston.

Women Fellows in the Fifties – FRCS 1954 to 1959
Women of the Fellowship into Plastic Surgery

Pamela Ball (née Pamela Margaret Moody) trained in Birmingham qualifying with the MB ChB in 1950 and took the FRCS in 1954, the first woman from Jamaica to be a Fellow of the Royal College of Surgeons. She was clinical assistant, then associate specialist, to the Regional Plastic Unit at the Wordsley Hospital, Stourbridge. A full account of her work is described in the Chapter 15.

Her father Dr Ludlow Moody was a well-loved and highly respected GP in Kingston, Jamaica, a JP and Custos of Jamaica. Her mother was a professional musician, a pianist who came from the Manley family and had studied in St Petersburg.

Pamela Moody, as she was then, was educated at Hamptons, where she was a contemporary of Monica Lewin, and then went on to Wolmer's, elite secondary schools in Kingston, Jamaica. She came to England on a scholarship from Jamaica to study medicine at Birmingham. She would like to have read mathematics but chose medicine like her father. During early posts she did both anaesthetics and surgery at a time when juniors were given much more responsibility and expected to do a wide variety of clinical tasks, giving anaesthetics at Birmingham General Hospital for the radium theatre lists of Beatrice Willmott Dobbie. She did the full gamut of general surgery and was a speedy and competent general surgeon. She took the FRCS in 1954 after an excellent correspondence course run by Dr Oates of Red Lion Square.

She entered plastic surgery almost by chance, going to work for Oliver Munsfield initially after she had given birth to one of her children, and later felt it would be a more compatible post with caring for her children and family. She married Dr John Ball, a GP who was much involved with BMA and GMC business, being in London two or three days mid-week and covering his general practice over the weekend.

Pamela was a highly competent plastic surgeon, known and well respected by her colleagues, tackling enormous lists, not only at Wordsley, the Regional Plastic Unit but also at Sutton Coldfield and at Sandwell. She was content to hold the clinical assistant post where she had a great degree of autonomy and found it fitted in with her family life. She was also a musician, playing the viola, and mathematician holding Open University degrees in mathematics.

Women Fellows in the Fifties – FRCS 1954 to 1959
Women of the Fellowship into the Ministry of Health

Catherine McRobert (Mrs Dennis) graduated with MB BS in Madras in 1943 and trained also in Aberdeen. She took the FRCS in 1954 and went into public health taking the DPH in 1956. She worked in the Ministry of Health, starting in Savile Row and moving with them to the Elephant and Castle. She retired to Truro and died in 2003.

Women Fellows in the Fifties – FRCS 1954 to 1959
Women of the Fellowship return to Australia

Elizabeth Ann Lewis took the FRCS in 1955 and returned to Australia.

Women Fellows in the Fifties – FRCS 1954 to 1959
Women of the Fellowship who returned to India

Dogdo Sohrab Bamji (Dogdo Rutha Mehta) took her FRCS in 1954 and returned to India where she worked full-time as a surgeon. She married. Her husband was not medical. She was still working full-time when we corresponded twenty-five years after getting her FRCS. Living in India, she had domestic help, one living in and one daily. Her opinion on part-time work, like that of many of her generation was that it was acceptable in helping women to stay in work, but it was not desirable while training which should be (her words) 'intensive full-time'. She herself had experienced no prejudice as a woman in medicine.

Sheroo Darebsha Broacha from Bombay took her FRCS in 1955 and returned to India.

Shakuntala Chandra went back to work at the medical college in Patiola in the Punjab in India after getting her FRCS in 1955.

Prem Virmani (Prem Mukerjee) 1928-1988 was educated at the Lady Hardinge Medical College in New Delhi graduating MB BS in Delhi where she was also lecturer in anatomy. She came to England for higher surgical experience and worked at the Hammersmith Hospital, the Royal Postgraduate Medical School, with Professor Ian Aird and Professor Charles Wells and took the FRCS in 1958 and later the ChM in Liverpool. She returned to Lady Hardinge to be head of surgery, had a particular interest in abdominal tuberculosis, did much research and put out more than a hundred publications.

She married Sandip Mukerjee FRCS at age thirty-three and they had a daughter, Ramona. Living in India, they had resident and daily help, four servants in all. She always worked full-time herself but agreed that part-time work might encourage some women to stay in work but was not in favour of specialist training being part-time. Nor had she experienced any prejudice against women in medicine, all predictable responses knowing how hard she herself has always worked and within the Lady Hardinge special woman-friendly environment.

Kamla Rupoharb Alimchandani came from Bombay and took the FRCS in 1958 and became FRCOG also. She had the MD higher degree. She returned to Bombay where she was consultant in obstetrics and gynaecology and assistant professor in the Grant Medical College and worked at the Cama & Albless Hospitals, the Jaslok Hospital & Research Centre, and the National Hospital Bombay as well as the Grant Medical College. She lived with her sister, brother-in-law, and their children and with two resident staff and two others.

In general, this surgeon was in favour of part-time training and felt it would be helpful for women. She herself had felt no prejudice against her as a woman in medicine.

Vimla Bhogilal Jhaveri took the FRCS in 1958 and returned to India.

Sumita Sen took the FRCS in 1958 and returned to India.

Susila Rajagopalan(Mrs Rajagopalan) took the FRCS in 1959 and returned to Pondicherry Hospital.

Women Fellows in the Fifties – FRCS 1954 to 1959
Women of the Fellowship into Private Practice and Unknown Careers

Cecilia Grieg trained at the West London Hospital Medical School where it was possible to qualify with the conjoint diploma rather than the university degree. She qualified LRCP MRCS, in 1944. She worked at St Mary Abbots Hospital, Epsom Cottage Hospital, and the Hammersmith Hospital/Royal Postgraduate Medical School and took the MRCOG in 1949 and the FRCS in 1955. She worked in private practice at 152 Harley Street, retiring at age sixty-five in 1985 and died in 1986.

Mary Kathleen Marchant obtained the FRCS in 1957. She had trained in Liverpool qualifying MB ChB in 1948.

Ellen Little received the FRCS in 1959.

Women Fellows in the Fifties – FRCS 1954 to 1959

Dorothy Rose Adams (Mrs Dorothy Campbell) 1902-1982 FRCS 1954
Gwen Hilton (Elfrida Lilian Gwendolen Hill, Mrs Hilton) 1898-1971 FRCS 1955
Mary Frances Lucas (Professor Mary Keene) 1885-1971 FRCS 1956
Ruth Elizabeth Mary Bowden (Professor Ruth Bowden) 1915 – 2001 FRCS 1973
Dame Lillian Margery Penson 1896-1963 Honorary FRCS 1959
Katharine Mary Fussell FRCS 1957
Mary Fredericka Richardson 1917-1993 FRCS 1956
Jean Anne Evans (Mrs Jean Green) FRCS 1957
Miss Jean Yolande Fowler-Wright died 1995 FRCS 1958
Pamela Mary Bacon (Mrs Pamela Spencer) died 2011 FRCS 1957
Valerie Mary Thompson (Mrs S C B Yorke) FRCS 1958
Una Kathleen Goddard (née Merrill) FRCS 1959 qualified 1955

Miss Mary Allan Craig Jones FRCS 1959
Mary Joan Starbuck FRCS 1959
Betsy Brown FRCS 1955
Peggy Kathleen Lilian Orton FRCS 1955
Joselen Ransome (Mrs Heron) FRCS 1958
Ruth Margaret Robinson (Mrs Ruth Hickson) FRCS 1956
Mary Elizabeth Shelswell FRCS 1956
Mini Hoshang Mehta FRCS 1959
Rosemary H M Adams (Mrs Campbell) FRCS 1955
Katharine Mary Burkill (Mrs Kit Taylor) 1929-1987 FRCS 1958
Irene Marion Irving (Mrs Irene Desmet) FRCS 1957
Eileen Rosemary Busby FRCS 1959
Pamela Ball (née Pamela Margaret Moody) FRCS 1954
Catherine Norah McRobert (Mrs Dennis) died 2003 FRCS 1954
Elizabeth Ann Lewis FRCS 1955 Australia
Dogdo Sohrab Bamji (Dogdo Rutha Mehta) FRCS 1954
Sheroo Darebsha Broacha FRCS 1955
Shakuntala Chandra FRCS 1955
Prem Virmani (Prem Mukerjee) 1928-1988 FRCS 1958
Kamla Rupoharb Alimchandani FRCS 1958
Vimla Bhogilal Jhaveri FRCS 1958
Sumita Sen FRCS 1958
Susila Rajagopalan FRCS 1959
Cecilia Grieg died 1986 FRCS 1955
Mary Kathleen Marchant FRCS 1957
Ellen Little FRCS 1959

CHAPTER 8

Women Fellows in the Sixties – FRCS 1960 to 1970

SIXTY-SEVEN women doctors attained the FRCS in the eleven years from 1960 to 1970.

Eighteen were from the Indian sub-continent who generally returned home to work once they had their Fellowship.

There were six new Fellows in 1960, six in 1961, five in 1962, five in 1963, eight in 1964, three in 1965, two in 1966, ten in 1967, none in 1968, two in 1969, two in 1970.

One was a paediatric surgeon who had the Edinburgh fellowship over twenty-five years before and belonged to the 1932 group. Six went to Australia, five returning to their home country including one from South Africa, an English graduate, emigrating there, another to South Africa, one to Canada, one to the USA, two to Barbados, some possibly returning to Ireland, five of unknown destiny. Four went to Africa, three to Catholic mission hospitals in Nigeria, one to Zambia.

This left twenty-eight new Fellows who were intending to make their future in the home country over the eleven years, on average two or three a year. Four Fellows achieved consultant posts in general surgery, one in Ashton-under-Lyne in the Manchester group, and three in London all within the umbrella of the teaching hospitals.

Women Fellows in the Sixties –FRCS 1960 to 1970
FRCS given to Distinguished Surgeons of Twenty Years Standing

Isabella Forshall (1902-1989) FRCS 1960. Isabella Forshall was one of the founders of paediatric and neonatal surgery in England. She was a consultant at the Alder Hey Children's Hospital in Liverpool.

She was educated privately at home in Sussex. Her mother had read classics at Girton College, Cambridge. She entered the London (Royal Free Hospital) School of Medicine and graduated in 1927 at age twenty-five. After early house jobs, she was appointed to the Royal Liverpool Children's Hospital in 1929 and also at the Birkenhead and Wirral Children's Hospital and Waterloo General Hospital. During the war she was actively involved in the treatment of many casualties from the bombing of the Liverpool dock area. She went on to Alder Hey Hospital where she remained for all her working life, making a great name for herself in the field of the new speciality of paediatric surgery.

She was involved in the formation of the Liverpool neonatal surgical centre, which had profound influences on the mortality of babies born with congenital abnormalities and was a lode star for other units to emulate. In 1958 she was the second president of the British Association of Paediatric Surgeons, in 1959 president of the Section of Paediatrics at the Royal Society of Medicine, in 1963 of the Liverpool Medical Institution. She had taken the Edinburgh fellowship in 1932 and belongs to that age of Fellows, though receiving the FRCS England in 1960.

Women Fellows in the Sixties – FRCS 1960 to 1970
Women of the Fellowship into General Surgery

Six women Fellows of the sixties made their career in general surgery, four achieved a consultant career in this country, one struggled to find suitable posts, one had an impressive career in Jamaica but found it difficult to find a similar post when she returned to England where she and her urologist surgeon husband had trained.

Tessa Morrell was consultant surgeon at the Tameside General Hospital in Ashton-under-Lyne in Lancashire.

Tessa was educated at Harrogate Grammar School and was one of two girls in her year who planned to study medicine. She took the entrance examination for Cambridge and went up there to study natural sciences, doing anatomy in part II in her third year. Her father was an agricultural merchant, there were no doctors in the family and her brother went into agriculture also. After Cambridge, Tessa went on to the Oxford clinical school for the clinical years, there being no medical training clinical school at Cambridge at that time. She graduated MA MB BChir in 1962.

She was house physician to Professor Witts at the Radcliffe and did house surgeon jobs there and went on to the Royal Northern Hospital in the Holloway Road, London to work in the accident and emergency department, where she also covered ENT, and then went on to an orthopaedic post there. She took the FRCS in 1965. She was registrar in urology at Leeds General Infirmary and lecturer in surgery at Oxford's Radcliffe Infirmary where she had plentiful operative experience. In Oxford she worked with Alf Gunning and did research on the epidemiology and pathology of pulmonary embolus, ascertaining experimentally that a thrombus and an embolus were indistinguishable.

Appointed consultant in general surgery and urology at Ashton-under-Lyne Tessa Morrell was one of three general surgeons being on emergency call '1 in 3'; they shared one registrar between them and had assistance from senior house officers who were generally overseas graduates. She was an assiduous member of the Surgical Research Society. Her colleagues Sewell and Samaji attended the Association of Surgeons meetings and because of the necessity for emergency cover it was not possible for her to join too. She retired to live near Cambridge.

Margaret Childe, Mrs Margaret Ghilchik. Margaret Ghilchik became a source of encouragement to generations of younger women by becoming a busy consultant surgeon and mother of a family. She worked continuously and full-time, operating until each of her four children was born and then taking her six weeks annual holiday.

Born in Hong Kong and speaking Cantonese before she spoke English, she was the middle daughter of a south China missionary, a Methodist minister. The hospitals and schools in Fo-shan and Suichow still stand, along with the vast diaspora of medical and education efforts that accompanied a century and a half of international missionary effort to the sub-continent of China that had brought literacy, medicine and education alongside the Bible. Her father elected to remain in China during World War II and was interned by the Japanese, but she and her sisters and mother were evacuated by the Red Cross to Australia.

She was educated in Melbourne at the Methodist Ladies' College where the wife of the headmaster, Dr Olive Wood, was an inspiration as a medical doctor, mother of six, and a generous warm-hearted woman of great Irish charm.

After the war on returning to England, she went to Rookery Road Elementary School in Handsworth, Birmingham, King Edward's High School (like Dame Hilda Lloyd and Beatrice Willmott Dobbie before her) and the North London Collegiate School, NLCS (like Dorothy Adams and

Betty Underhill and Elsie Visick Griffith). In spite of the excellent standing of NLCS, like many before her she found the science teaching inadequate, and attended technical college and night classes in Acton.

She trained at Barts, St Bartholomew's Hospital, and after the BSc spent a halcyon year at the Johns Hopkins University, USA, in biochemistry research. She won the William Harvey Prize in physiology, the Herbert Paterson medal in biochemistry and a university scholarship in science. She qualified MB BS London in 1961. The newly appointed professor of surgery at Barts decided to break with the traditions of his eminent predecessor Sir James Paterson Ross who disallowed women to take any of the house surgeon posts at Barts asserting that the jobs were too tough for girls. She was house surgeon, junior and senior, on the surgical professorial unit and went on to a third job on the thoracic unit.

As a house surgeon in Barts in the 1960s she had generous opportunity to operate, having an outpatient urethral bouginage list for stricture, a circumcision list, and diverse small operations to do under local or general anaesthetic. She was sent to the wards of the medical professorial unit to biopsy a lymph gland in the neck under local anaesthetic in order to provide a diagnosis and amongst other operations as a houseman she did an inguinal hernia and a cholecystectomy. On the thoracic unit, cardiac operations were done under conventional and profound hypothermia and she assisted in these and the insertion of an early pacemaker in 1962. She did tracheotomy under local anaesthetic on the ward and under general anaesthetic in theatre. She re-sutured the skin of a dehisced median sternotomy on the ward under local anaesthetic using a sterile Foley catheter as a drain.

After house posts she went on to research on an Aylwen Research Bursary while she took the primary FRCS. Like Jennifer Haley, she was unsuccessful in London but the primaries were interchangeable and she flew up to Glasgow on the shuttle and sat amongst the memorabilia of David Livingstone waiting her turn for warm and friendly vivas in the examination rooms.

She applied twice for all of the five surgical firms at Barts as junior registrar (SHO) without success. Even the professor who had appointed her felt that, because she was a woman, she should concentrate on surgical research, or consider going into paediatric surgery – he arranged for her to meet Peter Rickham – or into obstetrics and gynaecology where they were agreeable to have her. Sometimes at the appointment committees 'the feeling of the meeting' was not in her favour. Once coming to a vote with equal numbers between her and another candidate, the chairman, Mr Alec Badenoch, the urologist, made the casting vote with the words 'Let the man have it'.

She did her surgical training instead as resident surgical officer at Harold Wood Hospital, Essex, on the customary '1 in 2' resident-on-call rota, the old 100-110 hour week, and at the end of two years as RSO, the registrar 'cutting' years, she was accomplished in all the general elective and emergency operations and care of patients and took the FRCS in 1967. Under Mr John Talbot she developed an interest in the parathyroid, later to form the subject of her MS thesis.

She then worked for Professor Harold Ellis at the Westminster Hospital for a year trying to emulate his teaching talents and operative skills, assisting him at successful Whipple's operations, before going on to St Mary's as a lecturer in surgery, where she published extensively, in the transplant field, in vascular surgery, and presenting her MS thesis in 1972 on the localisation of the parathyroids, and becoming a senior lecturer.

Her consultant appointment was at St Charles' Hospital in Ladbroke Grove, mid-way between the Hammersmith and St Mary's in 1971 where she had forty beds, was on emergency call – 'a 1 in 2' – and operated on the whole range of general elective and emergency surgery. She ran the breast units at St Mary's, the Elizabeth Garrett Anderson and later the Central Middlesex Hospitals and breast cancer became her abiding interest. She was an early advocate of adjuvant chemotherapy and of breast conservation and reconstruction, embarking on these treatments as early as 1981. Together with the oncologist Dr Len Price and Dr Bridget Hill, the cancer cell biologist, she ran a conference on Safer Cancer Chemotherapy at the Royal College of Surgeons which was published as a book. She was Penrose May tutor at the College and lead the FRCS course for three years. In the breast field she collaborated with the research unit of Professor Mike Reed with many seminal publications in steroid chemistry and the biology of breast cancer.

She married Tony Ghilchik, an accountant, in 1969 and they had four children, she working and operating up to the day they were born and then taking her annual six weeks holiday only before returning to work. By being a successful consultant general surgeon and a mother of four she showed a generation of medical students and colleagues that it could be done. In retirement she continued to work for many years slotting in to locum appointments in breast units all over the country.

Elizabeth Mary Gordon (Betty) became a vastly accomplished consultant surgeon, much valued by her colleagues both in general surgery and in urology, in the surgical transplant field and in paediatric surgery at the Charing Cross Hospital and St George's. She worked at St James' Balham, at the South London Hospital for Women, in Australia, in Vietnam, and in India and Nigeria.

From her convent school in Clapham, La Rotraite, she left at age sixteen to do her A levels at Norwood Technical College where she had excellent teaching, winning a state scholarship. Her mother had been a teacher. Betty had had her early schooling in a Scottish village school, one teacher, fourteen children, in one room, when her father had worked for Lord Glenconner. Her decision to be a surgeon dated to the age of twelve on reading her brother's comic paper, *The Eagle*, where the operation of appendicectomy was described. She was always interested in the science side.

Betty Gordon did her medical training at Charing Cross when it was still in the Strand, nine girls and forty-five men students, and again excellent teaching. There was still the 'firm' spirit, as Constance Fozzard describes, and the students and their consultants took it in turns to host the end-of-firm party, once at the Ivy, sometimes at the consultant's home. Qualifying with honours in surgery and pharmacology, MB BS, she was house surgeon to Professor Harding Rains on the surgical professorial unit. Peter Philip was also on the firm, a superb technical surgeon. The professor of medicine was Hugh de Wardener and he was initiating renal dialysis, the Scribner shunt, and pioneering night time dialysis and home dialysis, later extending the concept to 'hospital-at-home'.

Betty did her medical house physician post at Putney Hospital at a time when the housemen were responsible for their own cross-matching of blood, their own blood sugar analyses and even were required to carry out their own post-mortems. She returned then to Charing Cross to do the accident & emergency post where she said you could tell the time of day by the patients who came in, whether from the Covent Garden market or bus men or the railways. She next went out to Stanmore to the Royal

National Orthopaedic Hospital which she enjoyed and entertained the idea of a career in orthopaedics. She went on to Hemel Hempstead, the 'cutting years', and took her FRCS in 1967.

By then the Charing Cross had moved from the Strand to Fulham and she re-joined Professor Harding Rains on the surgical professorial unit and was electrified one day to be asked whether she would like to go to Australia. She wondered at first what she had done to be banished, but it transpired that it was an Edward Wilson (the Arctic explorer and natural scientist of bird life) scholarship and she went to Melbourne, to Monash University, where she worked with Jim Watts (later to be at Flinders, Adelaide) on gastroduodenal function, looking at cholecystokinin in bile and doing pig liver perfusion experiments. She enjoyed her time there and elected to spend a second year doing operative surgery which included a stint in Vietnam with the Australian forces, working in Ben Hoa, a civilian hospital but receiving casualties from the war and where her orthopaedic, vascular and general surgical expertise was valuable. A child with a fractured femur would be put in a Gallow's splint and left there strung up to await healing; over the age of seven a hip spica was applied and the patient sent home. It was there that she was confronted for the first time with a patient being released by a medical colleague for interrogation and realised what was likely to befall him, and this sowed the seed for her later humanitarian work.

Never one to neglect an opportunity for the wider surgical experience, she worked for a month in Patna in India on her way home to England, and at some stage at a mission hospital in Nigeria where she recalls removing a spleen under local anaesthetic. Back in Charing Cross in Fulham, Grant Williams had started renal transplant surgery and as senior registrar and lecturer she was much involved with renal shunts, parathyroid surgery; Paton-Philip had started on his renowned transsexual surgical work. To give her a breathing space to complete her MS thesis which was on 'The Effect of Gastroduodenal Hormones on Bile Flow', she was sent to Cambridge to join Professor Roy Calne where the operating theatre was bathed in music from Mozart and Haydn and she got her MS 1977.

It was about that time that she went to a meeting in Stockwell of Amnesty International and was drawn into forming a medical group which became the Medical Foundation for Victims of Torture. She worked with Helen Bamber, Michael Korzinski and Rex Bloomstein and has been active in that sphere since.

It then became time to apply for consultant posts and Betty had interviews at Southampton and Liverpool where generally they had their own candidates. She had a difficult discussion with a woman consultant at the Royal Free where she was asked what she would do if she got married, and was then not called for interview, a situation similarly experienced there by Margaret Ghilchik when she was informally interviewed by the dean Dame Frances Gardner who quizzed her as to who made the evening meal and told her that it was unacceptable at the Royal Free that she should be cooking dinner.

She accepted an eight session consultant surgeon post at the South London Hospital for Women and kept four sessions at Charing Cross on the transplant and general side, and went on to work at St James' Balham, a very busy district general hospital. There they didn't need another general surgeon and she increasingly did urology and also paediatric surgery including neonates and premature babies with Alan Johnson, who later went to Leeds with his highly selective vagotomy innovation.

Eventually St James's Balham and the South London Hospital for Women had their day, and Betty went to St George's Tooting where again she settled down happily. The breadth of her surgical experience was illustrated when, on one occasion, the neurosurgeon needed to approach the spine at the T12 level. The thoracic surgeons when consulted averred it was a little low for them, the orthopaedic thought it a little higher than they were used to, and Betty provided access safely through an incision designed to approach the kidney.

She did some gender reassignment work at St George's on infants born with adrenal hyperplasia syndrome. She was invited to do a clinic once a month at Queen Mary Carshalton to see children with neuropathic bladders and did some bladder replacement surgery. She retired from St George's but continued on at Charing Cross until age sixty-seven when she was asked to do consultations and assessments for the Human Tissue Authority on living patients who wished to donate an organ, ensuring that they understood the consequences and had not been coerced. This fitted in well time-wise with her humanitarian work for the Medical Foundation for the Care of Victims of Torture which by then had centres in Hull, Manchester, Birmingham, Newcastle, and Glasgow as well as London, and where they have counsellors, therapists, gardens, allotments, and meeting centres. Elizabeth Gordon is a Trustee of the charity and an active worker for the cause.

Averil Olive Dring (later Averil Mansfield and Averil Bradley). Averil Dring qualified MB ChB Liverpool in 1960 and took the FRCS in 1967 and the ChM in 1973. She was lecturer in surgery at Liverpool Royal Infirmary and published papers on venous thrombosis, pulmonary embolism and fibrinolysis, giving a Hunterian lecture at the College on 'Control of pulmonary embolism by removal of residual thrombus from the iliac and femoral veins'.

Looking back, Averil recalls expressing her intention to be, not only a doctor, but a surgeon, at about the age of eight, after reading a children's book on early surgical advances which described a doctor operating opening the chest unaware whether a patient could live after such a procedure. Averil was an only child and her mother laid down a local rule that she could only say that she wanted to be a surgeon to her two parents, she was permitted to say that she might become a doctor to wider members of the family, but that she must respond to inquiries from the rest of the world by saying that she wanted to be a nurse. As Alan Bennett another Northerner would express it, she must not be thought to be 'getting above herself'.

Her mother had originally nurtured a desire to be a teacher but had been told that she was not strong enough, later living to the age of eighty-three, and had met her father in Blackpool Leisure Gardens. He was a scrap metal merchant who had left school at twelve and work was not always easy to find. Averil passed the eleven-plus and was educated at Blackpool Collegiate School for Girls where her musical ear was recognised in song and piano. Winning a local musical competition, her mother reminded her of the family rule and accordingly she appeared in the local paper with the header *Averil to nurse*. School and Headmistress were supportive and she passed the necessary three 'A' levels for medical school with a distinction in biology, her mother having written off for the A level syllabus and ensured that she covered the work. Medical school in Liverpool was a big step and one of her schoolteachers told her that if she were lonely in the hall of residence to go and find a piano and play it and she did just that and found herself surrounded by a friendly group. She did find music a solace.

She married firstly an architect, becoming Averil Mansfield. They had sung in the same choir, and she was known as Miss Mansfield throughout her working life. Averil always stoutly maintained that she had never met prejudice against her as a woman but students and junior doctors in Liverpool remember otherwise, recounting many incidents when the professor of the time would declare on a crowded ward-round that women could not be surgeons and when challenged, indicating that his senior lecturer was a woman, the professor would reply acidly 'Exactly!'

She spent some time in Berkeley, California, on a Harkness Foundation scholarship, and in Philadelphia, before becoming consultant in vascular surgery in Liverpool but later moving to London where she had posts at Paddington General Hospital (St Mary's Harrow Road), the Hammersmith and St Mary's Paddington. The operation for which she became known was carotid endarterectomy and she usually did such a procedure most weeks. She always had time to give a second opinion on knotty vascular cases. She married the surgeon Jack Bradley.

At St Mary's the Chair of Surgery became vacant with the removal back to Leeds of Professor Guillou after the untimely death of Professor Giles there, and there was hopes that Andrew Bradley, the transplant surgeon might be persuaded to come from Scotland to St Mary's where they had long had one of the earliest renal transplant units, but Bradley had his sights on Cambridge. Averil was on the selection committee and after hearing the many unsuccessful phone calls to Scotland, the committee asked her to fill a chair of vascular surgery. Having appointed a woman to the chair, St Mary's put out a statement that she had been appointed entirely on merit, doubtless with the intention of being supportive, in fact an unnecessary and unhelpful comment. Shortly after, she was elected on to the Council of the Royal College of Surgeons and she brought the reputation of the College appointment to St Mary's and was instrumental in the fund-raising for the up-grading of lecture theatre 2, commemorating the first woman surgeon Eleanor Davies-Colley, and the Paul Cox mural of women surgeons covering one wall of the lecture theatre and which is also seen on the cover of this book.

Averil Mansfield was the second woman surgeon to be elected to the Council and, like Phyllis George before her, was said to have taken fairy cakes that she had baked into the Council meetings for the men's tea. They felt perhaps a subtle flattery in providing home-baked cakes for male colleagues, a sign that their sex was recognised. Nevertheless, it was an outrage to feminists. From Hillary Clinton onwards, the wives of American Presidents have laid claim to professional lives of their own, eschewing the competition for the best home-baked cookies. She was a tall stately woman and, though associated with the College's attempts to be more female-friendly by the setting up the association WIST (Women in surgical training, a joint venture from the Department of Health's Virginia Bottomley and Angela Rumbold with the College), she was not always found to be supportive of other women surgeons. When asked the secret of her success in the male-dominated field of surgery, she replied that it was by keeping her head below the parapet. Later, in her retirement, she became President of the BMA for a year. In a retirement subscription dinner that she organised at the College, she entertained with a bravura recital in scouse dialect of an autobiographical epic poem that she had written, displaying her pride in her Liverpool origins and covering the highlights of her career. She added playing the cello to her skills at the piano and was a collector of the diminutive musical instruments of Haydn's *Toy opera*.

Clara Clothilde Zilahi studied at Cambridge University qualifying MB BChir in 1956 and took the FRCS in 1965. She lived in Downham Market, Norfolk. She did clinical assistant sessions as and when she could obtain them, usually about three sessions a week. She did feel that she had had prejudice against her as a woman in medicine. She felt strongly in favour of the availability of part-time work, even to senior house officer and registrar level.

Monica Cynthia Lewin was the second Jamaican woman to get the FRCS, after Pamela Ball the plastic surgeon. She and her husband David Atkinson were the first husband and wife both to be FRCS.

Monica was educated at Hayes Elementary School and the Hampton School in Jamaica where her sisters also studied and where she was a contemporary of Pamela Moody (Pamela Ball). It is an elite secondary school and it is said that she was the first black girl to become head girl. Her mother was a teacher and her father a headmaster and they were committed to education for their daughters. She came to London on a Jamaican scholarship to study medicine at the London (Royal Free Hospital) School of Medicine. She was house surgeon to Geraldine Barry at the Royal Free and had posts at St Margaret's Epping, Brighton, the Royal Homeopathic Hospital and the Elizabeth Garrett Anderson. She took the FRCS in 1962.

On her return to Jamaica she was Senior Registrar to Sir Harry Annamunthado and then was appointed consultant surgeon to Kingston Public Hospital, in 1963, where she dealt with machete and gun-shot wounds in the unrest of the 1960s.

She married the surgeon David Atkinson FRCS. They had been medical students together. In Kingston, he was Consultant Urologist at the University Hospital, surgeon i/c of firm B. He was known colloquially to the students by the nickname of 'Whispering Smith' because he spoke softly and because it was believed that he had been undercover in the Secret Service. They adopted children. They returned to England and David became Consultant Urologist at the North Middlesex Hospital and Monica did clinical assistant posts at the Royal Northern and Whittington Hospitals. To their surprise, when she was over age forty-five, they had two children of their own, David and Mary. Monica died in 1998.

Monica's sister, the renowned Dr Olive Lewin, also came to London on a Jamaican scholarship to study at the Royal Academy of Music and then at Queen's University Belfast and the Royal College of Music. She collected and published an iconic collection of Jamaican folk music. She was much decorated, including OJ (Order of Jamaica), CD, LRSM, LRAM, LTCL and FRCL (Trinity College of Music), ARCM (Associate Royal College of Music). Among her eight books are *Forty Folk Songs of Jamaica*, 1973, and *Rock It Come Over: the Folk Music of Jamaica*, 2000. She did many performances and video-audio recordings with the Jamaica Folk Singers, a group she inaugurated, such as 'Messengers', 'Timeless trial from humblest hearts', 'Dandy shandy', 'Beeny bud', 'Alle, alle, alle', 'Come mek me hol yu can'. In later years her recitals and singing were supported by her daughter Johanna.

Women Fellows in the Sixties – FRCS 1960 to 1970
Women and the Fellowship into Gynaecology

Six women Fellows went into gynaecology, Margaret Witt and Jill Evans, both trained at Barts; they were contemporaries. Maggie Witt did her postgraduate training around London at Queen Charlotte's, Soho and

Watford Peace Memorial and there was conjecture whether Barts might ever accept a female consultant. Jill Evans had been up at Cambridge for her preclinical years and after Barts went up to Sheffield for further postgraduate training and was appointed to the Royal Oldham Hospital. Constance Fozzard who had trained at Charing Cross was consultant in the Royal Cornwall Hospital, Truro, Dorothy Whitney (Mrs Raeburn) was Consultant in Cuckfield and the mid-Sussex group, Eunice Burton was at Harold Wood, Essex. Ann Mary Jequier, who after student days at the Royal Free, had been registrar at the celebrated Southend unit and become first lecturer at the Middlesex Hospital then Consultant at Nottingham, took her future to Perth, Australia where she headed an infertility unit doing original research.

Margaret Witt received her FRCS in 1961 and became MRCOG in 1966 and FRCOG in 1979. Maggie Witt trained at Barts and qualified MB BS London in 1955. She worked at Queen Charlotte's, the Hospital for Women Soho Square and the Peace Memorial Hospital in Watford and was senior registrar at Barts. She was appointed Consultant in Obstetrics and Gynaecology at the North Middlesex Hospital, Edmonton.

Jill (Margaret) Evans (1929-1995) was consultant in obstetrics and gynaecology in the Royal Oldham Hospital. She was educated in Brentwood High School, and went up to Girton College Cambridge on a scholarship. She did her clinical training at Barts. She graduated MB BCh Cambridge in 1954. She was house surgeon and registrar in obstetrics and gynaecology in Sheffield and took the MRCOG in 1959 (later becoming FRCOG) and the FRCS in 1962. She was appointed consultant in obstetrics and gynaecology to the Royal Hospital Oldham where she spent her working life. She was a keen hill-walker, doing the Munros, and loved trekking in the Himalayas, sailing and music. She died age sixty-five in 1995.

Constance Ethel Fozzard trained at the Charing Cross Hospital Medical School and qualified MB BS London in 1958. She was firm in her resolution to be a doctor while still at school. Her headmaster tried to persuade her on to the arts side and she had to resist that to study science in the sixth form. Her mother, who was a widow, was reluctant to support her, believing that her priority must be to fund Constance's brother in his engineering studies. Then she failed her A level physics which put a hoped-for botany scholarship out of reach. However she went to the Northern Polytechnic and took and passed her pre-medical exams and, to her delight, Charing Cross Hospital Medical School offered her a place. Charing Cross was then on the Strand and central to all London life.

She was fascinated by dissection and human anatomy and chose to go into the medical school during the holidays to dissect teaching specimens. In biochemistry, her neighbour on the bench livened things up with accidental fires and her own working partner never did any experiments: his contribution was to get out the apparatus, then disappear, and return at the end of the session to hear her findings and write up the results and put the equipment away.

Once she was into the clinical side, the firms had to go out to specialist hospitals for 'fevers' and 'midwifery' but in Charing Cross itself there were daily post-mortem demonstrations. Their firm dinners were often held at the famous Rules' restaurant.

Constance did her further training at the Italian Hospital and Queen Charlotte's and took the MRCOG in 1964 and the FRCS in 1967. She was senior registrar at Charing Cross and got her consultant appointment in obstetrics and gynaecology at the Royal Cornwall Hospital, Treliske, Truro. She was much involved in medical education and in the BMA Council and committees and a firm opinion on medical politics. In retirement she became Mayor of Truro.

Dorothy June Whitney (Mrs Raeburn) became consultant in obstetrics and gynaecology at the Cuckfield Hospital in Haywards Heath, Sussex and the Mid-Sussex Hospital Group. Dorothy trained at Guy's and qualified MB BS London in 1953. She was registrar on the professorial unit (obstetrics and gynaecology) at the Queen Elizabeth Hospital Birmingham, taking the DRCOG in 1955 and the MRCOG in 1958. She was registrar in general surgery at the Dundee Royal Infirmary and took the FRCS in 1962. She was senior registrar at St George's Hospital before being appointed consultant to the Mid-Sussex Hospitals.

Eunice (Ruth) Burton became consultant in obstetrics and gynaecology at Harold Wood Hospital, Essex. She trained at the Middlesex Hospital qualifying MB BS London in 1957 and after house appointments at the Middlesex took the DRCOG the following year. She was senior house officer at Queen Charlotte's and senior registrar at the Hammersmith Hospitals and took the MRCOG in 1961 and the FRCS in 1964. Her consultant appointment was at Harold Wood Hospital, Essex to a newly built obstetric and gynaecology block on the Harold Wood site of the EMS wooded single storey hospital originally designed to receive the projected casualties of the Blitz in World War II. She became FRCOG in 1977 and published in the field of obstetrics, on pregnancy and placental insufficiency.

She writes: 'I feel that one has had to choose between a "successful" consultant career and marriage: I could not leave (sic) that the heavy demands of my job and brought up a family without their being "deprived" emotionally , altho' cared for physically by "help"!'

When asked whether she felt she had experienced prejudice against her as a woman in medicine, she certainly felt there had been. When applying for consultant posts, some posts went to men less well qualified especially if there was a woman already in the area. She could see that part-time posts would be helpful to keep women doctors working in medicine but she was against part-time training posts, feeling that one should complete one's training before having a family.

Anne (Mary) Jequier became consultant at the University Hospital in Nottingham and went from there to Perth, Australia to be head of a service at the King Edward Memorial Hospital.

Anne Jequier trained at the Royal Free Hospital graduating MB BS London in 1961. After house physician and house surgeon appointments at the Royal Free, she was surgical registrar at Southend General Hospital. She took the FRCS in 1967. She was lecturer in obstetrics and gynaecology at the Middlesex Hospital and took the MRCOG in 1969. She became consultant and senior lecturer in obstetrics and gynaecology in the University of Nottingham and was FRCOG in 1982. She published in 1986 *Infertility in the Male and Semen Analysis: A Practical Guide*.

Anne Jequier went to Perth, Australia as consultant to the infertility clinic at the King Edward Memorial Hospital. She published papers on 'The founding father of modern andrology' and other papers in the infertility field.

Women Fellows in the Sixties – FRCS 1960 to 1970
Women and the Fellowship into Eye Surgery

Seven of the Fellows of the sixties became eye surgeons, Doreen Birks at St Thomas', Marian Handscombe, following on Dorothy Adams, at Coventry and Warwick, Enid Taylor at the North Middlesex and the Elizabeth Garrett Anderson Hospitals, Margaret Challis at Whipps Cross, and Doris Price at Harlow and Eileen Vale. Althea Connell, who came from this country where her parents were both doctors, had a distinguished career in Barbados.

Doreen Ann Birks became consultant ophthalmic surgeon to St Thomas's Hospital and the Sutton and West Merton Eye Unit at Sutton Hospital. She trained at the Royal Free Hospital qualifying MB BS London in 1949 and was house surgeon, and later senior registrar, at the Royal Eye Hospital and ophthalmic registrar at St James' Balham. She took the DO in 1953 and the FRCS in 1962. Her consultant appointments were not only at St Thomas' and Sutton but she was also the hon consulting surgeon for the School for the Blind in Leatherhead. She was a member of the Ophthalmological Society UK and was author of published papers.

Marion Christine Handscombe became consultant ophthalmic surgeon at Coventry and Warwick Hospitals. She went to school in Essex, at Mills Grammar School and the Sir John Lemon School and trained at UCH and then the London Hospital qualifying MB BS London in 1954. She married and had a baby during her houseman years and received surprised support from her consultants and warm help from her mother-in-law and was back at work in three months. She worked in Greenwich and the London and did the eye surgery training programme at Moorfields where she was senior registrar. She took the FRCS in 1962 and FCOphth in 1989. She was representative on the Council of the Royal College of Surgeons when the eye surgeons broke away and formed their own college.

Her consultant appointments were at Coventry and Warwick Hospitals where she spent her working life. She travelled to Africa, India, Ceylon and China to practise her eye surgery and teach, flying round in tiny aircraft, sometimes taking one of her two children, a student-nurse, with her. She retired to Banbury in Oxfordshire.

Enid Taylor (née Enid Wheldon) was consultant ophthalmic surgeon at the North Middlesex Hospital and the Elizabeth Garrett Anderson. Enid Wheldon studied at Cambridge University and did her clinical studies at the London Hospital and qualified MB BChir in 1957. She was registrar at the North Middlesex Hospital and at St James' Balham and senior registrar at Barts. She took the FRCS in 1965. She was appointed consultant at the North Middlesex Hospital and the Elizabeth Garrett Anderson and took the FRCOphth in 1988. She was a member of the Ophthalmological Society of the UK and Assistant of the Worshipful Company of Apothecaries and published on diabetic retinopathy. She was a married lady.

Margaret (Thornton) Challis trained at the London Hospital qualifying MB BS in 1957. She was house surgeon at Moorfields Eye Hospital and senior registrar in eyes at the London. She went on to be appointed consultant at Whipps Cross Hospital, a busy district general hospital, and the regional eye centre.

Her mother was a doctor and had worked in general practice for forty-one years. Margaret Challis's feelings on part-time posts were that they would be helpful to women. She herself worked a virtual full-time eight sessions including on-call commitments but, like many others, felt that part-time training was a step too far. On prejudice, she said that she lost many jobs initially because women were not wanted, then got one job because she was female!

Doris May Cleweth Price (neé Davies) became consultant ophthalmic surgeon to the Harlow Group of Hospitals. Doris Davies, as she was then, trained in Birmingham and graduated MB ChB in 1953. After house jobs she was registrar at the Coventry and Warwick Hospitals, and in Shrewsbury, and took the DO in 1956, then becoming senior registrar at Birmingham & Midland Eye Hospital and took both the Edinburgh and the English FRCS in 1963. She was a member of the Midlands Ophthalmological Society and the Royal Society of Medicine and became FRCOphth in 1988.

As consultant at the Harlow Group of Hospitals she covered West Essex and East Hertfordshire. Twenty years after getting the Fellowship, she was working full-time with some private practice and felt that both part-time work and part-time training would be helpful to women in surgical work, and she felt that many more part-time consultant posts should be available. She did not feel that there had been prejudice against her as a woman in medicine; however she did not find her colleagues helpful to her during her two pregnancies. She took only the minimum leave and returned to full responsibilities six weeks after giving birth. She would advise any young woman in medicine to obtain her higher degrees before she is married, as she did, as this was the better way to gain postgraduate experience.

She writes: 'To have a career in medicine doing full-time work + a family + a husband, who must agree to your work, is very difficult and demanding – but is equally very satisfying when it is achieved.'

Eileen Mary Vale did her medical training at the Royal Free Hospital and qualified MB BS London in 1944. She took the DO in 1962 and the FRCS in 1969. She died in Bexhill in January 1977.

Anthea Mary Stewart Connell (1925-2003) was the senior consultant ophthalmic surgeon at the Queen Elizabeth Hospital, Barbados for twenty-seven years and did important work documenting conditions of the eye in Barbados.

Anthea was the daughter of two doctors, her father John S M Connell was a surgeon and gynaecologist in the RAMC in World War Ii with the rank of colonel serving on hospital ships; her mother Constance B Challis trained in Cambridge and Birmingham and went into public health. Anthea was educated at Edgbaston High School, Birmingham and then at City Park Collegiate Institute, Saskatoon before moving on to the University of Saskatchewan, Canada and then to Birmingham University where she qualified MB ChB in 1952. She was resident and registrar at Moorfields and senior registrar/first assistant at Moorfields/Guy's/and the London Hospitals. She took the FRCS in 1964.

Anthea Connell was appointed senior consultant and head of department of ophthalmology in Barbados in 1969 and was assistant lecturer in the University of the West Indies. She initiated the Barbados Eye Study and conducted surveys and published on the incidence of glaucoma and on intraocular eye pressures in the population, presenting her work in the American Academy of Ophthalmology. She held courses and organised the Diploma of Ophthalmology examination for the College of Surgeons of England.

She married in 1963 George E P Dowglass, a wine merchant, and they had a daughter Charlotte, who worked at Hampton Court Palace and the Tower of London.

Like many surgeons, Anthea painted, in oils and acrylic, and showed her work. She died after a series of cerebrovascular accidents

Women Fellows in the Sixties – FRCS 1960 to 1970
Women of the Fellowship into ENT Surgery

Four of the sixties Fellows became ENT surgeons, Veronica Gammon in mid-Glamorgan, Romola Dunsmore in Doncaster, Noelin Fehily (Mrs Cook) in Worcester and Carol Wengref in Greenwich and Lewisham.

Veronica (May) Gammon became consultant ENT surgeon to the Mid-Glamorgan Health Authority in Wales. Trained at the Royal Free, qualifying MB BS in 1948, she was FRCS in 1961 and DLO in 1971.

Romola Diana Dunsmore became consultant ENT surgeon at Doncaster Royal Infirmary. Trained at the Royal Free, qualifying MB BS in 1949, she did her early jobs at the Free in surgery, obstetrics and gynaecology and ENT, and was surgical registrar in ENT. She took the FRCS in 1961. She retired to Settle in North Yorkshire.

Noelin Catherine Gertrude Fehily (Mrs Cook) qualified in 1963 in the NUI (University College, Dublin), and held surgical posts in Leicester Royal Infirmary, was surgical registrar at Victoria Hospital, Blackpool, and did ENT training in Brighton, UCH and senior registrar in Birmingham. She became FRCS in 1967 and consultant ENT surgeon in Worcester.

Carol Lindsay Wengref was Consultant ENT surgeon at the Greenwich, Lewisham and Woolwich Hospitals in South London. Trained at Guy's Hospital, graduating MB BS in 1962, and after house surgeon posts, was SHO in ENT at the Westminster Hospital, taking the FRCS in 1967 and became Senior Registrar in ENT at Guy's, before being appointed Consultant at Greenwich, Lewisham and Woolwich.

Women Fellows in the Sixties – FRCS 1960 to 1970
Women of the Fellowship into Orthopaedics

Three women Fellows went into orthopaedics, one working predominantly in research, one as an A & E Consultant and one in physical medicine.

Ruth Wynne-Davies went from orthopaedic surgery into research medical genetics specialising in the orthopaedic field and has become an authority on the epidemiology, genetic and other aetiological factors in developmental disorders of the musculoskeletal system.

She was educated at Eversfield School, Sutton and the Nonsuch County School for Girls and was evacuated in the war to Wales finishing her schooling at Oswestry High School for Girls. Her father John Welch Blower had worked for Lloyds Bank in Oswestry and in Sutton and was one of the Directors of the Sutton & Cheam Music Festival, being a baritone and a pianist himself and served in both world wars, in the first in Mesopotamia as a captain, in the second by 'reducing' his age by a decade and took part in the small vessels pool, ferrying small boats around the coast of Britain. Ruth had done secretarial work on leaving school during the war in local government and civil defence.

After the war, she entered the London (Royal Free Hospital) School of Medicine graduating MB BS London in 1953. She was married as a medical student and young doctor to a fellow medic, Arnold Danziger. She was attracted to an orthopaedic career as early as the preclinical years. As she put the appeal: bones have length and joints have angles. She did house jobs at the Metropolitan Hospital and the Royal Free and was demonstrator in anatomy at the Free. She got excellent surgical experience at Birmingham Accident Hospital as senior house officer and at Great Ormond Street and was surgical registrar at the Elizabeth Garrett Anderson Hospital and in Wrexham North Wales taking the surname Wynne-Davies of her uncle who had encouraged and sponsored her and achieving the FRCS in 1960.

She had decided on orthopaedics as a career and after a spell at the Royal Salop Infirmary, became orthopaedic registrar and then senior registrar in Exeter at the Princess Margaret Orthopaedic Hospital with Norman Capener in his outstanding orthopaedic unit. Her two years there determined the future direction of her career. As well as becoming a competent orthopaedic surgeon, she was 'bitten by the research bug'. She was awarded the Robert Jones Gold Medal and prize of the British Orthopaedic Association.

She went from Exeter to be an MRC research fellow in 1963 at the Medical Research Council's group on genetic problems in orthopaedic disease. (In the wake of the Thalidomide disaster, the Distillers Company had provided funds, a quarter of a million pounds, for Edinburgh University, which looked after the twenty-four people from Scotland and Northern Ireland affected by thalidomide.) The MRC research group was formed to look into genetic and familial causes of skeletal deformities.

Ruth Wynne-Davies was first senior lecturer, then reader (orthopaedics) in the Genetics Research Unit in Edinburgh University and took the PhD Edinburgh in 1973 while there.

Her eighteen years at Edinburgh were productive. Her research ranged over all the musculoskeletal disorders and she published upward of seventy research papers and a number of books and chapters in books. Together with Christine Hall as consultant radiologist and A Graham Apley, the orthopaedic surgeon at St Thomas' and St Peter's Chertsey whose Rowley Bristow Pyrford teaching course will be known to all surgical Fellows post World War II, she produced in 1985 *The Atlas of Skeletal Deformities*. With T J Fairbank she produced the second edition of *Atlas of General Affections of the Skeleton* in 1976 and in 1973 *Heritable Disorders in Orthopaedic Practice*.

During the first ten years she was concerned with large family and genetic surveys of the common development disorders, congenital dislocation of the hip, scoliosis and vertebral anomalies, talipes equinovarus (clubfoot), Perthes' disease, and congenital limb deformities. She drew originally on the register from the Princess Rose Hospital, Exeter, where they had records spanning back forty years. She set up a skeletal dysplasia clinics in Edinburgh, Oswestry, Nottingham, St Thomas' which met as specialist clinics once a quarter. She compiled joint family surveys with Edward J Riseborough on cases seen between 1967 and 1970 at the Children's Hospital, Boston, and visited centres in France, Germany, where Faber had published in 1934 a series of six hundred cases, and Australia. Her seminal paper on the study of the families of patients with scoliosis analysed the families of two hundred and eight children with scoliosis, one hundred and sixty-nine girls and thirty-nine boys, giving a sex ratio of 6:1, all right-sided curves, almost all thoracic. She divided the age groups into infantile – birth to three years, juvenile – four to nine years, and adolescent – age ten and over, this last group having the preponderance of cases. From the family studies she concluded the incidence as 3.9/1000 in girls and 0.3/1000 in boys, and noted small numbers of other abnormalities, concluding a multifactorial mode of inheritance.

With colleagues, she has contributed to genetic mapping, site on chromosome identification, and the connections and linkages with other inherited conditions.

Ruth Wynne-Davies was an early member of the British Orthopaedic Research Society, of which she was secretary and president in her time. The Skeletal Dysplasia Group, a multidisciplinary membership of orthopaedic surgeons, clinical geneticists, radiologists and paediatricians, meets for teaching and research, initially twelve members, now numbering two hundred and fifty and international.

In 1981, at the age of fifty-five, she took early retirement from Edinburgh, keeping contact with the Harlow Wood Orthopaedic Hospital, Mansfield, the Robert Jones and Agnes Hunt Orthopaedic Hospital, Oswestry, St Thomas' Hospital and the Oxford Radcliffe and Clinical Genetics Department where she was an honorary consultant. She studied English language & literature for the BA Oxon and settled in Oxford.

Delia (Margaret Helen Hernaman) Cothay was the first consultant to be appointed to the orthopaedic & trauma unit in the accident & emergency department of the Royal Surrey County Hospital, Guildford. When she retired, it was the time of improved staffing of A & E units, of increased recognition of medical, as opposed to surgical, emergencies, a rota system for cover, and increasingly a consultant-led service, but nevertheless it took six consultants to replace her.

Educated at Sunderland High School Delia Cothay lived with her grandparents in the north-east of England. Her parents were away in the Plateau State, central Nigeria, her father working as an engineer in tin-mining. Delia went on to finish her schooling at the Bedgebury Girls' Public School in Lillesden, near Hawkeshead in Surrey and spent a year with her parents after leaving school. By the second year of the war, Delia found a job, intercepting telegrams and radio messages from the Free

French. Because of her war service she was eligible for the further education training scheme (FETS) and she entered the Westminster Medical School as a medical student. They were the first entry post war, and William Goodenough had pressurised the great London teaching hospitals to open their doors to women students as well as men. They took only a quota of women; in Delia's year there were four girl students and twenty-four chaps. She worked under Sir Stanford Cade, whom she found supportive and not at all frightening (his daughter Irene was a medical student alongside her) and Bobby Cox and qualified MB BS in 1951. She did house surgeon posts at the Westminster and in the Isle of Wight.

What decided Delia Cothay for orthopaedics was a childhood observation. The woman who lived next door to her grandparents in Sunderland had a caliper on one leg that Delia regarded with interest – pondering why she had it, what was the necessity of it, how it worked.

Delia did training posts at the Royal National Orthopaedic Hospital at Stanmore and took the FRCS in 1960 and was orthopaedic surgical registrar at Treloar. In those days, in order to become a consultant, one had to obtain a senior registrar post and these were scarce and in the purlieus of the teaching hospitals. Delia did a locum and was then appointed consultant in orthopaedics and trauma to the Royal Surrey Hospital in Guildford – the Hospital's first A & E consultant – and where she spent her working life.

Helene (Valerie) Goodman, later Mrs Woolf, became a consultant in physical medicine and rheumatology in St Stephen's Hospital, Fulham, the Westminster Hospital and the Royal Marsden. She went up to Oxford where she qualified BM BCh in 1951, doing her clinical training at St George's. She was registrar in physical medicine at the Middlesex and senior registrar at St Thomas', taking the DPhysMed in 1958, the DM in 1961 and the FRCS in 1962. Her consultant appointments were at the Westminster Hospital, St Stephen's Fulham and the Marsden.

Women Fellows in the Sixties – FRCS 1960 to 1970
Women of the Fellowship into Neurosurgery

Jennifer (Jane) Haley trained at the Middlesex Hospital and graduated MB BS London in 1955. She had a distinguished career as a neurosurgeon, training at the Whittington and Central Middlesex Hospitals, the Liverpool neurosurgical unit at the Walton Hospital, and co-founded with her husband the neurosurgery unit in New Delhi in the Safdarjung Hospital, associated with the Lady Hardinge Medical College and the medical faculty at Delhi University. Her married name was Ahluwalia.

Jennifer Haley was one of the four children of William Haley. When her father started his career on the *Manchester Evening News*, he was judged to be too shy to be a newspaper reporter and they made him a sub-editor; he went on to be Director General of the BBC from 1944 to 1952 and Editor of *The Times* from 1952 to 1956. Jennifer went to seven different schools during war-time England, including a few weeks at St Paul's during the flying bombs and then on to Cheltenham Ladies' College. She was a keen medical student at the Middlesex Hospital and it was largely the surgical side which captured her interest: she recalls watching Diana Beck, the neurosurgeon doing an operation, harbinger of her surgical future, and assisting David Patey doing a painstakingly slow meticulous dissection of a parotid tumour. She got wonderful surgical and medical experience in house posts at the Central Middlesex Hospital, learning also from the outstanding diagnostic skills of Richard Asher and others. The medical mess sent a deputation to Dr Joules, Consultant Physician to the Hospital, to formally protest about the medical residence conditions there and he told them that they could all leave if they had any complaints; there were plenty of others who wanted their jobs.

When Jennifer Haley took the primary FRCS, she had the misfortune to meet Sir Gordon Gordon-Taylor whom she knew from her Middlesex student days was dead against women: he greeted her with 'If you can put down your bag, you silly woman, and be prepared to soil your fingers, tell me what this is' pointing to the optic nerve in the dissection. 'That's the optic nerve, sir.' He did not agree and they went around naming the cavernous sinus and optic chiasma and various other structures before returning to the optic nerve which he triumphantly identified to her. 'That's what she said in the beginning,' said the other examiner mildly before taking himself off for a cup of coffee. Primary fellowships were interchangeable and Glasgow was said to be the place to go and she and another student drove up in his Jaguar XK120 convertible which he let her drive and she returned triumphantly having passed the primary and driven a wonderful car. She had begun in Glasgow by making a mess of the first question of the day and the examiner had said sympathetically, 'It *is* rather early in the morning. Tell me what you are *really* interested in' and they spent a happy viva discussing extradural haematomas.

She had done a casualty job at the Whittington and during her surgical post at the Central Middlesex, working for Mr Roberts, she was offered neurosurgical training by Mr MrCall at the Whittington, who then got cold feet after offering the job to a woman and had to be encouraged by a phone call from Mr Roberts. She took the FRCS in 1964. She went on to become senior registrar in neurosurgery at the Walton Hospital Liverpool where she did four further years in training. During her time there, she contracted viral encephalitis from a patient whose cerebral abscess she had drained. Her work was well trusted at Liverpool; she called Mr Kerr, the chief, on one occasion to say that the tumour she was operating to remove did not look like the metastasis that they had thought it was, but an astrocytoma, and wondered whether he wanted to come and give his opinion or take over and do the operation, and the laconic reply from Kerr came back to theatre, 'Tell her to carry on'.

At the Walton Hospital, Liverpool, she met and worked with fellow neurosurgeon Har Paul Singh Ahluwalia and they agreed to marry, an arrangement that both sides of the family initially minded. They were both ready to become consultants and discussed Cardiff, Preston, or even Liverpool itself, as possible locations. Har Paul had trained in Calcutta, as had his sister, a gynaecologist, and done his initial surgical training in the UK at the Hammersmith Hospital. Three weeks before the wedding, the future in-laws arrived, the father, an ophthalmic surgeon put it to his son to consider a neurosurgical future in New Delhi. The pair set up the neurosurgical unit in the Safdarjung Hospital, the university hospital, and stayed there for six years. They worked well together in Liverpool and in New Delhi: they both graciously said about the other that their partner was the better neurosurgeon, but inside, they each knew that they were the better! There were at that time about eight neurosurgeons in the whole of India and they left the unit well looked after and set up. Their range of surgery was comprehensive. Financially they were not well off but they might have stayed working in India if they had gone to Chandigarh but mother-in-law was not in favour and they had two small children. Her son who was four and a half spoke English to his parents, Hindi with his friends and Punjabi locally. Her daughter Susan was three. She returned to the UK to Jersey where her father Sir William Haley had been born and where he had retired. There was no scope for a neurosurgical practice in the Channel Islands and Jennifer worked in the Morning Medical Clinic for ten years, and with her husband in general practice; he died at the early age of sixty-one. A fuller account of her life is in the chapter on neurosurgery.

In response to the 1981 questionnaire, she felt that part-time posts and part-time training would be helpful to keeping women working in medicine. Her own mother had worked. When the children were small she had a local live-in help to look after them when she was not there. She continued working in St Helier, half in the hospital and half in general practice, though not in the speciality for which she had been trained. She certainly felt that there was prejudice expressed against a woman in medicine.

Carys Bannister was an almost exact contemporary of Jennifer Haley and became a paediatric neurosurgeon specialising in neurodevelopmental defects founding and running the tertiary referral centre in Manchester Children's Hospital. She qualified at Charing Cross Hospital in 1958 and after early training posts took the Edinburgh Fellowship and then went to Oxford to study neurophysiology. Her research subject was the blood supply to the brain and spina bifida and hydrocephalus and at the neurosurgical unit at Leeds Infirmary subsequently she developed the extracranial-intracranial bypass technique. She was appointed consultant neurosurgeon to the North Manchester Hospital Group and Booth Hall Children's Hospital. She set up a tertiary referral centre for neurodevelopmental defects at St Mary's, the Manchester Children's Hospital. She helped to elucidate the importance of brain folate in hydrocephalus.

She was a successful surgeon and, remaining single and free of family commitments, she was able to indulge the sort of hobbies that some of her men colleagues took part in. She was an enthusiastic car rally driver, and her dogs won best of breed at Crufts. She died age seventy-five.

Women Fellows in the Sixties – FRCS 1960 to 1970
Women of the Fellowship into Thoracic Surgery

Mary (Patricia) Shepherd was consultant thoracic surgeon at Harefield. She trained at the Royal Free and qualified MB BS in 1957. After house appointments she went to the Hospital for Sick Children in Toronto and trained there in cardiovascular surgery. It was in Canada that she got her thoracic training. She was registrar in general surgery at the Royal Free Hospital and took the FRCS in 1964. She was senior registrar on the thoracic surgical unit at Harefield Hospital and later was appointed consultant there. She also covered the Central Middlesex, St Albans City, Queen Elizabeth Welwyn Garden City and Barnet General Hospitals.

Her Hunterian professorship lecture in 1969 was on 'Diaphragmatic muscle and cardiac surgery' and she enlarged it into an MS thesis on the same topic in 1972. She was a member of the Thoracic and Cardiovascular Society of Great Britain. In spite of operating on countless lungs, she was an inveterate cigarette smoker. She was a single lady, and had minimal daily help, once a week for a few hours. She had never felt any prejudice against her as a woman in medicine and was in favour of both part-time posts and part-time training if it would help other women to work, but she herself had always worked full-time.

Women Fellows in the Sixties – FRCS 1960 to 1970
Women of the Fellowship into Paediatric Surgery

Leela Kapila graduated MB BS in Madras in 1962, having trained at the Christian Medical College, Vellore. She did posts at Rush Green Hospital, Romford and the Hospital for Sick Children, Great Ormond Street and the London Hospital and took the FRCS in 1966. She became consultant paediatric surgeon in Nottingham at the University Hospital in Queen's Medical Centre. She became an examiner and a member of Council of the Royal College of Surgeons, the third woman on the Council and the first Indian. Wearing her sari, she entertained the members of Council to Indian food, perpetuating the women's cooking image.

Caroline Doig was a paediatric surgeon at the Children's Hospital in Manchester. She was educated at the Forfar Academy in County Angus. Her mother was a teacher and all her mother's family were teachers and headteachers. Her father was a master draper and in the family firm but his elder brother was a doctor, Chief Medical Officer for Scotland, and gave his niece a stethoscope with a cotton-reel at the end and as a child Caroline used to give her dolls 'blood confusions'. She studied at St

Andrews and took the MB ChB in 1962. She enjoyed surgery but the general feeling was that women didn't really do surgery, which she saw as a challenge. Two of the chiefs tried to put her off surgery but one, Willie Walker, when he saw her commitment, encouraged her and introduced her to Andrew Wilkinson, the paediatric surgeon. She did her training at Glasgow, the Dryburn Hospital, Durham, and Dundee Royal Infirmary. She applied for posts as C Doig and at interview was asked 'What if you get married?' to which she replied 'Do I have to?' She went as senior registrar to the Hospital for Sick Children Great Ormond Street with the FRCS Edinburgh and England, 1970, and the ChM with a thesis on staphylococci infection, theatre and ward dissemination and theatre wear.

She became a consultant paediatric surgeon in Booth Hall Hospital, Manchester where she was renowned for her gastrointestinal work and her enthusiasm and skill in the training of junior surgical staff.

Caroline Doig has the distinction of being the first woman on the Council of the Edinburgh Royal College of Surgeons. She took her seat on Council in 1984 and said it had taken her 400 years to get elected. In fact it was sixty-four years after the first two women became FRCS Edinburgh, 1920, Alice Hunter – who didn't stay to take her seat but left at once to be a missionary surgeon – and Gertrude Herzfeld who was assiduous in shepherding future women Fellows as they came through.

Caroline Doig served on the Council and committees of the General Medical Council for fifteen years. She inaugurated the Hunter-Doig medal to encourage future generations of young women surgeons.

Women Fellows in the Sixties – FRCS 1960 to 1970
Women of the Fellowship into Radiotherapy, Oncology and Nuclear Medicine in Oncology

(Margaret) Ruth Sandland became Consultant Radiotherapist at St Bartholomew's Hospital and the Hospital for Sick Children, Great Ormond Street. She trained in Melbourne graduating MB BS Melbourne in 1964. She was registrar in St Thomas's Hospital and both registrar and senior registrar at the Royal Marsden. She took the FRCS in 1969, the DMRT in 1971, the FFR in 1972, and the FRCR in 1975. She published extensively on the radiotherapy of childhood tumours. She was appointed

consultant in radiotherapy to St Bartholomew's Hospital and the Hospital for Sick Children, Great Ormond Street where she spent her working life.

Ann (Elizabeth) Johnson became a consultant surgical oncologist in the breast study centre at Mount Vernon Hospital. She trained at University College and Hospital, graduating with honours in the MB BS London with distinction in pharmacology and therapeutics in 1956. She had house surgeon posts at UCH and was resident surgical officer at the Miller Hospital Greenwich and took the FRCS in 1960. She then became registrar and later research assistant in the radiotherapy and oncology department at Mount Vernon, taking the DMRT in 1965 and the FRCR in 1975. She published papers on measurement in carcinoma of the breast and management of treatment. She was honorary surgical oncologist on the breast research unit at Mount Vernon Hospital, Northwood.

Gunes (Nurettin) Ege went into the field of nuclear medicine and published on the lymphoscintigraphy of nodes in breast and ovarian cancer. She worked in the Princess Margaret Hospital, Toronto, Canada. She was educated in the United States, where her father was a diplomat; and was Turkish in origin. She was an extremely accomplished concert pianist. She was a registrar in the Westminster Hospital in London and took the FRCS in 1964.

Twenty years after gaining the Fellowship, when she responded to the questionnaire as a Fellow of the English College, she wrote from Canada with strong opinions. She was working full-time and had moved from radiotherapy to the field of nuclear medicine where she had made signal developments in the field of lymphoscintigraphy, especially in the internal mammary nodes in breast cancer. She wrote she was single and needed no domestic help. She had experienced no prejudice against her as a woman in medicine. On the contrary, she saw no reason why any concessions should be made as regards part-time work or training. She wrote from Canada: 'All motivated women doctors I know have managed to find or fashion positions suitable to their particular circumstances'. She made the point that part-time specialist training would only prolong training and put the quality in jeopardy. Such part-time trainees would affect the functioning of the full-time trainees as well.

Women Fellows in the Sixties – FRCS 1960 to 1970
Women of the Fellowship to and from South Africa, Australia, Canada and the USA

Doreen Ashmel Birch (1926-1975) came from South Africa, practised in Australia. Doreen Birch came from South Africa where she had graduated MB ChB in Cape Town. She was research assistant to Professor Michael Boyd in the surgical professorial unit in Manchester and took the FRCS in 1961. She went on to practise in ENT surgery at the Royal Newcastle Infirmary in Newcastle, New South Wales and then in Mount Gambier in South Australia. She married Dr J C McCaffrey in 1963 at age thirty-seven and they had a son. Doreen Birch died early in 1975 age forty-nine.

Ruth (Valda) Magnus qualified in Melbourne MB BS in 1955 and was RMO at the Alfred Hospital, Melbourne and registrar in the Children's Hospital. She came to London to take the FRCS in 1961. On her return to Australia she became consultant paediatric surgeon to the Dandelong and District Hospital, Victoria, in 1974. She died early in 1980 at age about fifty.

Elizabeth (Anne) Lewis qualified MB BChir Cambridge in 1962 having come from Australia to take the Fellowship, which she obtained in 1966, and returned there to work. She was a single lady and worked full-time. She thought that part-time appointments might help women doctors to continue in work but was not in favour of part-time training.

Ann Louise Davies became FRCS in 1967. Subsequently she returned to Australia

Lena Elizabeth McEwan qualified in 1954. She took the FRCS in 1970 and returned to work in Seaton Park, South Australia.

Shirley Heather Knowles went to Sydney, Australia and took the FRACS the year after she had obtained the English fellowship in 1964. She was visiting ophthalmic surgeon to St Vincent's Hospital, Sydney

Clarice Ann Baker was an Oxford graduate BM BCh in 1958 and took the DRCOG in 1960, followed by the FRCS in 1963. She did posts at the

London Hospital, King George Ilford and the Forest Gate Hospital and went on to a career in obstetrics and gynaecology in Canada, being resident in Winnipeg General Hospital and tutor in the University of Manitoba.

Lynne Wilford Baker, FRCS 1960, was from South Africa and *Frances Selsnik*, FRCS 1964, was from the USA.

Women Fellows in the Sixties – FRCS 1960 to 1970
Career destinations unknown

Molly Elizabeth Wakely qualified in 1955 and did house posts at University College Hospital, a casualty SHO at Nottingham, and surgical registrar at Farnborough Hospital, Kent. She became FRCS 1960.

Dorothy May Davies and *Loris Freda Figgins* both became FRCS in 1963.

Shirley Jean Johnston qualified MB BS in 1959. Mrs Johnston became FRCS in 1964 and lived in Kincardineshire. *Judith McKenzie* became FRCS in 1967.

Women Fellows in the Sixties – FRCS 1960 to 1970
Women of the Fellowship into Africa

Four women went to Africa. Three of them, Catherine Mary Rosarii Lawler, Rosemary Carmel Garvey and Sister Mary Patricia Phelan, went to Catholic missionary hospitals in Nigeria. Anne Christine Bayley became Professor of Surgery in Zambia and played an important part in the discovery and elucidation of virulent HIV/Aids.

Catherine Mary Rosarii Lawler qualified MB BCh BAO at the National University of Ireland, the NUI, in 1957 in Dublin and amongst other training posts was SHO in general and thoracic surgery at the Hospital for Sick Children, Great Ormond Street. She went on to be surgeon to Our Lady of Lourdes Hospital, Ihiala, Onitsha Province, in Eastern Nigeria.

Rosemary (Carmel) Garvey went to work at the Marie Assumption Hospital in Ado-Ekita in Western Nigeria after she got her Fellowship in 1967.

(Sister) Mary (Patricia) Phelan (1925-2001) was educated at the Loreto Convent, Killarney. Her father was a lighthouse keeper. She trained at the University College of Cork and the University of Dublin where she took first place in her examinations, qualifying MB BCh, BAO, in 1948 in the National University of Ireland. She took the MCh and the FRCS in 1963. She was attached to the Medical Mission of Mary, Drogheda, County Louth, and was house surgeon at the Hammersmith Hospital, Royal Postgraduate Medical School, did obstetrics at Lourdes Hospital, Drogheda and went out to St Luke's Hospital, Anua, Nigeria.

Anne (Christine) Bayley became the professor of surgery in the University of Zambia. She has the distinction of being the first of the women general surgical Fellows to become a professor of surgery. Her major contribution to the recognition of the existence of the Aids virus in East Africa and the elucidation of its nature and epidemiology was of central importance to the world's understanding of this disease, acknowledged by the World Health Organisation. She was appointed OBE.

Anne Bayley had her early education at the Girls' Grammar School in Colchester and was encouraged by her father, an engineer, to take the Cambridge entrance examination. She went up to Girton College Cambridge and completed her clinical training at the Middlesex Hospital where she qualified MB BChir in 1959. Her first house surgeon post was equivalent to working on a surgical professorial unit, though Middlesex had no surgical professor and she worked for David Patey, director of surgical studies, and found his meticulous parotid surgery a practice to emulate. She was house physician in Stoke and after various hospital posts went to Ghana and worked in a mission hospital. It is almost impossible when a British-trained doctor finds themselves in a rural hospital in Africa, not to take part in the surgical emergencies that present themselves starting with caesarean section and Anne was no exception and rapidly became experienced in operative surgery, particularly of the massive and sometimes obstructed hernias. She greatly admired the capacity of the Ghanaians to enjoy a party making the visit of the examiners who came from Uganda on a surgical inspection visit a congenial gathering and receiving an offer to work in East Africa. Realising she must return to England first for more formal surgical training and obtain the Fellowship, she left Ghana. She had formed a friendly sponsorship of an eight-year-old girl who was being brought up by her grandmother and was keen to help her obtain secondary education. Back in England she worked at the Birmingham Accident Hospital on surgical emergencies, and in the burns unit, and at Bedford General Hospital as surgical registrar and took both the Edinburgh and the English FRCS in 1966. She was able to obtain a place for her 'unadopted daughter' as she calls her, at Whitby Grammar School and Anne's parents also looked after her while Anne was away working or abroad.

The plan was for Anne Bayley to go to Uganda but the political turmoil of Idi Amin resulted in the offer of the post there being withdrawn and considered unwise and she accepted instead a surgical appointment in the University Hospital in Zambia, only to find that Uganda was on offer again, but she was committed by then to Zambia where she worked for twenty years. When the professor retired, she applied for and was appointed to the chair, the first woman FRCS to hold a professorial chair in general surgery. She was active in the Association of Surgeons of East Africa, an important grouping involving Zambia, Kenya, Tanzania, Uganda, Malawi and to some extent Zimbabwe – though that last tended to look south toward South Africa – and was on the council, and the first woman to be president.

Amongst her special interests was Kaposi's sarcoma which, in 1980, presented itself in men and women equally as peripheral lesion on the toes and feet of the lower limb, and on the hands and forearms of the upper limb. The lesions regressed after some rather mild chemotherapy, and recurred. Anne Bayley noticed a change in pattern that was taking place in the disease and that was the topic of her presentation in 1983/1984 to the Association of Surgeons of East Africa in her inaugural address as president. She described graphically that it was as though when you left the house there was a pet dog there, you went out, and when you came back to tea, there was a rabid dog. She drew the connection between AIDS and Kaposi's sarcoma. At that time AIDS was thought to be possibly due to HTL-V3, the lymphoma virus, or the cytomegalic virus. Anne Bayley collaborated with Bob Dowling from the Porton Down laboratories in Salisbury and sent him specimens. He came out and, together with the surgeon Wilson Carswell, they visited small peripheral hospitals in villages and rural slums and took blood samples from patients sick with the wasting disease, diarrhoea, tuberculosis, Slim disease, and from these specimens, the human auto-immuno-deficient virus, AIDS, was identified as the causative agent. Linda Chalker, Minister for Overseas Development, visited and was made aware that the AIDS epidemic emerging in Africa was a heterosexual disease, in contrast to the initial perception on the west coast of the United States that the pandemic was of homosexual transmission. Anne Bayley sat on the committees of the WHO on the pandemic. She has published seminal papers on HIV-related Kaposi sarcoma and on HIV and been invitation speaker at many international conferences.

On her return to England Anne Bayley offered herself and was accepted for ordination to the Anglican priesthood. She would have considered that as a vocation when young but women were of course not accepted as ministers by the Church of England. The Bishop of London was insistent that she spent a year at St Stephen's and then took a curacy in Wembley, neither of which were happy times. She recounts that when she stood in St Paul's Cathedral for her ordination, she was lapped by the waves of less-than-approval from the male clergy, and in déjà vu she felt that she had been there before as she had stood forty years before to get the surgical FRCS being received into the Fellowship of the Royal College of Surgeons with a less than an enthusiastic welcome.

In retirement, she made visits again to Zambia and Malawi, covering surgical locum posts for colleagues who had been former students and, wearing her ecclesiastical robes, conducts services, feeling the warmth particularly from women in the congregation who, as women, feel empowered at receiving communion from a woman priest.

Her 'unadopted daughter' settled in England, became an occupational therapist, married here in England and has children and Anne has an 'unadopted granddaughter' just starting at Cambridge and two younger 'unadopted grandsons'.

Women Fellows in the Sixties – FRCS 1960 to 1970
Women of the Fellowship from the Indian subcontinent

Suniti Ratnakar Samsi. From Bombay, FRCS 1960
Dhun Dinshaw Dinsla Sumari. FRCS 1960
Sheena Bhatnagar. Mrs Bhatnagar was from Ludhiana; FRCS 1961
Karimpot Ramakrishnan. FRCS 1961
Shalina Krishna Agarwal. From New Delhi, FRCS 1961

Saulert Begum Jahan. Miss Jahan became FRCS 1962
Indra Skanda Rajah. Sri Rajah from Sri Lanka won the Hallett Prize after the Primary FRCS in 1961. FRCS 1963
Joya Chodury. FRCS 1964, died late 1970s.
Kishwar Nazli Mahmood. From Jinnah Postgrad Centre, Karachi, W. Pakistan, FRCS 1964
Pilloo Parvez Hakim. From Bombay, FRCS 1965
Javick Lilly. From Bombay, FRCS 1965
Mahjala Khokhar. From Gujranwok, West Pakistan, FRCS 1966
Tripty Adhy. From Colombo, Sri Lanka, FRCS 1966
Mahmooda Khan. Became associate professor of surgery at Srinagar. FRCS 1967
Urmila Khanna had her own clinic, the Khanna Nursing Home in Calcutta. FRCS 1967
Leela Kapik. FRCS 1969
Kochutravia Poovan. Christian Medical College, Vellore. FRCS 1969
Mehar Burzorji Mehta. FRCS 1970

Sixty-seven women surgical Fellows achieved the FRCS in the eleven years between 1960 and 1970. Eighteen who came from the Indian sub-continent returned with the Fellowship to practise there and a further sixteen returned overseas or went to work abroad. Four went to west and sub-Saharan Africa, others to Ireland, Australia, South Africa, and the West Indies and the destinations of four were unknown , leaving twenty-eight over the eleven years who were intent on making a career in England, still about two to three per year.

Six women surgical Fellows intended to make their career in general surgery. Four achieved this, becoming consultant general surgeons. These were Tessa Morell in Ashton under Lyne, Margaret Ghilchik (Childe), Elizabeth Gordon and Averil Mansfield in London. Monica Lewin who came from Jamaica and trained in the Royal Free in London and returned to Jamaica to work as a consultant, found it difficult to get an established post on return to London, as did Clara Zilhali. Six Women Fellows who chose careers in gynaecology all achieved consultant posts, one deciding to make her (third) consultant post in Australia. Similarly of the seven surgical Fellows who became eye surgeons, one decided to make her career in Barbados. The four who became ENT surgeons likewise were consultants in district general hospitals, the women's hospitals now playing a less prominent part. Of the three who went into orthopaedic surgery, two who were well trained on the surgical side found their future one in research, one in an accident & emergency unit, and the third in physical medicine.

Six returned to Australia, one who was originally from South Africa. One returned to South Africa, one to Canada, one to the USA.

Of the less common specialties, one went into thoracic surgery, one to neurosurgery who practised in Delhi with her husband, three into oncology/radiotherapy of whom one developed scinti-scan radiology of sentinel lymph glands in Canada. Two Fellows went into paediatric surgery and became consultants in England, one who had come originally from India and was the third woman to be elected to the College Council and one a Scot working in Manchester. Four went to Africa, three to Catholic mission hospitals in Nigeria and one with humanitarian intent to become surgical Professor in Zambia and teach and operate – and make ground-breaking discoveries. This completes our narrative of the early women in the fellowship of surgery.

Subsequent chapters are on the history of surgery in India particularly the foundation of the Lady Hardinge College in Delhi where Indian girls and young women can be taught medicine by a female faculty, and then chapters on the specialties, fields where the women surgeons found on the whole a greater acceptability than in general surgery. Then a chapter on some of the hospitals set up by women to treat women and children and to provide a clinical setting where women could work. The final chapter compares and contrasts the lives of the first women surgical Fellows with the experiences sixty years later, 1911 to 1970.

Women Fellows in the Sixties – FRCS 1960 to 1970

Isabella Forshall (1902-1989) FRCS 1960
Margaret Tessa Morrell FRCS 1965
Margaret Childe (Mrs Margaret Ghilchik) FRCS 1967 MS 1972
Elizabeth Mary Gordon FRCS 1967 MS 1977
Averil Olive Dring (Averil Mansfield/Averil Bradley) FRCS 1967 ChM 1973
Clara Clothilde Zilahi FRCS 1965

Monica Cynthia Lewin (1926-1998) FRCS 1962
Margaret Witt FRCS 1961 MRCOG 1966 FRCOG 1979
Jill Margaret Evans (1929-1995) FRCS 1961 FRCOG
Constance Ethel Fozzard FRCS 1967
Dorothy June Whitney (Mrs Raeburn) FRCS 1962
Eunice Ruth Burton FRCS 1964 FRCOG
Anne Mary Jequier FRCS 1967 FRCOG
Doreen Ann Birks FRCS 1962
(Mrs) Marion Christine Handscombe FRCS 1962 FRCOphth
Enid Taylor née Enid Wheldon FRCS 1965 FRCOphth
Margaret Thornton Challis FRCS 1967
Doris May Cleweth Price FRCS 1963 FRCOphth
Eileen Mary Vale (died 1977) FRCS 1969
Anthea Mary Stewart Connell (1925-2003) FRCS 1964
Veronica May Gammon FRCS 1961
Romola Diana Dunsmore FRCS 1961
Ruth Wynne-Davis FRCS 1960 PhD
Delia Margaret Helen Hernaman Cothay FRCS 1960
Helene Valerie Goodman (Mrs Woolf) FRCS 1962 DPhysMed DM
Jennifer Jane Haley (Jennifer Ahluwalia) FRCS 1964
Carys Bannister FRCS Ed
Mary Patricia Shepherd FRCS 1964 MS
Leela Kapila FRCS 1966
Caroline Mary Doig FRCS 1970 ChM
Margaret Ruth Sandland FRCS 1969 FRCR
Ann Elizabeth Johnson FRCS 1960 FRCR
Gunes Nurettin Ege FRCS 1963
Loris Freda Figgins FRCS 1963
Doreen Ashmel Birch (1926-1975) FRCS 1961
Ruth Valda Magnus FRCS 1961 died 1980
Elizabeth Anne Lewis FRCS 1966
Ann Louise Davies FRCS 1967
Lena Elizabeth McEwan FRCS 1970.
Lynne Wilford Baker FRCS 1960
Frances Selsnik FRCS 1964
Molly Elizabeth Wakeley FRCS 1960
Clarice Ann Baker FRCS 1963

Dorothy May Davies FRCS 1963
Sister Mary Patricia Phelan (1925-2001) FRCS 1963
(Mrs) Shirley Jean Johnston FRCS 1964
Shirley Heather Knowles FRCS 1964
Catherine Mary Rosarii Lawler FRCS 1964
Noelin Catherine Gertrude Fehily (Mrs Cook) FRCS 1967
Judith McKenzie FRCS 1967
Rosemary Carmel Garvey FRCS 1967
Carol Lindsay Wengref FRCS 1967
Anne Christine Bayley OBE FRCS 1966

CHAPTER 9

India – Transit in Two Directions

QUEEN Victoria was exceedingly concerned when she was told of the plight of women in India, some excluded from society by being in purdah, and who were without medical help, sometimes dying in childbirth rather than allowed to be attended by a male doctor.

Although the Queen had not been sympathetic to the idea of women as doctors in the home country, an opinion fuelled by her misogynist physician Sir William Jenner, she saw no hypocrisy in supporting women doctors trained in England travelling out to her far-flung Empire to work abroad. One by one she instructed the wives of successive Viceroys to make the medical care of women in India their especial concern. The Countess of Dufferin, as wife of the Viceroy of India, set up in 1885 the National Association for Supplying Female Medical Aid to the Women of India, known colloquially as the Countess of Dufferin Fund, set up to recruit and train women doctors, midwives and nurses to reach in particular those women in purdah and support hospitals and clinics.

The Queen had been made aware of the desperate situation by *Elizabeth Beilby*, a missionary who had been so moved by the problems out there that she had undergone some years of medical study at the London School of Medicine for Women, though not qualifying as a doctor (a partial training strongly disapproved of by Elizabeth Garrett Anderson who refused to endorse the sending out of half trained medical women). Elizabeth Beilby had opened a dispensary and small hospital in Lucknow for the Zenana and done some useful work. At home on furlough, she had requested an audience with the Queen and had given her a graphic description of the plight of the purdah women. The Zenana Bible and Medical Mission had entered India in the 1850s. An American Methodist missionary doctor, Dr Clara Swan had gone out in 1870 and there had been sporadic attempts to provide midwifery and nursing hygiene training for local women, but in the vast sub-continent of India, this was a drop in the ocean.

In 1883 *Dr Mary Scharlieb* was summoned to an audience with the Queen, and then also by the Prince and Princess of Wales, to give her account of the situation before she returned to India. She had just graduated from the London (Royal Free Hospital) School of Medicine for Women with first class honours MB BS and a gold medal in obstetrics and gynaecology, but she had already previously trained and got good practical experience in Madras. Once again the Queen was much concerned and issued her instructions.

Dr Mary Scharlieb's life had been an extraordinary one. She was born Mary Dacomb Bird in England in 1845 to a mother who died of puerperal fever ten days after giving birth and was therefore brought up initially by her paternal grandmother and her Aunt Lily and then by her father and step-mother who made sure she had a sound education in boarding school in Manchester and New Brighton and at Mrs Tyndall's in 16 Upper Hamilton Terrace in Hampstead. She was engaged at twenty to a law-student from the Middle Temple and married when he was called to the Bar and went with him to Madras in 1866 where he was to practise as a barrister. An intelligent woman, she assisted her husband in his work, keeping records, writing reports, and editing papers for his law journals. She had an ayah for her two small sons and daughter and kept other house-servants and took part in the social life of the expatriate community, but like the Queen her conscience was touched by the plight of local women living in purdah without medical help available to them, particularly during childbirth. Reading Fayre's *Medical Jurisprudence* from her husband's bookshelves gave her some medical insight.

Extraordinary to relate, she entered midwifery training in the Maternity Hospital in Madras in 1871, a married English woman and mother of two small boys, and at the end of one year was determined to complete a full medical education. This was at a time when, in England, the London School of Medicine for Women was only just beginning to establish itself in conjunction with the Royal Free Hospital though had not yet obtained a facility for the students to take their qualifying examinations and get on to the Medical Register, and no other medical school in Britain admitted women.

Negotiations in Madras took a year or two but accordingly in 1875 she was one of five women who enrolled on the medical course at Madras College and she completed the medical practitioners' certificate in 1879. Of the four who completed the course, Dora White went to work at Nizam Hospital and Miss D'Abreu became a medical missionary. On her return to London, she was an inspiration, because of her experience, to the other students at the London School of Medicine for Women. It was necessary to matriculate as well as complete her medical studies and she qualified MB BS London with first class Honours in 1881 and a gold medal and scholarship in obstetrics in 1882, the University of London having by then agreed to accept women to all their degrees, including medicine, on the same terms as men.

After meeting the Queen and exchanging information on the situation on Indian women, Dr Mary Scharlieb returned to India to become lecturer in forensic medicine and midwifery and diseases of women in the Madras Medical College and University. (She was later to return to England to practise, and as surgeon to Elizabeth Garrett Anderson's New Hospital and lecturer in the medical school).

The universities in Calcutta, Agra, Bombay and Lahore followed Madras by admitting women to their medical schools, not without obstacles. In the Calcutta Medical School, both a diploma course after a shortened medical training and a co-educational full medical degree were instituted. Although entrance was theoretically open to women as to men, there was a dearth of Indian girls; their families were reluctant to let them study in a co-educational setting. Nor was their education always adequate. The few who attended were Christians or Jewish or from the orphanage schools of the various missionary societies. It was important to have hospitals and medical schools staffed by women for local girl students.

In Bombay, an American businessman George T Kettridge and a Parsee gentleman Mr Pestonjee Cama establishing a women's hospital and medical school had to fight the Government of Bombay that it would be staffed and run by the women doctors and not put under male supervision. Dr Edith Pechey herself was persuaded to come and lead the new medical school in Bombay, an inspired choice, as it was she who, on visiting the Irish College of Physicians and the Queen's University of Ireland in Dublin, had charmed them with her diplomacy into allowing women to take their qualifying examinations there and to give recognition to the London School of Medicine for Women, thus breaking the log-jam against the women's entry into the medical profession in England.

With each new viceroy, the Queen adjured the wives in turn to make the health of native women their special concern. Lady Hardinge set herself at once to learn Hindi when she arrived in India and immersed herself in the solution to local problems and founded the Lady Hardinge

Medical School in New Delhi, the first in India to allow the medical education of Indian girls taught exclusively by women doctors.

The Lady Hardinge Medical College was opened in 1916 by the viceroy at the end of his time in India and the pomp of the occasion tells the story of its funding. Lady Hardinge had sadly died, as of course had Queen Victoria, but the Viceroy arrived with his daughter the Hon Diamond Hardinge in an open carriage with outriders and the full bodyguard. The reception took place in a huge shamiana erected opposite the entrance. Present were the Maharajas of Gwalior, Bikaner, Kotah, Patiala and Jhind and they did not arrive unaccompanied. General Baber Shumsher Jung Rama Bahadur of Nepal came, Lady Willingdon and the Commander-in-Chief and the Begum of Bhopal. The chairman of the Hospital Committee Sir Pardey Lukis made the opening speech. On a marble slab in the entrance hall was inscribed the names of the donors and the amounts they gave. A list informs us of the local provenance of the funding. One lakh is a hundred thousand rupees.

His Highness the Maharajah of Jaipur	Rs.	3,00,000
His Highness the Maharajah of Patiala	Rs.	1,25,000
His Highness the Nizam of Hyderabad	Rs.	1,00,000
His Highness the Maharajah of Baroda	Rs.	1,00,000
His Highness the Maharajah of Udaipur	Rs.	1,00,000
His Highness the Maharajah of Jodhpur	Rs.	1,00,000
His Highness the Maharajah of Kotah	Rs.	1,00,000
His Highness the Maharajah of Hutwa	Rs.	1,00,000
The Maharajah Bahadur of Darbhanga	Rs.	58,437
High Highness the Maharahah of Indore	Rs.	50,000
Her Highness the Begum of Bhopal	Rs.	30,000
Their Highnesses the Dowagar Maharani and the Maharani of Gwalior	Rs.	30,000
N.M.Wadia Trust	Rs.	30,000
The Dowagar Begum Agakhan	Rs.	20,000
Other donors	Rs.	1,00,000

His Highness the Maharajah of Jammu and Kashmir agreed an annual subscription of Rs. 3,500.

The Government of India granted one lakh of rupees annually for upkeep, one lakh being 100,000 rupees.

Finally the Countess of Dufferin Fund promised Rs 20,000 to defray the salaries of three medical women to fill Professorial Chairs and eighteen scholarships of Rs.25 each for students. The Punjab memorial fund for Lady Hardinge gave one lakh of rupees which was sufficient to build an outpatients department, planned to be the best in India. Bihar and Orissa sent 30,000 rupees as their share of the Memorial Fund to build the cottage wards. The contractor Sardar Narain Singh was awarded a silver Kaiser-I-Hind medal and several medals and khilats were given to various Indians associated with the building of the college. Dr Kate Platt MD was the first principal.

A photograph of the first faculty, taken in 1916, shows eleven English women, eight of them in academic robes, the other three perhaps the warden and administrators. In contrast, a photograph of the faculty in 1966 at the fifty-year Golden Jubilee portrays seventy-one Indian women, perhaps five Europeans among them, and nine men. On the listing of the whole faculty, there were eighty-four Indians listed and five European names.

The students came from all over India and there were planned separate residences for Hindus, Muhammeddans, Sikhs, and Christians including Brahmins and those who had adopted the European mode of living. The course of study originally started with two years pre-medical science years, the FSc before going on to the five years study, and at first students had to travel to Lahore to take their examinations, there being no medical faculty in the University of Delhi. The pre-science years were dropped twenty years later as the demand for places grew and the examinations took place and the degrees were awarded in the University of Delhi once it had a medical faculty.

The early faculty Staff had to be versatile. Dr Kate Platt, the principal could be found supervising the construction of the outpatients' gate. Dr Gertrude J Campbell, the professor of anatomy, was in charge of building the chapel, as well as planning the lay-out of the anatomy department. She was succeeded by Dr K MacDermott, one of the pioneer cohorts of the dozen or so first students at Lady Hardinge, and she, in turn, was later succeeded by Professor S Achaya FRCS, a renowned Indian professor. Dr Beadon was one of the first faculty. Dr Charlotte L Houlton, the professor of obstetrics and gynaecology, was also in those early times in charge of surgery, that being part of the same department until 1920; she had previously worked at the Lady Lyall Hospital, Agra. Dr Ruth Young was involved with the making of the swimming pool, sports and athletic activities being an important factor in the freedom of student life. She also provided a room for the Gurudwara for Sikh students, a worship and meditation room for the Hindus, and the Muslim students could attend a small mosque on the campus. She wrote an account *The Work of Medical Women in India* jointly with Margaret Balfour (Women's Hospitals in Ludhiana and in Patiala). Miss Jesson the Warden gave money for the establishment of a school for evening literacy classes for adults and a day school for the children of the staff and servants. A strong club atmosphere was developed, the students putting on plays, *She Stoops to Conquer in Rajputana*, to raise money for the swimming pool, and setting up debates such as 'This House believes that the training of women as doctors is a waste of national wealth' – thankfully defeated after lively exchanges. The students had the freedom to go by tonga or bicycle into Old Delhi. They not only went into neighbouring villages to run clinics and dispensaries and worked in the St Luke's Mission Hospital in Old Delhi but also were mobilised for catastrophes, helping after the earthquake of Quetta, famine in Bengal, floods and cyclones, and made collections for the Jawans (untouchables).

The climate and the work could take its toll on the health of the staff. Dr Kate Platt, the principal for the first five years, had already worked in the Dufferin Hospital in Calcutta for nine years; she travelled extensively throughout India during her time as dean, studying the principles of Indian education and visiting other universities and medical colleges. She had a furlough in England when she gained her MD London with first class honours and returned to Delhi, but after five years in the post returned to England where she regained her health and continued to work in London always keeping her interest in India, the Dufferin foundation and in her old college, the Lady Hardinge, and lost her life eventually in an air-raid in World War I.

The role of principal was covered by Dr Gertrude Campbell who had been professor of anatomy. She had been working in India as a medical missionary in Madras for ten years where she with two other Scottish Free church (Presbyterian) medical missionaries, Dr Matilda Macphail and Dr Margaret McNeil, had been instrumental in the building of a new hospital in Madras, so her appointment at the inauguration of the Lady Hardinge was a happy choice. She was a daring and skilful surgeon and a clear and interesting lecturer and her sharp wit and keen sense of humour were much appreciated. She was a gifted linguist, learning Tamil, Teluqu, Urdu, Pushtu, and Bengali, and was a government higher examiner in Tamil. After her stint at the Lady Hardinge as anatomist, surgeon and obstetrician, she went to live and work for twenty years in a small mission hospital in Mardan near the North-West Frontier carrying out surgery and conducting outpatients, her shrewd judgement appreciated by locals and royalty, Pathans and tribes people. When in her late seventies she was becoming deaf, then her sight began to fail, her wit did not desert her and she told her eye specialist, 'What I need now is a man with a megaphone to teach me Braille'. Astonishingly, after first learning the 'moon' characters, she did master Braille. An undaunted, intrepid woman.

There was a tradition also of early graduates returning to teach and work there. Dr K J MacDermott, one of the dozen girl students in the first year of Lady Hardinge, qualified in 1923, and later came back from England to be professor of anatomy from 1947 to 1949, and principal of the medical college and superintendent of the hospital. She made the grounds and gardens, always immaculately kept, her especial concern and care. Dr D P Bali, another Hardonian, succeeded her when she returned to England.

Dr H M Lazarus who had arrived at the Lady Hardinge in 1917 to work but had been drafted to Calcutta after only a few months, returned later to be the second principal from 1921 to 1925 when Dr Kate Platt retired. There was a fair turn-around of staff. Dr J Jhirad who was working in her practice in Bombay and felt that she was not using the postgraduate training that she had had in Birmingham Maternity Hospital, England, was summoned for a locum to New Delhi in 1919. She was faced with cases of vesico-vaginal fistulae that she had not dealt with before and she hastened to the library to read up the details of the corrective operations. Nor had she met osteomalacia of the pelvic bones before. Her Caesarean sections however were much admired as her English technique utilised a small neat scar, not involving eventration of the uterus.

In surgery, the first professor was Dr Wilson, then Dr Macmillan for five years from 1920 to 1925, surgery separating from gynaecology. Then Dr Pfeile was professor from 1925 to 1929 and was also principal of the medical school and superintendent of the hospital, and she was ably assisted by Dr Govind Kaur, another of the first graduates of the medical school. Next came Dr Hamilton-Browne, also principal and superintendent, who became very interested in orthopaedic surgery, founding the department. Her assistant was Dr Helen Reid, a Hardonian, who later did further training in America on a Rockefeller scholarship, and she returned to Lady Hardinge to be, first reader, and then professor in orthopaedic surgery. Dr Wingate followed in surgery from 1932 to 1934 and Dr H E Franklin from the Women's Medical Service from 1934 to 1938 who was also vice principal and joint medical superintendent. Dr B H Jolly, an FRCS Edinburgh, covered the war years from 1938 to 1947. At the difficult time of the partition of India in 1947, Professor Helen Reid did valiant work tending the wounded, men as well as women, aided by Dr Grace Lukose FRCS. The hospital corridors were filled with beds of casualties and the staff and students went out to the refugee camps at Old Delhi Railway Station and mass-vaccinated the teaming inhabitants.

Professor M Chaudhuri FRCS was appointed professor of surgery in 1948 and was head of surgery and principal of the hospital and dean of the medical faculty of Delhi University. She was the first Indian to hold the position of professor of surgery. She was still active working part-time in academic research over thirty years later. There was reorganisation of surgery in 1954, making the new post of a professorship of clinical surgery and expanding access to beds at the Willingdon Hospital, the Safdarjung Hospital and the Children's Hospital, Kalavati Saran, where the pathology department was partly financed from the USSR and staffed by Russians.

The Minister of Health in India at the time of the Jubilee in 1966 was Dr Sushila Nayar, an old Hardonian. The professor of haematology, Sujata Chaudhuri was an early graduate.

There is no doubt that, like the London School of Medicine for Women and the Royal Free Hospital, the all-women's Medical College and Hospital, the Lady Hardinge, staffed and run by women, fulfilled a unique and important and encouraging place in giving access to the training of women doctors in India. And in both countries, other co-educational medical schools grew up rapidly alongside, Manchester, Birmingham, Edinburgh, Liverpool, the two colleges of London University – Kings and University College – and their associated hospitals, and in India, Calcutta, Madras, Lahore and Bombay.

Furthermore, the growth of women's hospitals, staffed by women for women patients, provided a place for women doctors to work and gain clinical experience and employment, both in England and in India. In India, the women themselves formed the Association of Women Doctors of India in 1907, a strong institution that proved a powerful force for good, surrounding its members with a sense of security and friendliness, good fellowship and support, with mentors, and with a network that made overall a supportive atmosphere for learning and working. It was the first medical women's association in the world and the first medical association in India. In addition, the WMS, the Indian Women's Medical Service, effectively lobbied successive governments to support their women workers for pay and status and conditions equal to the men of the Indian Medical Service, an important powerhouse for equal pay and promotion. Not only did it provide jobs for the women doctors, and of course a service to the patients, but it also sponsored postgraduate courses of study. They repeatedly drew the government's attention to the shortage of women's beds in the hospitals, to the high infant and maternal mortality, and were an immense power for good, until the WMS was eventually disbanded in 1949 and the staff absorbed into the state health services when Independence came.

Eight English women who gained the surgical Fellowship between 1919 and 1970 came to work in India. Why did they come, where and for how long did they work in India?.

Mary Scharlieb herself never took the FRCS though she was a surgeon in the Elizabeth Garrett Anderson Hospital and lecturer on the teaching staff of the medical school. By the time the Royal College of Surgeons opened its doors to women, she was in her sixties.

Gladys Marchant had qualified in Calcutta MB BS in 1916, achieving the top marks in pathology and in ophthalmology and, after house jobs at the Lady Hardinge Hospital in Delhi and lecturing in anatomy there, where she was later briefly professor of anatomy, she came to London to study and gain experience and training, taking the conjoint diploma in 1922, and the FRCS in 1928. Gladys Marchant went back to India and worked at the Dufferin Hospital, Meerut and was resident at the Bangalore Maternity Hospital. It was at the J A Hospital at Gwalior that her exceptional operative skills were recognised and she was appointed to be the first professor of obstetrics and gynaecology in King George Medical School, Queen Mary Hospital in Lucknow. She travelled in Europe and the States visiting clinics and presented her thesis in French for the MD in Lausanne. There is a further Marchant, *Mary Kathleen Merchant* with the FRCS in 1957, and her destiny is not known; maybe they were related.

Keren Isabel Parkes, FRCS 1932 established a flourishing private general practice in London. She was requested to go by flying-boat and private train to attend the wife of a Rajah with successful outcome.

Muriel Hulke, FRCS 1933 went out to India to work as surgeon to the Lady Reading College, Simla and the Dufferin Hospital, Lucknow.

Muriel Long, FRCS 1934 was expected to go to be professor of surgery to the Lady Hardinge Medical College in 1939 but World War II intervened. She married during the war and she and her husband both became consultants, she a surgeon, he a physician, in Llandudno, North Wales for all their working lives so never got to go and serve in India.

Doris Brown, FRCS 1935 found herself the only medical officer in the Lady Hardinge Hospital as war broke out. New Delhi was thought to be on the line of a possible invasion by the Japanese and all female medical staff were evacuated. In order to allow her to stay, she was designated a man and given jungle training and equipment. For a time, she manned the surgical side solo and received a contingent of British soldiers, led by an officer, exhausted and some wounded who had escaped from a prisoner-of-war camp. She operated on the officer and some of the men. Two years later, still in war-time, she married the officer in Calcutta and became Mrs Wallace.

Margaret Shepherd, born Margaret Ferguson, FRCS 1938 came to India with her husband, Dr James Forrest Shepherd, a doctor who worked in the Indian Medical Service, the IMS. They had married in 1937. She spent three years in India working in several stations and was consultant surgeon to the King George Hospital, Vizagapatan, before returning to England during the War.

Mary Richardson, FRCS 1956 worked in India during the latter part of the war, initially doing orthopaedic and maxillofacial surgery, and then later as surgeon to the Johar General Hospital in Assam and from 1963 to 1970 was the County Medical Officer to the Johar Tea Company in Assam heading a hundred and twenty bed hospital, serving a population of fifty thousand working in India for more than eleven years in all.

She qualified from Oxford (where she was a rowing blue and president of the women's boat club) during the war and after house posts joined the RAMC for three years, one year in Anti-Aircraft Command and two years in India. She contracted tuberculosis and had to go back to England but after further training she took her FRCS and returned to work in Assam. Returning to England again in her fifties, she married Dick Clifford whom she had met in Assam.

Jennifer Ahluwhalia (née Jennifer Haley) FRCS 1964 came out to New Delhi with her husband Har Paul Singh Ahluwhalia to found a neurosurgical unit at the Sarjarjung Hospital in Delhi. They were both neurosurgeons who had trained in Liverpool and later returned with their children to practise in the Channel Islands.

Ruth Ansley Watson (1926 – 1976) FRCS 1976 went up to receive her FRCS *ad eundem* wearing a wig after treatment of a brain tumour. She was known as Ruth Watson of Nepal or 'Karachi doctor'. She was born 16 September 1926, the daughter of a motor engineer who had worked with Sir Frank Whittle on the invention of the jet engine. After her MB ChB Birmingham, she was house surgeon at Birmingham Accident Hospital and then spent a year in missionary training. In November 1952, at age twenty-six, she went to Pokhra in Nepal and founded the Shining Hospital, so called because of its corrugated iron roof. In spite of local limitations initially on whom she as a woman could operate, men and married women being originally forbidden territory, she was soon performing six hundred operations a year. There were many burns patients and contractures. In 1956, age thirty, she founded the Green Pastures Leprosy Hospital. In 1964, age thirty-eight, she went to India to pioneer leprosy surgery. In 1976 she developed a brain tumour and was to die age fifty later that year 15 November 1976, but not before having received the accolade of the FRCS awarded to her. That gives but a small flavour of her immensely useful and dedicated life, well described in the book *Karachi Doctor: Ruth Watson of Nepal* written by D Hawker in 1984.

Thirty-seven Indian women doctors all took the journey in the opposite direction to come to England to train further and take the FRCS. All but one or two returned home to work with the accolade of the Fellowship of the Royal College of Surgeons of England.

Miss Satapriya Ghosh had her medical degree from Calcutta in 1914 and came over to England to study and train, the first Indian woman to obtain the FRCS, 1921.

Seven years later, *Gladys Marchant*, FRCS 1928, MB BS Calcutta, 1916, returned to be professor of obstetrics and gynaecology in King George Hospital, Lucknow, in Uttah Pradesh, North India.

Miss Venketeswaraiya Sankarambal came to London to take the FRCS 1939 and returned to work at the Maharajah's Hospital in Pallusuthe, Cochin State, India.

Miss Perin Kavasji Mullaferoze came from Bombay to take the FRCS 1940 and returned to work there.

Sita Achaya was renowned for her legendary leadership in Delhi. She had been educated in an Indian government school, and at Madras University and medical school, where she won nineteen gold medals and qualified MB BS Madras in 1940. She came to Edinburgh for further training and experience and, though she had been surgical registrar in Edinburgh through the war years, she came down to London to take the FRCS England in 1947. On her return to India she became professor of anatomy at the Lady Hardinge Medical College and served as principal and superintendent of the Hospital and dean of the Medical Faculty of Delhi University. She was president of the Anatomy Society of India. She became deputy director of health and medicine in the Ministry of Health.

She married Lt Gen Iyappa who was chairman of a large electronic firm in India.

Miss Maitreyes Chaudhuri was taking the FRCS in London at the same time, 1947. She was the first alumna of Lady Hardinge to obtain the Fellowship. She returned the next year to become professor of surgery at Lady Hardinge, head of surgery, principal of the medical school and medical superintendent of the hospital. She was dean of the faculty of medical science of Delhi University.

Nursing theatre sister Edith H Paull recalled at the golden jubilee celebrations of the Foundation of Lady Hardinge her recollections of Maitreyes Chaudhuri as a young house surgeon. Sister Paull had been the first Indian to be appointed as a nursing sister in the Lady Hardinge Hospital, joining English, Canadian, Australian and those other antipodeans popularly called the 'Newsy Landers', in 1933, to be in charge of the theatres. She recalls 'Miss Chaudhuri was a young house surgeon and very keen on surgery. Her desire to be a good surgeon kept her extremely busy. She took every opportunity to perform minor operations and assist with major ones, both during the day and for all emergencies. Whether acute abdomens or impacted fractures, Dr Chaudhuri was always there to give a helping hand, both in the theatre and on the wards. I was not surprised to find her (later) at the helm of affairs as principal of this great medical college for women and superintendent of the hospital.'

An accolade all women surgical Fellows would be proud to have ascribed to their youthful selves.

Miss Prem Virmani took the Fellowship in 1958, ten years after Miss Chaudhuri. She had taught on the staff of the Lady Hardinge as a lecturer in anatomy. In London she trained at the Hammersmith Hospital Royal Postgraduate Medical School under Professor Ian Aird, and with Professor Charles Wells and took the MCh Liverpool. She married Sandip Mukerjee, also FRCS, and it was as *Dr P Mukerjee* that she returned to work in the Lady Hardinge as head of surgery. She was an excellent surgeon specialising in abdominal surgery and published more than one hundred papers being a particular expert on abdominal tuberculosis.

Grace Lukose FRCS 1951 took her BSc in Madras and then came to London to study at the London School of Medicine for Women where she qualified MB BS in 1946. Her mother was Dr Mary Pooter-Lukose, Surgeon-General to the Government of Travancore. Grace Lukose worked at the Lady Hardinge Hospital as assistant to Dr Helen Reid, the reader in orthopaedic surgery from 1947 to 1949 and experienced the unrest of partition, treating many casualties. She returned to London to take the FRCS in 1951. When she came back to India, she got scarlet fever, was unwell, and died in an accident with an overhead fan while on a visit to her mother.

I list others who came to London to take the Fellowship with the year of their FRCS:

Miss Sehar Panchalingan, 1951
Dogdo Sohrab Bamji; Dogdo Rutha Mehta, 1954
Sheroo Darebsha Broacha, 1955
Shakuntala Chandra, 1955. She went back to the medical college in Patiola, in the Punjab
Kamla Rupoharb Almchandani, 1958 Bombay
Vimla Bhogilal Jhaveri, 1958
Sumita Sen, 1958
Mini Hoshang Mehta, 1959 Calcutta
Mrs Susila Rajagopalan, 1959 Pondicherry
Suniti Ratnakar Samsi, 1960 Bombay
Dhun Dinshaw Dinsk Sumari, 1960
Mrs Sheena Bhatnagar, 1961 Ludhiana
Karimpot Ramakrishnan, 1961
Shalima Krishna Agarwal, 1961 New Delhi
Saulert Begum Jahan, 1962
Skanda Raj Sri, 1963
Jennifer Jane Ahluwalia, 1964 Neurosurgery, Safdarjag Hospital, New Delhi
Joya Chodury, 1964 (died 1970)
Kishwar Nazli Mahmood, 1964 Jinnah Postgrad Centre, Karachi, Pakistan
Pilloo-Parvez Hakim, 1965 Bombay
Javek Lilly, 1965 Bombay
Tripty Adlhy, 1966 Colombo, Sri Lanka
Mahjala Khokhar, 1966 Gujranwok, Pakistan
Leela Kapila, 1966 Madras MS 1962 Xian Medical College, Vellore
Mahmooda Khan, 1967 Associate Professor of Surgery, No 8. Govt Quarters Tulsi Bagn, Srinagar, Kashmiri, India

Leela Kapik, 1969
Kochutravia Poovan, 1969 Xian Medical College, Vellore
Urmila Khanna, 1970 Khanna Clinic, Calcutta
Mehar Burzoiji Mehta, 1970

Of these, *Leela Kapila*, FRCS 1966 stayed in England and, having trained further here at Rush Green Hospital, Romford, Essex, the London Hospital and the Hospital for Sick Children in Great Ormond Street, became the consultant paediatric surgeon in Nottingham. She married. No children. She became the third woman to be elected to the Council of the College of Surgeons. Though she did not bake fairy cakes or honey cakes for the men on the Council like her two predecessors, Phyllis George and Averil Mansfield, it is apparently a tradition that a newly elected Fellow to the Council provide some entertainment or outside visit for the Council, and, wearing her sari, she did provide an Indian tasting of food. Strangely, from a feminist point of view that was less objectionable than the gesture of appeasement that constituted the baking and bringing in of the honey cakes.

CHAPTER 10

Orthopaedic Surgeons

ORTHOPAEDIC surgery was an emerging speciality in the early part of the twentieth century, the scope and volume of the work accelerated by the need to treat the casualties of war. Some general surgeons of course developed a particular interest in orthopaedics and the early figures in the nineteenth century, William John Little and Hugh Owen Thomas, were clearly specialists, and there were orthopaedic hospitals in London, but much orthopaedics was still carried out by general surgeons, and fractures and dislocations dealt with by medical practitioners. The authoritative figures who dominated the field of orthopaedics and set it in place as a distinctive branch of surgery were Sir Robert Jones and G R Girdlestone. During World War I, Sir Robert Jones was director of Army orthopaedic services, his clinics in Liverpool and Oswestry a hub of learning and innovation. Girdlestone in Oxford, where he became the first professor of orthopaedics, led a similar centre of excellence. After the war, those two instigated a national scheme to set up orthopaedic hospitals, clinics and centres.

Eight of our women Fellows specialized in orthopaedics, eight only out of the two hundred who became Fellows between 1911 and 1971. These eight are Erna Jebens, Maud Forrester-Brown, Eugenie Willis, Cicely Pepler, Ruth Hickson, Mary Shelswell, Delia Cothay and Ruth Wynne-Davis.

Maud Forrester-Brown took the primary FRCS in 1920 and, it must be admitted, never got round to the final, but so singular was her contribution that her inclusion in the pantheon of women orthopaedic surgeons must be allowed. She dominated the field of paediatric orthopaedics over three counties, Wiltshire, Somerset and Dorset, but her influence spread much wider by her visits to clinics both at home and abroad, by her writing, books and papers, and by her pertinent contributions in meetings.

Maud Forrester-Brown did her medical training at the London (Royal Free Hospital) School of Medicine for Women which she entered with a scholarship after education at Bedford High School, and graduated MB BS in 1912 with Honours in Pathology and Forensic Medicine. Her father was a civil engineer and worked for some time in Bombay where Maud spent some of her childhood. She did house jobs at the Brompton, the National Hospital for Nervous Diseases, Queen Charlotte's, and the Royal Hospital, Newcastle-upon-Tyne, thus obtaining wide early experience in chest diseases, neurosurgery, gynaecology and general surgery. On a University of London fellowship she visited Berlin studying surgical anatomy, radiology, paediatrics, cystoscopy and operative gynaecology. By the onset of the war, 1914, she was in Glasgow doing an obstetric course and gaining an MD London in gynaecology. The entry to junior hospital posts for a woman became a little easier with the war with male doctors volunteering and leaving posts unoccupied, and Maud did rewarding jobs in Glasgow, Dundee, Liverpool and the Royal Free.

To a certain extent, in a career, one must follow one's star. Maud went to work at the Royal Hospital for Sick Children in Edinburgh with Sir Harold Stiles. She went on from there to be senior resident in surgery at Sheffield, but when war broke out and casualties began to flow in, Stiles recalled her to work with him at the War Hospital in Bangour, Edinburgh. Here she did her pioneer work on nerve injuries, two-stage operations, gaining experience in complex gun-shot wounds. Sir Harold Stiles had been a general surgeon taking a special interest in tuberculosis of the bones and joints in children. As a house surgeon he had been 'spray doctor' for Lister himself in Edinburgh, responsible for keeping a film of carbolic spray between the operators and the wound, but in his work on children his preference was for asepsis rather than the antisepsis of the carbolic. Now they were both dealing with battle injuries. Together they wrote *Treatment of Injuries of the Peripheral Spinal Nerves*.

Sir Robert Jones came to visit at the Bangour Emergency Hospital and became known to Miss Forrester-Brown, who in turn was free to visit him at his units in Liverpool and Oswestry, and to visit Girdlestone at Oxford after the war. She did her MS London in 1920 with a thesis on 'The results of operations for peripheral nerve injury' and took the primary FRCS, obviously intending to take the final. She presented her work at the newly formed, three-year-old British Orthopaedic Association meeting and was the recipient of scathing comments from two of the founder members, Harry Platt and Blundell Bankart. Harry Platt had also been a war surgeon working on nerve injuries. He was not disposed to be chivalrous to a young woman surgeon presenting her results in what he regarded as his field of expertise.

Maud Forrester-Brown was left in charge of the Emergency War Hospital, three hundred beds, for two years after the end of the war and wrote papers on 'Difficulties in the diagnosis of nerve function' and 'Study of some methods of bone grafting' in the *British Journal of Surgery* and 'The possibilities of end-to-end suture after extensive nerve injuries' for the *Journal of Orthopaedic Surgery* and a chapter for Robert Jones' book *Orthopaedic Surgery of Injuries* on her war-time experience 'A study of operations for nerve injury at Bangour'. She worked in Dundee and obtained more experience of the management of tuberculosis of bone and joint.

Five years after the war she was awarded the William Gibson Research Scholarship and for three years was able to visit clinic and hospitals throughout the world making life-long friends: Putti, of Putti-Platt fame, in Italy, France, Norway, Denmark, Sweden and many centres in Britain, thus setting a life-long tradition that every year she would spend her holidays in that way. Her appointment as visiting consultant orthopaedic surgeon to the Children's Hospital in Bath started the process of revolutionizing children's orthopaedic treatment in the West Country. She set up and then attended at fourteen major clinics and fourteen minor (follow-up) clinics across Wiltshire, Dorset and Somerset, in her 'away-week' once a month or so, arriving on horse-back, taking time and providing continuity with her expertise, and operating at Bath. Like many surgeons of her era, she had eccentric predilections of practice, making her own chromic catgut, emptying neat iodine into the wound before closure. She continued attendance at meetings, being a fearless commentator in her turn at the British Orthopaedic Association not daunted by her initial reception. She was a pioneer not only in the study of nerve injury and of the effects of paralysis, but published some of the earliest work on tendon transfers, innovated sliding osteotomies for bone and joint deformities resulting from trauma, and reported one of the earliest cases of re-modelling of the femoral head and neck after slipped femoral epiphysis. Her splint for congenital dislocation of the hip and other conditions was well-known. She recognized the value of compression of cancellous bone surfaces in the acceleration of bone union which she described in 1939.

Over the next twenty-five years, she and her colleagues provided an extraordinary service, the advent of antibiotics allowing more ambitious surgery. World War II found the Bath Hospital designated as an emergency hospital. Child patients were put under their metal beds as make-shift Morrison shelters during an air-raid.

With the advent of the National Health Service, she was appointed consultant orthopaedic surgeon. Retirement at age sixty-five in 1950 was not going to be an easy transition for Maud Forrester-Brown. She spent some time with Professor James Learmonth in Edinburgh working on nerve repair, did locums in Huddersfield and Kirkaldy and then went to South Africa to work in a remote hospital in the Transkei where conditions were not so very different from her early days in Bangour. She continued her visits to other centres all over the world and at age seventy-eight in 1963 on being shown round the Philippines National Orthopaedic Hospital, she told them, 'I don't just want to see the buildings; I want to see the work.' In her eighty-second year she published details of a flanged and perforated plastic dome for the conservative management and protection of a myelomeningocoele.

Her outstanding contribution to the management of congenital deformity, of scoliosis, of tuberculosis of bone and joints, of children with poliomyelitis, was testament to a useful and extraordinary life.

The direction her career took was influenced by the chance of her working for Sir Harold Stiles and the advent of the World War I and the need to treat casualties; to which might be added the generous support of Robert Jones and Gathorne Girdlestone. Above all, were her refusal to be daunted by opposition, a strong healthy egotism, and her own depth of dedication and well-directed energy.

Another woman surgeon who had harboured a fierce ambition to be a paediatric orthopaedic surgeon found no opening available to her. *Margaret Moore White* had initially worked in physiotherapy at St George's, at the National Hospital for Nervous Disease, Queen Square and at the Royal National Orthopaedic Hospital, Stanmore, after leaving the Belmont School in Derby and the Tremarth School in Hampstead and matriculating at Birkbeck night school. She had trained at the London (Royal Free Hospital) School of Medicine for Women graduating MB BS in 1930 and was house surgeon to Cecil Joll and to Hamilton Bailey and took the FRCS in 1931, one of an outstanding number of new women Fellows that year. She was resident surgical officer, at the West Norfolk Hospital and Kings Lynn but could not then find a suitable post where she could go forward to train in paediatric orthopaedics. Accordingly, she accepted a gynaecology registrar post at the Royal Free and Willesden General Hospital and took her MRCOG in 1939. Then the World War II intervened and she went to the Three Counties Hospital at Arlesey, as part of the Emergency Medical Service.

After the war, she became consultant gynaecologist at the Lister Hospital, Hitchin, the Letchworth Hospital, the Three Counties Hospital, and finally to the Royal Free Hospital where she founded an Infertility clinic with Miss Gertrude Dearnley, one of the first ever, and where pelvic tuberculosis was thought to be one of the main problems. She married Dr Leonard Page, a medical psychologist, in 1942 and they had two sons, one of whom became a doctor. Her wish to be a paediatric orthopaedic surgeon was not fulfilled.

Erna Jebens founded the orthopaedic department in the Battersea General Hospital. She was an anatomist, publishing original research in the Journal of Anatomy.

Erna Henrietta Jebens was born in 1890, educated privately in London and in Paris. As a young woman, she was a keen motorist and bought her first car in 1911 when she was twenty-one. She loved to drive and characteristically took a course in motor mechanics. At the beginning of the World War I she was returning from Europe back to England and saw the casualties among the soldiers and as a skilled driver offered herself as an ambulance driver and the ambition to be a doctor was born in her as she dealt with the injured soldiers.

She studied at the London School of Medicine for Women but was one of the small elite cohort of women students selected to study at St Mary's, chosen for their intelligence, decorum and diplomacy not to offend the sensibilities of the previously all-male medical school as it faced financial problems in the war because of lack of tuition fees from the rank of men medical students, depleted by the volunteering and then conscription of the young men in World War I.

At St Mary's, she was particularly attracted to anatomy and worked in Professor Fraser's department there but was told that she must keep out of the way of the misogynist Almroth Wright. She became a lecturer in anatomy at the Royal Free and taught there, a memorable teacher, continuing to teach alongside her other clinical and surgical work until retirement in 1954 at age sixty-four. She published research with Mrs Monk Jones MSc on the pH and viscosity of synovial fluid. Erna Jebens took the FRCS in 1926 and was appointed consultant surgeon to Battersea General Hospital, where she founded the department of orthopaedic surgery.

Battersea General Hospital was a unique idiosyncratic hospital. It stood on the corner of the Prince of Wales Road and the Albert Bridge Road, on the southern side of the river Thames. Founded originally as an anti-vivisectionist hospital, it had required all those who worked in it to be dedicated to a refusal to countenance scientific experimental work on animals. Bus-drivers and conductors announcing the next stop near the hospital would shout the Anti-Vivies Hospital. To commemorate that stance a charming statue of a little brown dog was erected outside, and all would have been well, save for a long and libellous inscription beneath the plinth giving an account of the supposed suffering of the little brown dog in a students' demonstration in a lecture at University College Hospital. In fact the animal had been anaesthetized throughout and the medical students, incensed by the accusation of wanton cruelty, repeatedly tried to deface and remove the statue. Battersea Borough Council eventually tired of having to provide a bobby to protect the statue and had the little brown dog removed and, it was presumed, destroyed. Another brown dog statue was commissioned and set up in Battersea Park, without the inflammatory inscription, but the sculptor used her own small terrier as model and it lacks the mongrel charm of the original little brown dog. Battersea Dogs' Home, nearby, vehemently denied that any of their stray dogs were ever sent to advance science.

The hospital had enlarged and changed by the time Erna Jebens had joined and set about developing an orthopaedic service. She was known for her conscientiousness and thoroughness. Her particular mentor was Sir Thomas Fairbank and she took pains to visit and learn from all the great exponents of the day. She was a Fellow of the British Orthopaedic Association and presented papers there and at the Royal Society of Medicine and enjoyed foreign travel. She ran a successful private practice from her house in Wimpole Street.

Erna Jebens was fluent in French, German and Italian, as well as English. She was a sociable person and loved the theatre and literature and travel. She was very committed to the Royal Institution and was on the committee of managers.

In the World War II, she also served as assistant surgeon at the Royal Free Hospital and to the East Ham General, within the EMS, the Emergency Medical Service Hospitals.

Eugenie Willis was resident surgical officer, at the Royal Infirmary, Oldham and treated hundreds of casualties during World War II when she was chief assistant in orthopaedics at the Royal Infirmary, Manchester from 1942 to 1945. After the war, she was appointed consultant orthopaedic surgeon to Oldham Royal Infirmary and to the Woods Hospital, Glossop.

Eugenie Leeson Willis, born in 1910, was the daughter of Captain Frank R Willis RN. She was educated at the Blackheath High School for Girls, a GPDST school and went up to Girton College Cambridge where she took first class honours in her BA and did her clinical work at the Royal Free Hospital, London. She took her Fellowship in 1939. Amongst her junior posts she was registrar at the Duchess of York Hospital for Babies, Manchester. She died in hospital in 1948, three years after the war ended, at the early age of thirty-eight of a chronic illness.

Cicely Pepler was consultant orthopaedic surgeon at the Great Yarmouth, Gorleston and Lowestoft Hospitals. She graduated MB BS London in 1944 and worked as a lecturer in anatomy at the Royal Free. She was a Nuffield scholar when she was senior registrar in orthopaedics at Oxford. She took the FRCS in 1952. She was a member of the Girdlestone Society. She died in 1977 in her late fifties before reaching retirement age.

Ruth Hickson worked as an associate specialist in orthopaedics in the West Midlands. It had been her intention to practise general surgery but, like others, to a certain extent one must follow ones star.

Ruth Margaret Hickson trained at the London (Royal Free Hospital) School of Medicine for Women where she was a prize-winner and graduated MB BS London in 1951. When she was a junior student, Phyllis George was a senior on the same firm and she felt even then that

Phyllis was destined for high things. She got to know her a little because she bought a car off her when Phyllis was going to America.

Ruth was house surgeon to Geraldine Barry who was an excellent surgeon and ran a well-organised unit as befitted the successor to Cecil Joll. She assisted Miss Barry in meticulous thyroid surgery and Radley Smith doing hypophysectomies. Miss Barry also sent her out to do general practice locums when needed for her GP sister Dr Frances Barry. Ruth also worked at the Elizabeth Garrett Anderson Hospital for Miss Alfreda Baker. She was interested in pathology as well as surgery but during her house physician post at Southampton she, with three or four others, was summoned to interview at the Free for a grant for further training. She had looked in at the Royal College of Surgeons on her way to the interview and was attracted by the course for the primary FRCS and she used the award for this. She went on then as surgical house officer to the surgical professorial unit at Bristol, working for Professor Milnes Walker, who gave her the following advice, that she think long and hard about the unlikelihood of a future in this country in general surgery for a woman. He asked her to consider, when she had the Fellowship, offering to work overseas where there was a desperate need for women surgeons to treat Muslim women and mentioned India and Uganda.

Ruth went from Bristol to Weston-super-Mare, an associated hospital, for further surgical experience and passed the FRCS and went from there back to the Royal Free as surgical registrar to work for Dorothy Barclay from whom, specifically, she learned a great deal about communication, talking to relatives, dealing with patients and their families. She shared a flat at one stage with Cicely Saunders who later founded the Hospice movement. While she was surgical registrar at the Royal Free, Dr Arthur Robinson, who had been her house surgeon at Weston-super-Mare, followed her to London and they decided to marry. He had been an engineer before taking up medicine and had the offer of a good practice in Stoke. Ruth completed her surgical registrar post at the Royal Free, and once settled in Stoke became a locum registrar on the orthopaedic unit in the hospital there, which became her entrée to orthopaedic surgery. She worked for Denys Wainwright, a celebrated orthopaedic surgeon who had a special interest in children's orthopaedics, children with Perthes' disease and CDH, congenital dislocation of the hip. Together over the years they ran clinics with the paediatricians. She manned the fracture clinics, and also held clinics within the special schools for the handicapped alongside physiotherapists and teachers and parents in a less threatening environment than the hospital, in Biddulph Grange, an orthopaedic offshoot of Liverpool with Harry Platt himself coming to visit. Originally it had been a children's unit and later it became a geriatric orthopaedic rehabilitation unit. She was an associate specialist in orthopaedics and worked solidly over the years, dovetailing the clinics with family life. When she gave birth to one of her three children, she told her husband – phone Denys and tell him I've had the baby and won't be in for the clinic tomorrow morning. She retired at sixty-five.

Her motivation to become a doctor was, she thinks, was a local GP and his family who lived who nearby and befriended her widowed mother. She was educated at Torquay Grammar School for Girls; she was a schoolgirl during the war years 1938 to 1946 and they had classes from nine am to one pm and then an evacuated school took over the premises from one until five, but nevertheless her schooling was excellent, better she felt than that of her children and grandchildren. Once she had been awarded a place at medical school, the GP family-friend took her on visits to the local hospital and clinics. Her wish to become a surgeon was inspired by working for Geraldine Barry. Marriage and children, but also the force of the pessimistic viewpoint of Professor Milnes Walker, determined the later extent of her surgical career. Her energy and intelligence found an outlet for a lifetime of useful work under the umbrella of Denys Wainwright's commitment to children's orthopaedic problems.

Mary Shelswell became consultant orthopaedic surgeon at the Portsmouth group of hospitals. Mary Elizabeth Shelswell trained at St Andrews and graduated MB ChB in 1948. She was orthopaedic house surgeon at the Royal Portsmouth Hospital which determined her interest in her future career. She did further jobs at the Royal Cancer Hospital, the Royal Marsden, and was lecturer in anatomy at the Royal Free Hospital. She took the FRCS in 1956. As well as being consultant orthopaedic surgeon at the Royal Portsmouth Hospital she was a fellow of the British Orthopaedic Association and member of the British Society of Hand Surgeons.

Delia Margaret Helen Hernaman Cothay, FRCS 1960 became the first consultant to the orthopaedic & trauma unit in the accident & emergency department of the Royal Surrey County Hospital, Guildford. When she retired, it was the time of improved staffing of A & E units, of increased recognition of medical, as opposed to surgical, emergencies, a rota system for cover, and increasingly a consultant-led service, but nevertheless it took six consultants to replace her.

She went to school at Sunderland High School when she lived with her grandparents in the north-east. Her father was an engineer in tin-mining in Nigeria and her parents were out there in the Plateau State in Central Nigeria. Delia went on to finish her schooling at the Bedgebury Girls' Public School in Lillesden, near Hawkhurst in Surrey and was promised a year with her parents in Jos after finishing her schooling. The Plateau State is the twelfth largest state of Nigeria and though the grasslands have been scored by deep gorges and lakes in places by the tin-mining, it is still a place of great natural beauty, now designated the Home of Peace and Tourism, with mountains to the north, supplied by three rivers, and with captivating rock-forms, and bare rocks scattered around. Buffalo, lions, leopard, baboon, monkeys, derby elands, pythons, crocodiles, chimpanzees, jackals, and the rare pygmy hippopotamus are indigenous. Because of the altitude three thousand feet above sea level, although tropical, the climate was reasonable and malaria not a hazard. It was the first year of World War II and all was quiet. By the second year as hostilities increased, Delia found a job. A girl friend recommended her and she spent the next two years of the war intercepting telegrams and radio-operations from the Free French and dealing with the information. Because of her War Service she was entitled to FETS, the Further Education Training Scheme and entered the Westminster Medical School as a medical student. They were the first entry post-war, and William Goodenough had pressurised the great London teaching hospitals that if they wanted to receive the grant from the UGS, the University Grant Scheme, they must open their doors to women students as to men. They capitulated but only to a quota of women. Accordingly, in Delia's year there were four girls and twenty-four chaps. Her medical training went smoothly and she worked under Sir Stanford Cade, whom she found supportive and not at all frightening as was his reputation (his daughter Irene was a medical student alongside her) and under Bobby Cox and qualified MB BS in 1951. She did house surgeon posts at the Westminster and in the Isle of Wight.

What decided her for orthopaedics was a childhood observation. The woman who lived next door to her grandparents in Sunderland had a caliper on one leg that Delia regarded with interest – pondering why she had it, what was the necessity of it, how it worked.

Delia did training posts at the Royal National Orthopaedic Hospital at Stanmore and took the FRCS in 1960 and was orthopaedic surgical registrar at Treloar. In those days, in order to become a consultant, one had to obtain a senior registrar post and these were scarce and in the purlieus of the teaching hospitals. Delia did a locum and was then appointed consultant in orthopaedics and trauma to the Royal Surrey Hospital in Guildford – the Hospital's first A & E Consultant – and where she spent her working life. She was a single lady.

Ruth Wynne-Davies, FRCS 1960 went from orthopaedic surgery into research medical genetics specialising in the orthopaedic field and has become a major authority on genetic and other aetiological factors in developmental disorders of the musculoskeletal system.

She was educated at Eversfield School, Sutton and the Nonsuch County School for Girls and was evacuated in the war to Wales and finished her schooling at Oswestry High School for Girls. Her father John Welch Blower had worked for Lloyds Bank in Oswestry and in Sutton and was one of the directors of the Sutton & Cheam Music Festival, being a baritone and a pianist himself and served in both World Wars, in the first in Mesopotamia as a captain, and in the second by 'reducing' his age by a decade, he took part in the Small Vessels Pool, ferrying small boats around the coast of Britain. Ruth had done secretarial work on leaving school during the war in local government and civil defence.

After the war, she entered the London (Royal Free Hospital) School of Medicine graduating MB BS London in 1953. She was married as a medical student and young doctor to a fellow medic, Arnold Danziger. She was attracted to an orthopaedic career as early as the preclinical years. As she put it, the appeal of orthopaedics to her was: bones have length and joints have angles. It was clean surgery. She did house jobs at the Metropolitan Hospital and the Royal Free and was demonstrator in anatomy at the Free. She got excellent surgical experience as SHO at Birmingham Accident Hospital and Great Ormond Street and was surgical registrar at the Elizabeth Garrett Anderson Hospital and in

Wrexham North Wales taking the surname Wynne-Davies of her uncle who had encouraged and sponsored her and achieving the FRCS in 1960.

She had decided on orthopaedics as a career and after a spell at the Royal Salop Infirmary, became orthopaedic registrar and then senior registrar in Exeter at the Princess Margaret Orthopaedic Hospital with Norman Capener. Her two years there determined the future direction of her career. As well as becoming a competent orthopaedic surgeon, she was 'bitten by the research bug'. She was awarded the Robert Jones Gold Medal and prize of the British Orthopaedic Association.

She went from Exeter to be an MRC research fellow in 1963 at the Medical Research Council's group on genetic problems in orthopaedic disease. (In the wake of the thalidomide disaster, the Distillers company had provided funds, a quarter of a million pounds, for Edinburgh University, which did look after the twenty-four people from Scotland and Northern Ireland affected by thalidomide). The MRC research group was formed to look into genetic and familial causes of skeletal deformities.

Ruth Wynne-Davies was first senior lecturer, then reader (orthopaedics) in the genetics research unit in Edinburgh University and took the PhD Edinburgh in 1973 while there.

Her eighteen years at Edinburgh were productive. Her research ranged over all the musculoskeletal disorders and she published upward of seventy research papers and a number of books and chapters in books. During the first ten years she was concerned with large family and genetic surveys of the common development disorders, congenital dislocation of the hip, scoliosis and vertebral anomalies, talipes equinovarus (clubfoot), Perthes' disease, congenital limb deformities, arthrogryposis, spondylolisthesis. She drew originally on the register from the Princess Rose Hospital, Exeter, where they had records spanning back 40 years. She set up a skeletal dysplasia clinic in Edinburgh and extended it to Oswestry, Nottingham, St Thomas' Hospital in London which met as specialist clinics once a quarter or so and later at the Nuffield Orthopaedic Centre in Oxford. She travelled to the States and compiled joint family surveys with Ted Riseborough on scoliosis in Boston, Massachusetts and Wilmington, Delaware, visited centres in France and Germany, and spent six weeks in Australia in connection with the research of the epidemiology of arthrogryposis multiplex congenital.

Ruth Wynne-Davies is renowned for her work on the familial and congenital aspects of skeletal deformities in children, both of scoliosis and limb abnormalities, and is the recognised authority on the subject in this country. With colleagues, she has also contributed to genetic mapping, site on chromosome identification, and the connections with other inherited conditions such as neurofibromatosis, and linkages with other conditions.

Together with Christine Hall as Consultant Radiologist and A Graham Apley, the orthopaedic surgeon at St Thomas' and St Peter's Chertsey whose Rowley Bristow Pyrford teaching course will be known to all surgical fellows post World War II, she produced in 1985 *The Atlas of Skeletal Deformities*. With T J Fairbank she put out the second edition of *Atlas of General Affections of the Skeleton* in 1976 and in 1973 wrote *Heritable Disorders in Orthopaedic Practice*.

Her seminal paper on the study of the families of patients with scoliosis was produced when she was reader in orthopaedics in Edinburgh and analysed the families of two hundred and eight children with scoliosis, one hundred and sixty-nine girls and thirty-nine boys, giving a sex ratio of 6:1, all right sided curves, almost all thoracic. She divided the age groups into infantile – birth to three years, juvenile – four to nine years, and adolescent – age ten and over, this last group having the preponderance of cases. From the family studies she concluded the incidence as 3.9/1000 in girls and 0.3/1000 in boys. She noted seven girl patients with cleft palates, two with club-feet, one with a PDA, patent ductus arteriosus, and one boy patient with talipes calcaneovalgus. She concluded a multifactorial mode of inheritance. There were studies from Faber in Germany in 1934 of six hundred cases and a Canadian study from Toronto. With Edward J Riseborough she gathered a further series of cases seen between 1967 and 1970 at the Children's Hospital, Boston, where she went out to Massachusetts for several weeks at a time to gather and collate the work for publication.

She also wrote on polydactyly, absence of the fibula, talipes equinovarus, capital femoral epiphysis abnormalities, Perthes' disease, and congenital dislocation of the hip.

Within the British Orthopaedic Research Society, of which she was secretary and president in her time, she formed a multidisciplinary group of orthopaedic surgeons, clinical geneticists, radiologists and paediatricians, the Skeletal Dysplasia Group for teaching and research, initially twelve members, now numbering two hundred and fifty and holding an international gathering every six years; a meeting at the Royal College of Surgeons being scheduled for March 2011.

In 1981, at the age of fifty-five, she took early retirement from the Edinburgh appointment, keeping contact with the Harlow Wood Orthopaedic Hospital, Mansfield, The Robert Jones and Agnes Hunt Orthopaedic Hospital, Oswestry, St Thomas' Hospital and the Oxford Radcliffe and clinical genetics department where she was an honorary consultant. She studied English language & literature for the BA Oxon. and settled in Oxford where she was honorary consultant in medical genetics at the Churchill Hospital.

Erna Jebens, Maud Forrester-Brown, Eugenie Willis, Cicely Pepler, Ruth Hickson (Mrs Ruth Robinson), Mary Shelswell, Delia Cothay and Ruth Wynne-Davies, these are our eight orthopaedic Fellows.

One Fellow in India, *Dr Grace Lukose*, FRCS 1951, assisted Dr Helen Reid the reader in orthopaedic surgery at the Lady Hardinge Hospital and did valiant work during the unrest and riots of partition.

A further Fellow, *Barbara Ansell*, became an authority, pioneering paediatric rheumatoid conditions. She worked particularly in the Canadian Red Cross Hospital, Taplow.

Two further Fellows undertook the speciality of being in charge of accident and emergency units, *Rosemary Adams (Mrs Rosemary Campbell)* at the Norfolk and Norwich Hospital and *Katharine Burkill (Mrs Kit Taylor)* in the Royal Hallamshire Hospital and the Northern Hospital.

One Fellow went into the speciality of physical medicine: *Helene Goodman (Mrs Woolf)*.

CHAPTER 11

Eye Surgeons

SURGERY on the eye, to a general surgeon, carries the conviction that operations involve a delicate intricate precise controlled technique. It might be thought that dexterity of that degree, control of action, might make eye surgery a suitable province for women practising surgery.

The responsibility is extreme. To lose eyesight is a different order of magnitude to losing part of the colon or the rest of the body. Nor can the eye surgeon, nor indeed can the neurosurgeon, depend to the same degree on the wonderful facility of the body to repair.

Four, all distinguished, had qualified before World War II and are Dame Ida Mann, Philippa Martin and Jean Dollar; and Dorothy Adams whose English Fellowship was bestowed later after twenty years as a consultant. All made a remarkable contribution. In all, seventeen of the two hundred women Fellows chose ophthalmic surgery as their speciality.

The Ophthalmological Society began as long ago as 1880. From Ida Mann onwards, the breadth and depth of the knowledge of general surgery that was required for the FRCS was a demanding burden for those who had early decided on a future specialising in eye surgery. But the early women surgeons did take this route. In addition, the DOMS, diploma of ophthalmology in medicine and surgery, or the DO, diploma of ophthalmology, was a popular qualification particularly in those returning to India and practising general surgery including the treatment of cataracts. Those who intended to specialise in the surgery of the eye in Britain generally took the FRCS as well. Within the Royal College of Surgeons, the Faculty of Ophthalmic Surgery was formed in 1946 and it became possible to take the specialist eye FRCS. Inevitably, in 1988, the Royal College of Ophthalmologists was formed and the eye surgeons left the College.

Ida Mann was among the first group of women ever to attain the Fellowship. She stood to get the FRCS in 1924 with Erna Jebens and Esther Rickards as London School of Medicine for Women students who had been seconded to St Mary's Medical School for part of their training during World War I.

The factors that stimulated Ida Mann to embark on a career in medicine at all emphasise the extent to which chance plays a part in the direction of life choices. As a seventeen year old clerk in the Post Office Savings Bank, earning sixteen shillings a week, she none-the-less gave sixpence from her small earnings to a collection that was being made for the London Hospital. As a thank-you, those who donated were later invited to Whitechapel to be taken on a tour of the hospital by the governor. Ida Mann was totally bowled over, not by the sick patients, nor the wards, but by the apparatus, the equipment, the X-ray rooms, the machines, the casualty department, the laboratories. The tour completed, she sought out the governor to inquire whether she might become a student there. He was amused and told her that he could not accept her but added that the only medical school in the country that would accept girls was the London School of Medicine for Women in Bloomsbury.

Ida Mann, dressed as she thought suitable in a brown gabardine suit with useful large pockets in the jacket, her hat enlivened by vivid pheasant tail feathers, a colourful touch characteristic of her, presented herself at the women's medical school and filled in an application form, assuring them that she would be matriculated by the time of her entry.

She had been educated at Wycombe House, a small non-denominational international school, had left at sixteen with Cambridge Juniors and gone to Clarke's Business College on the corner of Walm Lane and Cricklewood High Road in West Hampstead where the Mann family lived, with a view to sitting the civil service examination that led on to the clerkship in the Post Office Savings Bank. She was envious and admiring of her brother, six years her senior, who had gone to boarding school in Broadstairs and on to Wadham College Oxford. A friend of her brother's, a medical student, had intrigued her on a family holiday with stories about his work. Ida enrolled herself in evening classes at the Regent Street Polytechnic in order to matriculate, as did future fellow student Esther Rickards. English, mathematics, a science (she chose chemistry), history with geography, French, she could manage. Latin was about to defeat her, but at the last moment, the authorities ordained that a second modern language could be substituted and she chose German. She sat the examination in the vast Imperial Institute Examinations Hall in Kensington, and counted only eight women amongst the hundreds of men, and duly passed. Her father paid his two hundred pounds outright for the full course of her medical training. He gave her an allowance of four pounds a month all the time she was a student.

At the London School of Medicine for Women, Ida got started, approaching the pre-medical studies with the enthusiasm which characterised all her work throughout her life. It was 1914. The physics lecturer, Miss Stoney, had a sister who was a radiologist at Fulham Military Hospital and Ida went to be a part-time switch-girl for the x-ray machines to earn some pocket money and she caught the eye of Major Lee the surgeon who used her help in the operating theatres, digging out shrapnel from the POWs and sewing wounds up, her first taste of surgery while still a first year student.

Professor Wood Jones, charismatic teacher of anatomy, encouraged some of his students to take the primary FRCS, the Royal College of Surgeons having opened its doors to women, and some, Ida amongst them, took his summer course: Margaret Basden was the only one who passed. The students were told that the skeletons they had each purchased in a box had been taken from bodies in the Napoleonic wars. Because it was war-time, there was talk of some of the students being seconded to other London medical schools for teaching and Ida Mann went to see the authorities of the London Hospital in Whitechapel again, this time bearding the chairman, and put her case to him that, with the young men in the Forces, he might open the doors to women. He said he would think about it – and while it was of no benefit to Ida, the London did accept women a year later for the duration of the war, and it may be that Ida's inquiry paved the way for Constance Ottley later.

However Ida Mann, together with Erna Jebens and Esther Rickards and Sybil Mocatta, was among the girl students who were seconded to St Mary's for their studies, chosen for their intelligence, sober appearance and decorum, not to upset the sensitivities of the all-male medical school. Even so, Sir Almroth Wright would not abide a girl student in his propinquity; they dubbed him Old Mr Almost Right in revenge, and they had to keep out of his sight. The women students were obliged to return to the Royal Free Hospital for some of their clinical teaching, including obstetrics, going out on 'the district' into the community, an eye-opener to Ida on the habitations and way-of-life of the poor.

Piqued by her failure in the primary FRCS under Professor Wood Jones, Ida struck up a friendship with Professor J E S Frazer in the anatomy department at St Mary's and she not only passed the primary but embarked on what was to be a long and fruitful collaboration on comparative structure and embryology. Frazer had a unique collection of human embryos at all stages of development that had been sent to him by former students from their subsequent practices which enabled Ida to study the development of the human eye. Later when she needed chicken eyes for one of her studies, she located a rabbi in Paddington authorised to dispatch chickens by slitting their throats with a razor blade; he threw the heads over a wall to Ida where she equally deftly removed their eyes for her research. Frazer and Ida Mann together wrote more than nineteen papers and presentations to the Anatomical Society and Ida was pleased to find herself accepted in the scientific world with no sex prejudice. There is irony that the comment made of her 'A male mind in a female body' pleased her. She later gathered the work together for a DSc which was also published as a book *The Development of the Eye*. She later wrote *Abnormal Developments of the Eye*.

When her student year graduated MB BS in 1920 they all applied for all the house jobs going and she was allotted the ophthalmic house surgeon to Leslie Paton and Frank Juler. Her work on the embryology of the mammalian eye had not gone unnoticed and Paton suggested a future for her in ophthalmic surgery and she found herself agreeing. Telling her mother about the seniors she had met at a formal dinner, her mother commented how nice it was for her to meet these people. 'Meeting them is nothing, Mother,' she said. 'I have to be one of them.' She took the DOMS, diploma of ophthalmology in medicine & surgery, in 1922.

To get the FRCS though she had to complete more general surgery and joined Ernest Lane, an exceedingly quick surgeon of the old school and Maynard Smith, slower and meticulous, and was able to assess the relative outcomes and choose her future style – a rapid four and a half minute cataract operation, that was later totally outclassed in speed when she subsequently visited India.

She had obtained a clinical assistant post in ophthalmology at St Mary's and was appointed consultant at the Elizabeth Garrett Anderson Hospital where she worked for a few years. She set about visiting centres of innovation abroad: she undertook a course run by Professor Vogt on the use of the Scandinavian invention of Gullstrand's slit-lamp; she visited Professor Axenfeld in Freiburg-im-Brusgau and saw Professor Weve's work on the detached retina. She took the final FRCS in 1924 in some trepidation because she was more experienced in ophthalmic surgery than in general surgery. In the viva, Sir Arthur Keith asked her what a slit lamp was as he had never heard of it and thankfully she spent the oral explaining this miraculous new invention that enabled one to see the blood corpuscles moving in the vessels at the back of the eye – and was duly passed.

Ida Mann was junior clinical assistant at Moorfields Hospital for six years from 1922 to 1928 working for A C Hudson, 'Huddie', and joined the Central London Eye Hospital in Judd Street in 1925, a stepping-stone to Moorfields, which she achieved in 1927. She and Stewart Duke-Elder were competitors, he a witty Aberdonian, protégé of Sir John Parsons, she with her DSc and many seminal publications on embryology. When she was summoned back in before the selection committee after the interview to be told that she had the job, Sir John Parsons said to her, 'I did my best to keep you out, but as you have won, I will say no more.' Her competitor was later appointed also when the next vacancy arose.

The same year she attended the International Ophthalmic Council in Holland, flying there with Stewart Duke-Elder and his wife in a small blue KLM plane equipped like a ship with a salon, the passengers seated round a table. She sought out contact with the big names in ophthalmology, found Professor Seefelder standing on his head in the sand, and was placed to sit at dinner by Professor Ernest Fuchs, the oldest and the youngest members. She was not averse to using her unique position as a young woman amongst mature older men. She won the Gifford Edmonds prize on development of the retina. She gave an Arris & Gale lecture at the Royal College on retinal differentiation. She did some work at the Zoo, experimental work, and operated on a python's infected eye, replacing it later with a brown glass bead, and refrigerating the snake to put it to sleep as she was told that giving an anaesthetic would kill it, and presented her findings to the Ophthalmological Society, once with a snake draped around her neck. One of the elderly eye surgeons commented, 'Horrid girl'. She set up in private practice and began to earn well, her hospital appointments all being 'honoraries', unpaid. She had a charming flat in Queen Anne Street with her consulting rooms below, a cottage in the Chilterns, a car, clothes, books, the theatre, women friends. She went on holiday with Erna Henrietta Jebens, and with other doctor friends from Royal Free days, including an intrepid trip walking with a donkey across the Breche de Roland from France to Spain, and later with young doctors who had been her students. And all the time she was operating and doing clinics at Moorfields and the Royal Free and seeing her patients.

In 1937 Ida Mann flew to Australia on an Imperial Airways flying boat. It left from Southampton water and took a week. The journey by boat would have taken ten weeks. The flying boat was spacious on board like a shipboard salon, ten passengers, tables to sit at, a promenade deck with a brass rail to hold on to. It flew at six thousand feet but over France they had to go above the clouds, the temperature dropped to 19 °F and they were all blue with cold. They were given hot Bovril but it cooled between leaving the flask and drinking it. They put down at Marseilles, Rome, Naples, Piraeus, Alexandria, Tiberia, Palestine, Iraq, Karachi, Allahabad, Calcutta, Penang, Singapore, Bitavia, Surabaya and Darwin.

As the situation in Europe deteriorated in 1938, she carried out an amazing Scarlet Pimpernel rescue of Josef Dallos, who had developed a mold for making Zeiss type contact lenses using a pliable material Negocoll, she driving him around Budapest in a taxi, while he agonised whether he needed to leave all he had in Hungary and come to England. He settled eventually with Hamlins to continue his work.

World War II approached and Ida signed a form stating that she would go anywhere, do anything. She was to be part of the team of Sir Hugh Cairns, the Oxford Professor of Neurosurgery. The anticipation of massive casualties led the government to disband all specialist hospitals and their staff in order to create enough EMS, Emergency Medical Service, beds. Charles Goulden on behalf of the Ministry of Health ordered Moorfields Eye Hospital to be shut, disbanded the hospital, bolted the doors, and designated it a first aid post. He wanted eighty-two beds. On Monday morning, one hundred and fifty eye patients turned up and sat on the steps. The intrepid porter opened up, saying that Moorfields had been open for forty years and was not going to close now. Ida Mann went to see Theodore Luling, Chairman of the lay-board, and both Moorfields and the Central London Eye Hospital defied the edict to close. They drove around the country north of London to find hospital accommodation to act as an overflow for patients seen in the City Road Moorfields, viewing a manor house vacated by a school in Radlett in

Hertfordshire, an abandoned convent hospital in the Priory of the Holy Sepulchre, and a site in Edgware that was deemed to be too close to Hendon airfield, and settled on Mount Vernon Hospital in Northwood. A year after war was declared, when the hundred days of day-and-night bombing of the Blitz started, part of the City Road Moorfields Hospital was indeed bombed and co-operated with the Central Eye to share facilities and keep open; Ida Mann's flat in Queen Anne Street was devastated beyond being able to live and sleep there. Ida commuted in her Morris Oxford car when she could get petrol between Mill Hill where she lived with friends and Oxford where she stayed with her brother's parents-in-law. During the war, 'Honoraries' were not allowed to resign from their consultant posts at a civilian hospital and she continued to see patients. She did important war-work in the Imperial Cancer Research Fund laboratories at Mill Hill, refuting the idea that ascorbic acid, vitamin C, protected the eye against the effects of mustard gas, a late corneal ulceration that occurred ten to fifteen years after exposure and she worked on BAL, British Anti-Lewisite. The director at Mill Hill was the scientist Professor William Gye FRS.

At Oxford she was asked to set in order the archaic eye hospital and, with twenty-five thousand pounds from Lord Nuffield, to set up a research laboratory. 'That woman has gone through Oxford like a tornado', was one comment. The Eye Hospital was in a primitive state. There was one phone that nobody answered. The matron resigned, to be replaced by a sister from Moorfields. Elderly members of the Board were dispatched. Outpatient attendances shot up from two thousand a year pre-war to twenty-two thousand. Patients paid sixpence a visit. The Nuffield Laboratory of Ophthalmology was set up with Ida's friend and colleague Antoinette Pirie as biochemist and research began. Her book *The Science of Seeing* was written with Antoinette Pirie during those war years and was published by Penguin in the Pelican series and can still be read today as an instructive insight into *seeing* from single cell organisms to the eyes of fish, reptiles, birds, and the human eye, and is popular and entertaining without compromising its scientific credence.

Ida was appointed Margaret Ogilvie Reader in Ophthalmology, entitled still to see private patients, and later became titular professor of ophthalmology at Oxford, the first woman professor in any subject in Oxford University. She had rooms in Holywell Manor, part of Balliol

College, where St Hugh's had moved, the women's college having become a military hospital. Every Monday morning Ida took the early train to London to operate at Moorfields. Disruption in the war was extreme and had to be accepted. Everyone sometimes did mad things. She received a proposal of marriage, far from her first, from a colleague now a major in the war in some far-flung part of the world, accepted him, changed her mind, but fortunately he married someone else. She discussed it over tea with Elsa, Professor Gye's wife, an ex-suffragist, and a strong-minded woman, whose name he had taken to Elsa Gye's delight because there would have been two Professor William Bullocks in the Pathology Department in Edinburgh. Elsa was to die of her breast cancer and Ida and William Gye fell in love and married, she a devoted wife and involved mother to her stepsons, Jack, Richard and Charles.

With the war ended and William Gye in retirement, Ida sought sunny climes for her husband's health and they settled in Perth. Moorfields Hospital were unhappy with her resignation from the staff and insisted she return to give her papers at an International Congress; she honoured her commitment, flying there and back.

After her husband's death, devastated but needing a new challenge, she criss-crossed Australia compiling records of the incidence of eye diseases at the request of the Public Health Department and with the help of the Flying Doctor Service, plotting trachoma in the Aboriginal population, an important cause of later blindness. She and her colleagues investigated the distribution, the type of the disease, the relation of its severity to the environment, the probable sources of infection, and speculated on its original arrival. They went on to extend the survey into first Papua New Guinea and then, at the request of the World Health Organisation, in Taiwan. Apart from the official reports, she wrote her account of this work in her books *The Cockney and the Crocodile*, and *China 13*, both quirky fascinating books showing her to be a graphic writer. Reading her books, Ida's delight in colour is manifest as she gives vivid descriptions of deserts of red sand-dunes, gold spinifex on black mountains, sky and stars and sunsets, silver-sanded beach and turquoise sea, all amidst her unflagging enjoyment of intrepid voyages, seemingly never daunted, always ready to encounter new people and situations viewing them with the shrewd analysis of an anthropologist as well as an investigative ophthalmologist and always with a humanitarian eye.

Philippa Parry Martin (1897-1981) FRCS 1930 was born Philippa Parry Pughe in Australia. Her father was an Anglican clergyman, Canon Thomas St John Pughe. She went to school at Toowoomba High School.

Canon Pughe sent his daughter back to England to finish her education at St Felix, Southwold, and after a year in Switzerland, she went up to Cambridge to read for the natural science tripos at Newnham College. Philippa Pughe however had had enough of the restrictions of an all-girls boarding school and faced with a repetition of this in the confines and petty rules of an all-women's Cambridge College, she left after only three weeks. She found herself a place as a medical student at University College London and the freedom of London life suited her better. She went on to University College Hospital, UCH, where she qualified with the conjoint diploma in 1921 and the MB BS with honours in surgery in 1922 at the age of twenty-five. She became house surgeon at UCH and married her consultant, the surgeon Edward Kenneth Martin, at the age of twenty-six.

She then went on to make a tremendous success of her career, taking the FRCS in 1930, the MS in 1932, the sixth woman to get this higher degree in surgery; she gave a Hunterian lecture at the College in 1936, the first woman to be a Hunterian professor. Her oration was on 'The effect on the eye of radium used for the treatment of malignant disease in the neighbourhood'. She was ophthalmic registrar at UCH and became the consultant at the Elizabeth Garrett Anderson, the Maida Vale Hospital for Neurology and Neurosurgery and the Western Eye Hospital. They had a happy marriage, with three daughters – two of them doctors and one an architect – and they enjoyed travelling, driving all over Europe. She was still operating in her eighties. Her husband was ninety-six when he died and she eighty-three.

An outside observer might have wondered whether her promising surgical career might have been about to be jeopardised by her early marriage when still a house surgeon to her consultant; far from it. As to those who take a stereotypic stance in their opinions on other people's life choices, insisting that women must decide between one course or another and cannot have everything, let them learn from the splendid example of Philippa Martin.

Old habits die hard. Fifty years later, a woman surgeon with the MS and FRCS, a consultant, sat at a College dinner, with her non-medical husband beside her, several children at home, and had to listen while a member of council, later to be president, pontificated voicing his firm opinion that a woman could not be both a good surgeon and a good mother. Philippa Martin certainly disproved that.

The liberal instincts of the 'godless institution of Gower Street' (University College) prevailed again with Gwen Hill. She qualified two years after Philippa Martin at UCH and married Reginald Hilton the year after she had graduated and none-the-less went on to specialise and to found the radiotherapy department at UCH, becoming its first director and to have a daughter, who followed her into the profession and speciality. Gwen Hill worked all her life.

Dorothy Rose Adams (Mrs Dorothy Campbell) 1902-1982 FRCS 1954 was made an FRCS by election as a distinguished surgeon of twenty years standing, qualifying in 1927 and becoming a consultant in 1937. She was a consultant eye surgeon and director of the research department of the Birmingham & Midland Eye Hospital.

As a Cambridge University student she made a landmark contribution to the understanding of the causation of cataract in glass-workers, and her academic commitment continued right through to her founding of the research unit that helped to make the Birmingham Eye Hospital outstanding. Her sphere of interest included the biochemistry of the lens, retinitis pigmentosa, and vitamin A and the eye.

Dorothy Adams was educated at the North London Collegiate School after Claire House Preparatory School and then won an entrance exhibition to Girton College Cambridge where she took a double first in 1923. She had a brilliant university career winning many medals and prizes and was awarded the Scientific and Industrial Research Studentship for a piece of work entitled 'The metabolism of the Crystalline lens' for the Glassblowers Cataract Committee of the Royal Society. The government had funded research on Glassworker's Cataract after the Workman's Compensation Acts were passed in 1896 and 1906. Sir William Crookes, an analytical chemist and President of the Royal Society and discoverer of the element thallium, had worked on the premise that infra-red and ultraviolet radiation in the extreme conditions where the glassblowers worked was responsible for clouding of the lens of the eye and this had led him to the inclusion of rare earth metals into glass and the development of tinted glass spectacles for industrial protection and indeed against strong sunlight and glare for leisure use. Although the glassworkers, puddlers and tin-platers did not take to the wearing of industrial protective glasses, the innovation did found the sun glass industry. After the end of World War I, the research was re-started supported by the Gilchrist fund and was handed to Dorothy Adams by Gowland Hopkins of vitamin and trace element fame. Using fresh ox and sheep eyes, she brilliantly showed that opacification of the lens was due to an autooxidation process reminiscent of that described in muscle by Gowland Hopkins and that chemical reaction reduced the amount of glutathione, leading to clouding of the lens.

Dorothy Adam's clinical training followed at University College Hospital, UCH, in London and she qualified MB BS London in 1927. She held early posts at the Royal London Ophthalmic Hospital, the Central London Ophthalmic Hospital and took the DOMS in 1930. The stimulus for academic biochemical research had come while she was still at Cambridge. In the first three years after qualifying she carried out further research on the biochemistry of the lens for the Medical Research Council. She went on to training posts to qualify as an ophthalmic surgeon. Her first appointment was as consultant to the Hospital of New Cross, Rugby and the Birmingham Midland and Eye Hospital where she worked from 1934 to 1940.

She married Dr George Campbell MA BM BCh Oxford, in 1938, at the age of thirty-six and they had a son and a daughter. She was a consultant for thirty-five years in the Coventry area, and in the war years she joined the EMS, the Emergency Medical Service, and covered Coventry, Warwick, Leamington and Nuneaton. Her husband, who was a GP, served in the war as a lieutenant commander in the RNVR and was a support to her in her work. She had a good woman friend who was Froebel-trained who looked to the care of her children. Dorothy makes the point that it was realized from the start that she had to earn enough to help cover the extra domestic expenses of her working. It was essential for her to have her consulting rooms away from the home as her husband's practice was there.

After the war, she went on to found the research department of the Birmingham & Midland Eye Hospital from 1947 to 1965, which helped to make the Birmingham Eye a beacon in the Midlands. She felt fortunate in working with many distinguished ophthalmologists.

She won the Nettleship Medal in 1940, gave the Middlemore Lecture in 1946 and again in 1960, the Doyne Memorial Lecture and Medal in 1952, the Percival Hay Memorial Lecture in 1962. Her research was supported by the Medical Research Council, MRC. She was a member and Vice-President of the Ophthalmological Society of the UK and a member and deputy-master of the Oxford Ophthalmological Congress.

She writes, when asked about women and surgery and the consideration of part-time work: 'Medicine is such a rewarding occupation but the choice of part-time work is important. Ophthalmology is one of the best possible for women. In part-time work, medical women would be well advised to choose a speciality rather than general practice – to avoid the mix-up between professional and domestic duties'. Then she adds (like most women of her generation): 'I feel that specialist training must be a whole-time commitment.'

She and her husband were enthusiasts for small-boat sailing, chiefly in the Royal Corinthian 1 design class in Burnham-on-Crouch. She was also a keen horse-rider.

Jean Marguerite Dollar (1901-1982) FRCS 1936 became an eye surgeon, practised all her working life and made an original and important contribution in her field describing a new technique after exenteration of the orbit with immediate reconstruction with a prosthesis, a boon to young patients with sarcoma to help them to adapt to their situation. She presented her work as a dissertation to the College as a Hunterian professor in 1945 and the work was also published in *The Lancet*, and was entitled 'The use of plastics in ophthalmology'. She was known as a deft and gentle surgeon.

Her father and grandfather were veterinary surgeons with a city practice based in Bond Street. She trained at the London School of Medicine and the Royal Free Hospital qualifying MB BS in 1927, took the DOMS in 1929, the MS in 1935 and the FRCS in 1936. She was Consultant to the Royal Eye Hospital which was her main concern, but also gave service to St Olave's, the Elizabeth Garrett Anderson and the Royal Free Hospitals.

During World War II, she was one of the few surgeons not on active service and so concomitantly busy. For a short time the Royal Eye amalgamated with King's College Hospital but separated again and her diplomacy was influential at that time. She was a good teacher and colleague with a fund of clinical anecdotes and quiet wit. In retirement she travelled and enjoyed visiting places of archaeological and wild fauna interest and was a great reader.

Mary Savory (1911-1999) FRCS 1949 was consultant eye surgeon at the Royal Eye Hospital London, St James' Hospital Balham and the South London Hospital for Women, and practised from Devonshire Place.

She went up to Cambridge and did her clinical studies at University College Hospital London and qualified MB BChir Cambridge in 1939. She was a BMA Research Scholar in 1946-7 and took the DOMS in 1946 and the FRCS in 1949. She was a member of the Oxford Ophthalmological Congress and the Ophthalmological Society. This society was founded in 1909 by Robert W Doyne and holds an annual academic and social meeting which extends an invitation to a few overseas doctors who would benefit from interaction with colleagues, and funds them. The laudable stated aims of the society are 'For the cultivation of the spirit of good fellowship and of unconventionality, the right of our youngest member to rank with his oldest colleague and last, but assuredly not least, the frank, free and tolerant discussion of scientific matters brought before it felt any prejudice in her/his gathering.'

Mary Savory became consultant at the Royal Eye Hospital, St James' Balham and the South London Hospital for Women where she spent her working life, retiring at age sixty-seven. She had not felt any prejudice in her career as a woman in medicine and, though not against part-time posts in principle, commented that she felt that they should be available to men as well as to women, a view-point eccentric at the time, but one that would find resonance today.

Elisabeth Davis Liken Simpson FRCS 1952 was consultant eye surgeon to St James' Balham, St George's Tooting and the South London Hospital for Women. She was also Ophthalmic Surgeon to Queen Mary's Hospital for Children, Carshalton and earlier at St John's Hospital, Battersea. She had a private practice from Harley Street.

She trained in Dublin, qualifying MB BCh BAO in 1941 and took the DOMS England in 1944. She was chief clinical assistant at Moorfields Eye Hospital and chief assistant at the Hospital for Sick Children, Great Ormond Street. During the War she was a squadron leader in the RAF. .

Irene Dorothy Rosalie Gregory FRCS 1953 trained in Bristol qualifying MB ChB Bristol 1944. She was house surgeon at Bristol Royal Infirmary, to the Bristol Eye Hospital and took the DOMS in 1946. She was senior registrar at Guy's. She was consultant eye surgeon to Sidcup Hospital and to the Greater London Council Inner London Educational Authority.

Kate Goddard, Una Kathleen Goddard, née Merrill FRCS 1959, became a consultant ophthalmic surgeon at Hull Royal Infirmary. She trained at Sheffield qualifying MB ChB in 1955 and served as house surgeon at the Central Middlesex Hospital and went on to Sunderland Eye Infirmary as senior house surgeon and took the DO and the FRCS in 1959, She was senior ophthalmic registrar at the United Sheffield Hospitals, before being appointed to her consultant post at Hull Royal Infirmary. She studied and took the LlB in 1985 and the FCOphth in 1988.

Like many other surgeons of her generation, she thought that the availability of part-time work might well help women to stay in medical practice, but also like nearly all, felt that part-time *training* in the surgical specialties was unacceptable. She had not felt prejudice against her as a woman in medicine. However she had an insightful and penetrating response to the question in the survey as to whether her own mother had worked – the attempt was being made to try to correlate whether a working mother helped encourage the daughter to a medical working lifetime. She pointed out that, since the husband's attitudes are so crucial to a working woman, a factor of at least equal, or she suspected more importance, would be whether one's *husband's mother* was a working woman. She added that she hoped that she had brought up her own son to accept a working wife in due course.

Mary Allan Craig Jones FRCS 1959 became consultant ophthalmic surgeon at the Royal Hallamshire Hospital, Sheffield. She trained in Birmingham graduating MB ChB in 1948. Her consultant appointment was to the Royal Hallamshire Hospital, Sheffield. She worked full-time and had some private practice. She had domestic help by two people covering every weekday from 8.30 to 4 pm. She was single.

She had not been aware of any prejudice against her in medicine because she was a woman. Like her fellows, she felt that part-time work might help women but was not in favour of it during surgical training.

Mary Joan Starbuck FRCS 1959 became consultant ophthalmic surgeon at Canterbury and Thanet and the South-East Hospitals.

Mary trained at King's College Hospital qualifying MB BS London in 1952 and where she held house officer posts. She sat the DRCOG in 1954 was house officer in the eye department and took the DO in 1956. She became senior ophthalmic registrar at Kings and also clinical assistant at Moorfields Eye Hospital. Her consultant appointment was to Canterbury Hospital where she spent her working life. She was a member of the Ophthalmic Society of the UK. In Canterbury, she was a colleague of Jean Rosemary Campbell Burton Brown and wrote her obituary in the BMJ.

Doreen Ann Birks FRCS 1962 became consultant ophthalmic surgeon to St Thomas's Hospital and the Sutton and West Merton Eye Unit at Sutton Hospital.

She trained at the Royal Free Hospital qualifying MB BS London in 1949 and was house surgeon and later senior registrar at the Royal Eye Hospital and ophthalmic registrar at St James' Balham. She took the DO in 1953.

Her consultant appointments were not only at St Thomas' and Sutton but she was also the honorary consulting surgeon for the School for the Blind in Leatherhead. She was a member of the Ophthalmological Society UK and published papers.

Marion Christine Handscombe received her FRCS in 1962. Mrs Handscombe became consultant ophthalmic surgeon at Coventry and Warwick Hospitals.

She went to school at the Mills Grammar School and the Sir John Leman School at Laindon in Essex, did her pre-clinical training at UCL and her clinical training at the London Hospital, qualifying MB BS London in 1954. and did house jobs in Greenwich and the London and was senior registrar at Moorfields. She took the FCOphth in 1989. She was instrumental in the founding of the College of Ophthalmologists and its splitting away from the Royal College of Surgeons and to that end attended Council meetings as special representative. Her consultant appointments were at Coventry and Warwick Hospitals where she spent her working life and she went abroad to practice her eye surgery and teach in Africa, India, Ceylon and China. She retired to Banbury in Oxfordshire.

Doris May Cleweth Price FRCS 1963 became consultant ophthalmic surgeon to the Harlow Group of Hospitals.

As Doris Davies, she trained in Birmingham and graduated MB ChB in 1953. After house jobs she was registrar at the Coventry and Warwick Hospitals, and in Shrewsbury, and took the DO in 1956, then becoming Senior Registrar at Birmingham & Midland Eye Hospital and took both the Edinburgh and the English FRCS in 1963. She was a member of the Midlands Ophthalmic Society and the Royal Society of Medicine and became FRCOphth in 1988.

She was appointed Consultant at the Harlow Group of Hospitals and covered West Essex and East Hertfordshire. Twenty years after getting the Fellowship, she was working full-time with some private practice and felt that both part-time work and part-time training would be helpful to women in surgical work, and she felt that many more part-time consultant posts should be available. She did not feel that there had been prejudice against her as a woman in medicine; however she did not find her colleagues helpful to her during her two pregnancies. She took only the minimum leave and returned to full responsibilities six weeks after their birth. She would advise any young woman in medicine to obtain her higher degrees before she is married, as she did, as this was the better way to gain postgraduate experience.

She writes graphically that to have a career in medicine doing full-time work plus a family, plus a husband – who must agree to your work – is very difficult and demanding but is equally very satisfying when it is achieved.

Anthea Mary Stewart Connell (1925-2003) FRCS 1964 was the senior consultant ophthalmic surgeon at the Queen Elizabeth Hospital, Barbados for twenty-seven years and did important work documenting conditions of the eye in Barbados.

Anthea was the daughter of two doctors, her father John S M Connell was a surgeon and gynaecologist in the RAMC in the War, with the rank of colonel, serving on hospital ships; her mother Constance B Challis trained in Cambridge and Birmingham and went into public health.

Anthea was educated at Edgbaston High School Birmingham and then at City Park Collegiate Institute, Saskatoon before moving on to the University of Saskatchewan and then to Birmingham University where she qualified MB ChB in 1952. She was resident and registrar at Moorfields and senior registrar/first assistant at Moorfields and the London Hospitals.

She was appointed senior consultant and head of department of ophthalmology in Barbados in 1969 and was assistant lecturer in the University of the West Indies. She initiated the Barbados Eye Study and conducted surveys and published on the incidence of glaucoma and on intraocular eye pressures in the population, presenting her work to the American Academy of Ophthalmology. She held courses and organised the diploma of ophthalmology examination for the College of Surgeons of England.

She married in 1963 George E P Dowglass, a wine merchant, and they had a daughter Charlotte, who worked in Hampton Court Palace and the Tower of London.

Like many surgeons, Anthea painted, in oils and acrylic, and showed her work. She died after a series of cerebrovascular accidents.

Enid Taylor neé Enid Wheldon FRCS 1965 was consultant ophthalmic surgeon at the North Middlesex Hospital and the Elizabeth Garrett Anderson.

Enid Wheldon studied at Cambridge University and did her clinical studies at the London Hospital and qualified MB BChir in 1957. She was registrar at the North Middlesex Hospital and at St James' Balham and senior registrar at Barts. She was appointed consultant at the North Middlesex Hospital and the Elizabeth Garrett Anderson and took the FRCOphth in 1988. She was a member of the Ophthalmological Society of the UK and assistant of the Worshipful Company of Apothecaries and published on diabetic retinopathy.

She was a married lady. She declined to take part in the questionnaire.

Margaret Thornton Challis FRCS 1967 became consultant eye surgeon at Whipps Cross Hospital and the Regional Eye Centre.

Her mother was a doctor and had worked in general practice for forty-one years. Margaret Challis trained at the London Hospital, Whitechapel, qualifying MB BS in 1957. She was house surgeon at Moorfields Eye Hospital and senior registrar in eyes at the London. She was appointed consultant at Whipps Cross Hospital, a busy district general hospital and the regional eye centre.

Her feelings on part-time posts were that they would be helpful to women. She herself worked a virtual full-time eight sessions including on-call commitments but, like many others, felt that part-time training was a step too far. On the existence of prejudice, she said that she lost many jobs initially because women were not wanted, then got one job because she was female!

A general point worth making is that the number of emergency call-outs for eye surgeons to the hospital at night fell dramatically after the clampdown on drinking and driving but, even more so, after the introduction by Barbara Castle on behalf of the government of the compulsory wearing of seat-belts, markedly reducing the injuries to the eye from impaction with the car windscreen.

Eileen Mary Vale, who died in 1977, did her medical training at the Royal Free Hospital and qualified MB BS London 1944. She took the DO in 1962 and the FRCS in 1969.

Seventeen women surgical Fellows became eye surgeons and enjoyed a uniquely successful and fulfilling career as consultants. From the first, the women seem to have been accepted as equal colleagues and the camaraderie and professional development fostered by the Ophthalmological Societies, the Oxford Society, regional societies such as the north-east society, the national and international Societies were well organised and supported.

To conclude the chapter, I quote a few words the Oxford Society uses to describe its aims... 'For the cultivation of the spirit of good fellowship and of unconventionality, the right of our youngest member to rank with his oldest colleague and last, but assuredly not least, the frank, free and tolerant discussion of scientific matters brought before it felt any prejudice in her/his gathering.' And a few words from Dorothy Campbell Adams: 'Medicine is such a rewarding occupation but the choice of part-time work is important. Ophthalmology is one of the best possible for women. In part-time work, medical women would be well advised to choose a speciality rather than general practice – to avoid the mix-up between professional and domestic duties'.

CHAPTER 12

ENT – Ear, Nose and Throat Surgery

THERE are fourteen women Fellows who specialized in Ear, Nose and Throat Surgery. Amongst them are two who made unique contributions in the ENT field, one for the investigation and treatment of the deaf child, one in the field of occupational cancer. First the lives and special contribution of these two unique Fellows, Edith Whetnall and Esme Hadfield, will be recounted and then the lives of the twelve, Mildred Warde (Faulkner), Dorothy Hall, Dorothy Collier, Winifred Wadge, Margaret Mason. Betsy Brown, Peggy Orton, Joselen Ransome, Doreen Birch, Veronica Gammon, Romola Dunsmore, Carol Wengref.

Edith Whetnall wrought a revolution in the investigation and treatment of the deaf child. She knew right away when she qualified at King's College Hospital, MB BS London, in 1938 that it was in ENT that her interests lay. The recital of her career pathway does nothing to describe the transformation that she brought about in the detection and treatment of the hearing impaired baby and child.

Two important precepts guided her work. Firstly that all, or practically all, the children who were clinically deaf, had a useful residuum of hearing which could be exploited by early diagnosis. Second, that *early* correction of a hearing loss, even in the first few months of life, of a deaf infant was necessary if successful rehabilitation and speech was to be achieved.

She was house surgeon in Horton Hospital in the Surrey group then became registrar at King's in ENT. She took the FRCS in 1940 and was clinical assistant in otological research at the National Hospital and took the MS in 1944. She was appointed consultant otologist to the LCC (London County Council) School Medical Service, succeeding Sir Terence Cawthorne. She became assistant surgeon to the Royal National Throat, Nose and Ear. Although she had trained as an otological surgeon, she was not deterred by the apparently bleak prospect of relieving hearing loss. She founded a clinic in Golden Square Hospital in 1947 to detect and treat deafness in young children.

By fitting hearing-aids to babies and small children, she made use of residual hearing by amplification, resulting in the important auditory feed-back loop that allowed the child to hear his own voice and develop speech.

Early detection was of prime importance, suspicion of the possibility of lack of hearing, and then early diagnosis using the Ewing distraction tests were employed but she also pioneered the introduction of electrophysiological tests of hearing. The development of the Medresco hearing-aid by Dr Tom Littler in the MRC Wernher Unit at Kings and its availability at that time was an important factor in the success of her work.

The third arm of Edith Whetnall's drive though, after the importance of recognition of a residuum of hearing, and of early exploitation and correction by amplification, was the recognition of the vital importance of the mother and family- counselling. In her Ealing hostel for mothers and babies, teachers-of-the-deaf, speech therapists, psychologists, nurses and doctors explained the importance of the baby or child wearing his hearing-aid at all times, and the mother and child having face-to-face contact and expression and clear and continuous speaking to the child. Many deaf children treated in her clinics achieved clear and acceptable speech.

A similar hostel was opened for older children. Her contribution and proselytizing zeal attracted the interest of the Nuffield Foundation which donated £100,000 to establish the Nuffield Hearing and Speech Centre.

Her hospital appointments were as Consultant Aural Surgeon to St Giles Hospital Camberwell and the Queen Mary Hospital Carshalton, and she practiced in Wimpole Street.

Her staff in the many clinics that she set up, nurses, speech therapists, and others held her in a respectful terror as she was intolerant of any level of professional activity that did not match up to her high standards.

Her early definitive book *The Deaf Child* was written jointly with D B Fry and she wrote many papers and delivered lectures and took part in conferences.

She married Dr Robert A Niven MD FRCP who completed her writings that she had left unfinished when she died, and he wrote *Learning to Hear with Niven.* Edith Whetnall had suffered injuries in a severe road accident many years earlier and it affected her health. She died early at age 55. Her name is celebrated in the Edith Whetnall Memorial lectures given at the Royal Society of Medicine.

Esme Hadfield is renowned for identifying the link between nasal carcinoma and the sawdust of the woodworkers of High Wycombe. Discovery comes to the prepared mind.

Esme Havelock Hadfield came from an eminent medical family. Both brothers were surgeons, John at Stoke Mandeville, Gordon at Bedford, and their father was Professor of Pathology at Barts, and then at the Institute of Medical Sciences at the Royal College of Surgeons. Esme was educated at Clifton High School and went up to Oxford to St Hilda's College completing her clinical work by staying up at Oxford in the Radcliffe Infirmary and graduating BM BCh in 1945. She was house surgeon and later 1st Assistant at the Radcliffe working for R G Macbeth and G H Livingstone, taking the FRCS in 1951. She travelled to clinics in Zurich, and as a BECC, British Empire Cancer Campaign Fellow, to Vancouver and Toronto.

She was appointed Consultant ENT Surgeon at the High Wycombe and Amersham Hospitals. It was there that she noticed the incidence of nasal sinus carcinomas in the woodworkers of High Wycombe and described the industrial disease. She described the working practices of the woodworkers, the bodgers working in sheds in an atmosphere of sawdust (hence a botched job), and two men working on sawing and bending wood, one in a pit – the under-dog, one above, the top-dog, She described the pre-cancerous changes of squamous metaplasia of the mucosa of the middle turbinate of the ethmoid sinus, showed the effect of sawdust on the cilia with reduction in the clearance of radioactive technesium, described the incubation period of 39 years exposure before the cancer developed,, and the metastatic site of spread to the frontal lobe of the brain through the cribriform plate. She presented her work in a Hunterian lecture as Professor at the Royal College of Surgeons.

She spent all her working life at High Wycombe, retiring at age 65. She was a keen fisherman particularly in Scottish waters and traveller. An inveterate smoker, she was reputed to close her desk drawer on a lighted cigarette during a long clinic, all the while exhorting her patient not to smoke.

Mildred Warde was the eleventh woman to gain the Fellowship. She was a doctor's daughter and started her preclinical studies at Manchester University after school at Hamilton House in Tunbridge Wells. She came down to the London School of Medicine for Women to do her clinical work, graduating MB BS in 1921, working as a surgical registrar at the Royal Free and obtaining the FRCS in 1922. She was the first woman to win a gold medal in the MS, 1929, the higher degree in surgery.

She set up in private ENT practice in Harley Street and worked there for ten years. She then met and married O T Faulkner and gave up her active medical work to mother his two sons, Denis and Alan, having two more of her own, Henry and Tony.

She sat on the Council of the Medical Defence Union and was active in the Samaritans, giving phone advice to depressed, anxious and suicidal people. Like many surgeons, she became a painter, chairman of the Norfolk and Norwich Art Circle.

Dorothy Hall became Consultant ENT surgeon first to the Mildmay Mission Hospital, Shoreditch and the Western Hospital, Fulham and then to the Elizabeth Garrett Anderson Hospital. The Eastern Hospital Homerton, St Ann's Tottenham and Clare Hall Hospital South Mimms.

She was the only daughter of a professor of Music and went to Aigburth Vale High School in Liverpool and on to the University of Liverpool where she graduated MB BCh Liverpool in 1919 and went on to be Holt Fellow in Physiology from 1919 to 1920. She came to London on a postgraduate course at St Mary's and was registrar and 1st assistant at the Central London Nose and Throat Hospital. She took the FRCS in 1928 and became ENT Surgeon at Mildmay Mission and the Western Hospital Fulham, later appointed to the Elizabeth Garrett Anderson, the Eastern Hospital Homerton, St Ann's Tottenham, and covering Clare Hall in South Mimms when she went out to live in Hatfield. She ran a private practice in Queen Anne Street and Harley Street. She was a staunch supporter of the Medical Women Federation. She died before reaching full retirement age, age sixty-one, in the Royal Free Hospital.

Dorothy Collier was Consultant ENT Surgeon at the Royal Free Hospital, the South London Hospital for Women and Children and was Assistant Lecturer in the Institute of Laryngology and Otology.

Dorothy went from the Convent of Notre Dame up to Oxford and did her clinical training in London at University College Hospital, graduating MB BCh Oxon in 1922. She was house surgeon at King Edward VIIth Hospital Windsor and house surgeon, registrar and 1st assistant in ENT at UCH, and registrar at the Central London Throat and Ear Hospital, taking the FRCS in 1932 and becoming Consultant at the Royal Free, the South London Hospital and Assistant lecturer at the Institute of Laryngology and Otology, and ran a private practice at Harley Street and Upper Wimpole Street.

She wrote a text-book *Diseases of the Ear Nose and Throat*, J D McLaggan and Josephine Collier which ran into a 2nd edition.

She was Hunterian professor at the Royal College of Surgeons describing reparative surgery after facial nerve paralysis.

During World War II, she served in North Africa and Italy. Interestingly, before that, in the Spanish Civil War, she was responsible for rescuing Professor Joseph Trueta and his family from the fascists and bringing them from Barcelona to England. With a Spanish woman friend, she went on a hazardous expedition to the Orinoco Delta in Venezuela.

She was an elegant discerning highly educated artistic lady and a skilled and valued surgeon.

Winifred Wadge became Consultant to the ENT Unit at University College Hospital and to the Department of Diseases of Throat, Nose and Ear at the Nelson Hospital, Wimbledon, and ran a private practice from Devonshire Place.

Winifred Wadge was first up at Cambridge studying for an MA and then went to University College and University College Hospital where she graduated MB BS London in 1936. She took the FRCS in 1939.

Margaret Mason went up to Newnham College Cambridge and did her clinical studies at Kings College Hospital graduating MB BChir in 1945. She was house surgeon in ENT at the Institute of Laryngology and Otology and the Princess Beatrice Hospital, and worked in ENT at Sutton General Hospital and King George Hospital Ilford. She was Consultant at St Mary Abbotts Hospital Kensington. She retired in 1984 and died a year later in St Christopher's Hospice Sydenham at age about 65.

Betsy Brown became Consultant ENT Surgeon at Bradford Royal Infirmary.

She trained in Glasgow qualifying MB ChB Glasgow in 1945, considered a career in Public Health and took the DPH in 1948, but then was attracted to ENT and took the DLO in 1950 and the FRCS in 1955. She was Lecturer in Otorhinolaryngology in Manchester before she got her consultant post at Bradford Royal Infirmary. She published on tumours of the larynx and sinuses and their treatment.

Peggy Orton became Consultant in Otolaryngology at Queen Mary Carshalton for Children, the St Helier Hospital and the South London Hospital for Women and Children.

She trained at the London (Royal Free Hospital) School of Medicine and qualified with the Conjoint Diploma in 1943. She did house surgeon posts at the Royal Cancer Hospital (the Marsden) and took the DLO in 1947. She became 1st Assistant at the London Hospital, Senior Registrar at the Royal Free Hospital, and took the FRCS in 1955. She became Consultant to the three hospitals, the South London Hospital, Queen Mary Carshalton and St Helier Hospital, Sidcup.

Joselen Ransome trained at the London (Royal Free Hospital) School of Medicine qualifying MB BS London in 1949. She was house surgeon at the Radcliffe Infirmary and there decided on ENT as a career. She became registrar at the Royal Throat Nose and Ear Hospital and took the FRCS in 1958 and went on to Senior Registrar at the Royal Free Hospital. She became Consultant at the Metropolitan Ear Nose and Throat Hospital and at St Stephen's Hospital Chelsea, and later to the Charing Cross.

She published and edited books on ENT surgery in the Recent Advances series and in the Operative Surgery volumes.

Doreen Birch came from Cape Town South Africa to England to take the FRCS and went to Australia to practise.

She trained initially at the University of Cape Town graduating MB ChB Cape Town. In England she became research assistant to Professor Michael Boyd, the Professor of Surgery at Manchester University. She took the FRCS in 1961. Once in Australia, she went into ENT at the Royal Newcastle Hospital and practised eventually in Mount Gambier in South

Australia. She married Dr J C McCaffery in 1963 at age thirty-seven and they had a son. She died in Australia at the early age of forty-nine.

Veronica Gammon became Consultant ENT surgeon to the mid-Glamorgan Group of Hospitals in mid Wales.

She graduated from the London (Royal Free) School of Medicine MB BS London in 1948 and took the FRCS in 1961 and the DLO in 1970.

Romola Dunsmore became the Consultant ENT surgeon to Doncaster Royal Infirmary. She graduated MB BS from the London (Royal Free) Hospital School of Medicine in 1949 and did house surgeon posts at the Royal Free in surgery, obstetrics and gynaecology and in ENT and was then surgical registrar in ENT, taking the FRCS in 1962. After a lifetime's work in Doncaster, she retired in North Yorkshire in Settle.

Carol Lindsay Wengref was Consultant ENT surgeon at the Greenwich, Lewisham and Woolwich Hospitals in South London.

She trained at Guy's Hospital, graduating MB BS London in 1962 After house surgeon posts, she was SHO in ENT at the Westminster Hospital, taking the FRCS in 1967 and became Senior Registrar in ENT at Guy's, before being appointed Consultant at Greenwich, Lewisham and Woolwich. She published on tinnitus and on pharyngeal cheadronate.

Noelin Catherine Gertrude Fehily (Mrs Cook) qualified in 1963 in the NUI (University College, Dublin) and held surgical posts in Leicester Royal Infirmary, was surgical registrar at Victoria Hospital, Blackpool, and did ENT training in Brighton, UCH and senior registrar in Birmingham. She became FRCS in 1967 and consultant ENT surgeon in Worcester.

CHAPTER 13

Radiotherapy

FIVE of our women fellows found their final career in radiotherapy, Margaret Snelling, Gwen Hilton, Irene Cade (Irene McEwen), Eileen Busby and Ruth Sandland.

It is striking that the Director of the Radiotherapy Departments at the two great adjacent teaching hospitals in London, the Middlesex Hospital and University College Hospital, now amalgamated into one institution, should both have surgeons, and *women surgical Fellows* to boot, as their first pioneering leaders.

Margaret Snelling had two careers, one as a surgeon, then as a distinguished radiotherapist, the first Director of the Myerstein Institute of Radiotherapy and Oncology at the Middlesex Hospital.

Margaret Dorothy Snelling was educated at Wimbledon High School, a GPDST school, and at the London (Royal Free Hospital) School of Medicine for Women, graduating MB BS in 1935. She did house surgeon posts at the Royal Free, Chelmsford, and the Hospital for Sick Children, Great Ormond Street. During World War II she was surgeon to Chase Farm Hospital doing general surgery, neurosurgery and orthopaedics, taking her FRCS in 1944, and was assistant surgeon, again doing neurosurgery, at the South London Hospital for Women and Children.

During the War also, she took the MRCP in 1941, the DMR in 1942, and after the War, specialized in radiotherapy, taking the FFR in 1952, and becoming FRCP in 1968. As Director of the Myerstein Institute of Radiotherapy at the Middlesex Hospital, she did pioneering work on the treatment of cancer of the cervix and uterus, and with her special expertise in this field, visited India, Egypt and the Sudan, lecturing and sharing her knowledge in hospitals and clinics.

She was the first woman to be President of the European Association of Radiology. In her international work she gave generous help and encouragement to emerging radiotherapy units in the developing countries world-wide.

Although she herself had an untreated heart condition, she was an athletic vigorous person, playing a good game of tennis and enjoying fencing. A single lady, she mothered her brother's children when her sister-in-law died.

Gwen Hilton was the first radiotherapist at University College Hospital, appointed in 1938, and became Director of the new Department in 1948.

She was born Elfrida Lilian Gwendolen Hill in 1898, the daughter of a professor of mathematics, the Fellow of the Royal Society Professor Hill. She was educated at Roedean School and went on to University College London and University College Hospital where she took First Class honours in her BSc and a gold medal in Physiology, graduating MB BS London in 1924.

She was the first radiotherapist to be appointed to the staff of University College Hospital, founding the new department, and became Director ten years later. She married Reginald Hilton a year after qualifying in 1925 at age twenty-seven and they had a daughter Clare Terrall who is a radiotherapist. She was elected FRCS as a member of twenty years standing in 1955.

At interview, candidates are sometimes asked to enumerate strengths and weaknesses, and *Irene Cade* must have entered medicine with a feeling both of the advantages of bearing the name of the towering figure in surgical oncology, Sir Stanford Cade, and possibly some drawbacks. He was a forthright commentator on the surgical problems of the day. He was remembered as tackling Dr Robert McWhirter at the Royal Society of Medicine when he had come down from Edinburgh to present the work equating the outcome of simple mastectomy and radiotherapy with Hadfield's radical mastectomy. Cade's aphorisms were remembered and quoted and acted on for decades, *A linear scar is a death sentence in malignant melanoma.* Maybe not considered true today but emphasizing the importance of clear margins. He was a radical and bold surgeon.

Irene Cade was educated at Queens College Harley Street, Aylesbury College and the Malvern Girls' College. She was a prize-winner during her time at the London (Royal Free Hospital) School of Medicine, taking the prize in surgery and graduating MB BS London in 1947. She did house surgeon posts in the Royal Free and at East Ham Memorial

Hospital, the Royal Sussex Hospital and the Hospital for Sick Children, Great Ormond Street and took the FRCS in 1952. She then decided on radiotherapy as a career and took both her MS with a thesis on hypophysectomy and carcinoma of the breast and her DMRT the same year in 1959, and in 1961 took the FFR and became consultant radiotherapist in Portsmouth. She worked on megavoltage therapy and published also on hyperbaric oxygen. She came up to the Westminster Hospital Radiotherapy Clinic and Meeting every Wednesday and took part in the discussions, an important further education opportunity in its day. Her married name was Irene McEwen. She died age seventy-five in the year 2000.

Eileen Rosemary Busby trained at Charing Cross and graduated MB BS London with honours in surgery in 1955. She was surgical registrar at the Royal Marsden Hospital and took her FRCS in 1959. She was 1st Assistant at St George's Hospital and took the DMRT in 1966, the FFR in 1972, the FRCR in 1975. She was Senior Registrar and 1st Assistant at the Royal Marsden Hospital and Associate Specialist there. She was appointed consultant radiotherapist and oncologist to the Kingston Hospital.

Ruth Sandland became consultant radiotherapist at St Bartholomew's Hospital, Barts, and the Hospital for Sick Children, Great Ormond Street working on the radiotherapy of childhood tumours. She trained in Melbourne, Australia graduating MB BS in 1964. She came to England and was registrar at St Thomas', and registrar and senior registrar at the Royal Marsden Hospital, London. She took the FRCS in 1969, the DMRT in 1971, the FFR in 1972, and the FRCR in 1975. She has published extensively on her work on the radiotherapy and treatment of childhood tumours.

CHAPTER 14

Thoracic Surgery

THREE women surgical Fellows specialized in thoracic surgery, Doreen Nightingale, Betty Slessor and Mary Shepherd.

Doreen Nightingale was the first thoracic surgeon to be appointed to University College Hospital. She joined the Professorial Surgical Unit in 1955 as 1st assistant and deputy director. She was a technically excellent and speedy surgeon.

She graduated MB BS London in 1940 and the MS in 1945. She learned her thoracic surgery at the Harvard Medical School and on her return was appointed to UCH at the age of thirty-nine. She operated extensively on the lung but did not extend her practice into the development of open heart surgery. She contracted tuberculosis herself.

She married Hugh Burt, a longstanding friend, toward the end of her life, perhaps feeling that an earlier marriage would not be acceptable in the hospital to her work.

Betty Slessor was a confident and experienced thoracic surgeon who was Consultant at the Groby Road Hospital, Leicester. Many male thoracic surgeons trained in her unit as registrar.

Betty Vivian Slessor was educated at Edinburgh graduating MB ChB in 1941. She was surgical registrar at Plymouth and 1st assistant on the Professorial Surgical Unit at Sheffield before being appointed to the Groby Road Hospital in Leicester where she pioneered the development of open heart surgery.

After closing a hole-in-the-heart of a small patient, ably assisted by Philip Slade her registrar, she sat up all night with the little girl on the Intensive Care Unit, as related by the patient when seen thirty years later and questioned on the provenance of her sternal scar. The patient treasures the photograph of herself, aged eight, and Miss Slessor on the ward at Christmas. She married J A Chatterton and retired to Thurcaston, Leicester.

Mary Shepherd was one of the thoracic surgeons at Harefield Hospital, the hospital renowned because of the pioneering work of the heart surgeon Magdi Yacoub, but where the full panoply of thoracic surgery nevertheless was also carried out.

Mary Patricia Shepherd trained at the Royal Free Hospital graduating MB BS London in 1957. She was surgical registrar at the Royal Free, taking her FRCS in 1964. She did her cardiovascular training at the Hospital for Sick Children in Toronto and came back to be Senior Registrar at first, then Consultant, at Harefield Hospital. She provided specialist thoracic cover to the Central Middlesex Hospital, the Queen Elizabeth Hospital Welwyn Garden City, St Albans City, and Barnet General Hospitals.

She was a Hunterian Professor at the Royal College of Surgeons in 1969 and wrote her MS thesis on the diaphragm muscle and cardiac surgery. She operated extensively at Harefield Hospital, particularly on the lung and oesophagus and diaphragm. In spite of operating on so many lungs with carcinoma, she was an inveterate cigarette smoker.

CHAPTER 15

Plastic Surgery – 'Force of Circumstance'

ONLY one of our Women Fellows with the FRCS went into Plastic and Reconstructive Surgery. Pamela Ball worked in the Regional Plastic Centre at Wordsley, Stourbridge, in the Midlands. When I asked her why she thought she had not become a consultant in spite of holding a locum senior registrar post, she replied 'Force of circumstance'. When I asked a young plastic surgery consultant the same question, he said thoughtfully, that it was a reflection of the time. Probably today, things would be different.

Pamela Ball FRCS 1954 was born Pamela Margaret Moody. She trained in Birmingham qualifying with the MB ChB in 1950 and took the FRCS in 1954, the first woman from Jamaica to be a Fellow of the Royal College of Surgeons of England. She was Clinical Assistant, then Associate Specialist, to the Regional Plastic Unit at the Wordsley Hospital, Stourbridge.

Her father, Dr Ludlow Moody, was a remarkable man, a well-loved and highly respected Jamaican GP, an MRCP, never stinting on the demands of his work. His daughter remembers him being carried in on a stretcher from the boat when he had conscientiously been visiting a patient on one of the islands; he had always been a poor sailor.

Her father had gone to London for his medical training, as had his brother, and at King's College London medical school he carried off a cluster of prizes, the Warneford scholarship, the Huxley prize in physiology, and the Todd prize in clinical medicine. He was the first Jamaican to obtain the MRCP. He worked in the departments of physiology and bacteriology at KCH.

On his return to Jamaica, he worked as government bacteriologist, and continued his specialist interest in laboratory medicine alongside his clinical practice, carrying out his own pathology services, diagnosing malaria, doing other blood tests, doing his own microbiology. He was a man given to philanthropy. At his old school where he was a Trustee, he developed a preparatory school. He was an excellent shot and captained the successful

Jamaican team at Bisley in 1938. He was a man of many parts. He developed an interest in breeding pedigree dairy cattle. He held many public offices with distinction. He was a Justice of the Peace, a member of the Jamaica Public Services Commission, and served as Custos of Kingston from 1961 to 1963. An honorary doctorate of Laws was bestowed on him by the University of the West Indies. He was appointed CBE.

Pamela's mother was a professional musician, a pianist who was studying in St Petersburg during the Russian Revolution. She came from the Manley family of Jamaican, Yorkshire and Irish heritage; her brother Norman Manley was the first Prime Minister of Jamaica. A brilliant scholar and athlete, he studied law at Jesus College Oxford as a Rhodes scholar, fought in World War II in the Royal Field Artillery, strove for universal suffrage in the colony of Jamaica and served as Chief Minister and as Premier.

Music and mathematics and medicine ran through her family.

Pamela Moody, as she was then, was a highly intelligent girl at school where she was at first at Hamptons, where she was a contemporary of Monica Lewin, FRCS 1962, and then went on to Woolmer's, elite secondary schools. She came to England on a scholarship from Jamaica to study medicine at Birmingham. She would like to have read mathematics but she felt that the only avenue that would then have been open to her in Jamaica with a mathematics degree would have been teaching and that she didn't want to do, so she studied medicine like her father. During her early posts she did both surgery and anaesthetics at a time when juniors were given much more responsibility and allowed to do a wide variety of clinical tasks. She recalls giving a series of rapid anaesthetics at Birmingham General Hospital for the theatre lists of Beatrice Willmott Dobbie, FRCS 1931 who was carrying out her radium list and had to achieve one after the other, a safely anaesthetized patient, for the quick procedure and then, recovering the patient, and on to the next. She recalls also doing a hysterectomy toward the end of a theatre list when she was RSO at Kidderminster by the light of a held torch, the lights having been necessarily turned off. On occasion she had to give the anaesthetic herself, then go round and do the operation. She did the full gamut of general surgery and was a speedy and competent general surgeon. She was a contemporary at Birmingham General Hospital of Peter Bevan who nearly killed her once when she went to him for a tetanus injection when she had impaled her foot and went into a full blown anaphylactic reaction having been previously exposed to horse antitoxin serum. To prepare herself for the taking of the Final examination of the FRCS, she took an excellent correspondence course run by Dr Oates of Red Lion Square. She remembers that on the day that she completed the Final clinical exam, she was one of five who passed and went forward to shake hands with the examiners.

She entered plastic surgery almost by chance. The senior registrar in the Plastics Unit was time-expired and had his contract renewed haphazardly so that when he got his consultant post elsewhere, he was free to take himself off at once leaving the post unfilled and Pamela, who had recently been off work having a baby, went to work for Oliver Munsfield to fill the gap which she did admirably. Later while she was working in Accident and Emergency, incredibly busy, never getting home to see her family, the post was again available as Clinical Assistant and Pamela sought the job feeling that it would be more compatible with her time with children and family. She had married Dr John Ball, a 6 foot 6 inch GP who was also much involved with BMA and GMC business, being in London two or three days mid-week and covering his general practice during the rest of the week sharing the work with his partners and being on-call over the week-end.

Pamela became a highly competent plastic surgeon, known and well respected by her colleagues. She tackled enormous lists, doing clinics and operating not only at Wordsley, the regional plastics unit, but also at Sutton Coldfield and at Sandwell. The work at Wordsley covered the full range of plastic work, though not burns which went to the unit at the Birmingham Accident Hospital. She wasted no time on niceties. In her long lists of cases to be done under local anaesthetic, her patients were all seen and examined and Pamela went down the line with Sister, Pamela holding one enormous syringe of local anaesthetic, Sister changing the needle for each patient. In those days it was a heavy glass syringe, washed and sterilized, the plunger greased, the metal needles also re-usable, a thin metal wire threaded down the lumen during sterilisation and housed in individual tins. Each patient in turn then walked into the operating theatre and had the procedure beautifully and speedily operated on.

She took part in the West Midlands UK Mole Study with a paper in the Archives of Dermatology on benign pigmented naevi in children.

Her senior consultant, Henry Goldin, would write his findings and opinion in painstaking long-hand in a patient's notes, outlining his instructions, *this is a probable basal cell carcinoma but maybe with some squamous activity and needs wide excision with clear margins and full depth excision*; Pamela's clinical notes would read, *Needs to be done.* Then the operation note, *Done.*

Pamela Ball did not become a consultant. She was probably born in the wrong age, a colleague said. Force of circumstances, Pamela said. The route to consultant then was necessarily through a training senior registrar post and Pamela did hold a locum senior registrar position but she says she was content to hold the clinical assistant post where, because of her competence and energetic capacity for work, she had a great degree of autonomy and it fitted in with her family life, the household, husband and children. She worked for all her working life and for a further seven years in retirement as Clinical Assistant to the Regional Plastic Surgery Unit in Wordsley Hospital, Stourbridge, in the A and E Department and in her husband's general practice.

Alongside her surgical work she pursued her study of mathematics. She taught and coached in maths. She was in the first cohort of students of the Open University when it was newly formed by Harold Wilson, when he was Prime Minister, and Jennie Lee. When she enrolled, at first the class had to take part in a Foundation year, a course run by the National Extension College, before going on to the mathematics degree. In her group of fellow students, a maths teacher from the local grammar school who had not yet got a University degree and a whiz kid from IBM, were studying together. Later, she went on to take the Open University MSc in Mathematics.

Mathematics, medicine, music and mother. In spite of both parents being doctors, none of her three children embarked on a career in medicine. Musical ability came down through the generations. Pamela's instrument is the viola and she plays in the Stourbridge orchestra. Two of her children have degrees in music. Her daughter plays violin and flute, her son is a cellist and the son's children, her grandchildren, play piano and cello. Her daughter is a lay-canon of the Anglican Church and a member of the Synod and works in Bristol in the hospital. One son became an engineer, the other an accountant, one works in the music business in London.

On her medical career, Pamela Ball revelled in her work, enjoyed the patients, still hears from former patients, remembers particularly the melanoma patients, relishes the people of the Black Country as salt of the earth, and clearly achieved mountains of work in her time as Specialist Plastic Surgeon. Mathematician and musician as well as surgeon, her family life as mother has also been a joy to her.

CHAPTER 16

Neurosurgery

THREE women neurosurgeons, Diana Beck, Carys Bannister and Jennifer Haley Ahluwalia have their lives recounted.

Diana Jean Kinloch Beck (1902-1956) FRCS 1931 is the first neurosurgeon amongst our women Fellows.

She was educated at the Queen's School, Chester and went on to the London School of Medicine and the Royal Free Hospital where she was a prize-winner and qualified MB BS in 1925. She worked for a few years as a general surgeon taking the FRCS in 1931. Then in 1939 she went to work with Sir Hugh Cairns in Oxford on the William Gibson research fellowship from the Royal Free and thus started her career as a neurosurgeon. During World War II, she worked at first in Oxford, in Enfield and in Bristol and in 1943 was appointed Consultant Neurosurgeon at the Royal Free Hospital. In 1947 she was appointed to the Middlesex Hospital, the first woman to hold a post on the teaching staff of a major London teaching hospital. She published papers in *Brain*, in the *British Journal of Surgery*, the *Journal of Neurosurgery*, in the *Archives of the Middlesex Hospital* and in *Transactions of the Association of Industrial Medicine*. She died prematurely at age fifty-four after surgery in the Royal Free Hospital.

Carys Margaret Bannister qualified at Charing Cross Hospital two years after Diana Beck died and after early training posts took the Edinburgh Fellowship and then went to Oxford to study neurophysiology. Her research subject was the blood supply to the brain and spina bifida and hydrocephalus and at the neurosurgical unit at Leeds Infirmary subsequently she developed the extracranial-intracranial bypass technique. She was appointed consultant neurosurgeon to the North Manchester Hospital Group and Booth Hall Children's Hospital. She set up a tertiary referral centre at St Mary's, the Manchester Children's Hospital, for neurodevelopmental defects. She helped to elucidate the importance of brain folate in hydrocephalus.

She was a successful surgeon and, remaining single and free of family commitments, she was able to indulge the sort of hobbies that some of her men colleagues took part in. She was an enthusiastic car rally driver, and her dogs won best of breed at Crufts. She was a tall woman with a rosy complexion and gave little credence to appearance: her notes and equipment accompanied her in carrier bags. Every Christmas she toured her wards, pushing a trolley decorated with a present for each patient and with the pair of corgi dogs like small reindeer trotting in front. Her hands and forearms bore the evidence of handling and dipping her sheep. But her neurosurgical technique was precision tuned. She owed her break-through to become a consultant surgeon to the original research contribution that she achieved in Oxford and to her development of the shunts to relieve hydrocephalus in babies and children in Leeds. Her clinical care on the children's wards and her communication with the parents was exemplary. She died age seventy-eight.

Jennifer Jane Haley (Jennifer Ahluwalia) FRCS 1964 trained at the Middlesex Hospital and graduated MB BS London in 1955. She had a distinguished career as a neurosurgeon, training at the Whittington and Central Middlesex Hospitals, the Liverpool neurosurgical unit at the Walton Hospital, and co-founded neurosurgery with her husband in New Delhi in the Safdarjung Hospital, associated with the Lady Hardinge Medical College and the medical faculty at Delhi University. Her married name was Ahluwalia.

Jennifer Haley was one of the four children of William Haley. When her father started his career on the Manchester Evening News, he was judged to be too shy to be a newspaper reporter and they made him a sub-editor; he went on to be Director General of the BBC from 1944 to 1952 and Editor of The Times from 1952 to 1956. Jennifer went to seven different schools during war-time England, including a few weeks at St Paul's during the flying bombs and then on to Cheltenham Ladies' College. She was a keen medical student at the Middlesex Hospital and it was largely the surgical side which captured her interest: she recalls watching Diana Beck, the neurosurgeon doing an operation, harbinger of her surgical future, and assisting David Patey doing a painstakingly slow meticulous dissection of a parotid tumour and, after what seemed like hours, he asking the sister for some additional instrument not on her trolley and when she unwisely said she knew where it was, told her that he would sit down and wait while she fetched it and sterilised it and produced it for him – those were the days! She got wonderful surgical and medical experience in house posts at the Central Middlesex Hospital, learning from the outstanding diagnostic and holistic skills of Richard Asher and others. The medical mess sent a deputation to Dr Joules to formally protest about the medical residence conditions there and he told them that they could all leave if they had any complaints, there were plenty of others who wanted their jobs.

When she took the Primary FRCS, she had the misfortune to meet Sir Gordon Gordon-Taylor whom she knew from her Middlesex student days was dead against women: he greeted her with "If you can put down your bag, you silly woman, and be prepared to soil your fingers, tell me what this is" pointing to the optic nerve in the dissection. "That's the optic nerve, Sir." However he did not agree and they went around naming the cavernous sinus and optic chiasma and various other structures before returning to the optic nerve which he triumphantly identified to her. "That's what she said in the beginning," said the other examiner mildly before taking himself off for a cup of coffee. Primary fellowships were interchangeable and Glasgow was said to be the place to go and she and another student drove all the way up in his Jaguar XK120 convertible which he let her drive and she returned triumphantly having passed the Primary and driven a wonderful car. She had begun in Glasgow by making a mess of the first question of the day and the Examiner had said sympathetically , "It *is* rather early in the morning. Tell me what you are *really* interested in" and they spent a happy viva discussing extradural haematomas.

She had done a Casualty job at the Whittington and during her surgical post at the Central Middlesex working for Mr Roberts she was offered neurosurgical training by Mr MrCall at the Whittington, who then almost got cold feet after offering her, a woman, the job at the interview and had to be encouraged by a phone call from Mr Roberts, that she would be alright. She took the FRCS in 1964. At both hospitals there was excellent training. She was on call continuously for neurosurgery at the Whittington always within reach of the hospital during her two years there apart from one night when she attended the Middlesex Hospital Ball.

She went on to become Senior Registrar in Neurosurgery at the Walton Hospital Liverpool where she did four further years in training. During her time there, she contracted viral encephalitis from a patient whose cerebral abscess she had drained. Her work was well trusted at Liverpool; she called Mr Kerr, the chief, on one occasion to say that the tumour she was operating to remove did not look like the metastasis that they had judged it to be but an astrocytoma, a tumour, and wondered whether he wanted to come and give his opinion or take over and do the operation, and the reply from Kerr came back to theatre, Tell her to carry on.

At the Walton Hospital, Liverpool, she met and worked with fellow neurosurgeon Har Paul Singh Ahluwalia and they agreed to marry, an arrangement that both sides of the family initially minded. They were both well qualified and ready to become consultants and Cardiff, Preston, or even Liverpool itself, were all possibilities for their consultant appointments. Har Paul had trained in Calcutta, as had his sister, a gynaecologist, and done his initial surgical training in the UK at the Hammersmith Hospital. Three weeks before the wedding, the future in-laws arrived, the father, who was an ophthalmic surgeon and had worked for the Army and the Railways in India, persuaded his son to consider a neurosurgical future in New Delhi which was how the pair came to go and set up the neurosurgical unit in the University Hospital, the Safdarjung Hospital there and where they stayed for six years. They worked well together in Liverpool and in New Delhi: they both graciously said about the other that their partner was the better neurosurgeon, but inside, they each knew that they were the better! There were at that time about eight neurosurgeons in the whole of India and they left the unit well looked after and set up. Their range of surgery was comprehensive. One patient stuck in her mind, an Afghan with a prolapsed disc who paid them with a sack of almonds. Financially they were not well off but they might have stayed working in India if they had gone to Chandigarh but mother-in-law was not in favour and they had two small children. Her son who was four and a half spoke English to his parents, Hindi with his friends and Punjabi locally. Her daughter Susan was three. She returned to the UK to Jersey where her father Sir William Haley had been born and where he had retired.

They lived in St Helier, Jersey, in the Channel Islands and the children grew up and went to school there. There was no scope for a neurosurgical practice in the Channel Islands, but remembering the teaching and example of Richard Asher at the Central Middlesex she took on a hospital psychiatry post for some months and then worked in the Morning Medical Clinic for ten years and worked with her husband in a general practice that he had there. He had a heart attack and then a subarachnoid haemorrhage and died early, age sixty-one. When the children were small she had a local live-in help to look after them when she was not there.

In response to the 1981 questionnaire, she felt that part-time posts and part-time training would be helpful to keeping women working in medicine. Her own mother had worked. She continued working in St Helier, half in the hospital and half in general practice, though not in the speciality for which she had been trained. She certainly felt that there was prejudice expressed against a woman in medicine.

CHAPTER 17

Gynaecology

ABOUT one sixth of the whole number of women surgical Fellows, 37 of the 200, became gynaecologists. Even in this 'women's field', all was not always plain sailing for them. Training appointments outside the women's hospitals, in the general hospitals of the land, were not always accessible to women. During World War I, with the exodus of men to the Forces, women were able to obtain resident posts in Queen Charlotte's Hospital in London, sought-after elite obstetric training posts, and they continued to be appointed for a few years post-war; similarly in Liverpool and Manchester. Then in the late twenties and thirties it proved difficult for women to get posts at Queen Charlotte's and the men took the jobs, only to find that during World War II women were being appointed again.

Not quite all the women surgical Fellows who practised in obstetrics and gynaecology chose to became members or fellows of the new College of Obstetricians and Gynaecologists when it was formed in 1929; there was a feeling at first that it was going to be a men's club. It was certainly true that amongst the group of men who formed the nucleus of the foundation of the College, there was a degree of bonding in shooting parties on country estates and meetings in gentlemen's clubs, and indeed the thirty members of the Gynaecological Visiting Society founded by Blair Bell, and which was the starting blocks of the new College, were all male. However at the formation of the College in 1929 the Council made a welcome decision to include a woman consultant as a co-opted member and this sensible early decision was repeated every three years until Professor Hilda Lloyd was elected President – the first woman to be President of any Royal College – in 1939. Most of the women surgical Fellows who were gynaecologists (37) did join the College, all but three or four in fact, and many were amongst the first Founder members and fellows.

In the *Lives* book of the Fellows of the Royal College of Obstetricians and Gynaecologists that records those Fellows who had died between 1929 and 1970, twenty-one only were women, forming about 5% of the whole, and of these only three were surgical Fellows with the FRCS, Edith Hall, Katharine Liebert and Gladys Marchant. Of these twenty-one, five went to India to work, one – Margaret Fairlie – became the first woman Professor of Obstetrics and Gynaecology in Scotland, in Dundee, in 1940, four had been surgeons in the battlefield hospitals during World War I – Frances Huxley, Frances Ivens (Knowles), Ruth Nicholson and Dame Louise McIlroy, one specialised in radiotherapy as well as surgery for cervical and breast cancer – Louisa Martindale. Their consultant appointments were impressive in being to the general hospitals of the land, Nottingham, the Whittington, two to Liverpool, Withington, Orsett, St Andrews Billericay, Plaistow, as well as the women's hospitals, Marie Curie, the South London, Elizabeth Garrett Anderson and the New Sussex in Brighton. One went home to South Africa and one to Sydney, Australia.

In 1936 the Women's Gynaecological Visiting Club was formed for the Royal College of Obstetricians and Gynaecologists and early members included Frances Huxley, Louisa Martindale, Hilda Lloyd, and Alice Bloomfield, of whom the latter two were surgical Fellows. There were in fact more than one such club and they were variously named: the Gynaecological Travellers Club and the Gynaecological Visiting Society of Great Britain and Ireland. Their function was to hold meetings, present work and papers, and visit each other's departments. As well as sharing new ideas and practices, their establishment did much to promote collegiate relationships between their members. There were also regional obstetric societies: the Obstetrical Society of London and the North of England Obstetrical and Gynaecological Society.

The first such society was the Gynaecological Visiting Society, founded in 1911 by Blair Bell of Liverpool. There were thirty members, mostly young when it was formed, all men, and mostly from the medical schools. They met twice a year at home or abroad.

The founding of the College, later Royal College, of Obstetricians and Gynaecologists in 1929 provoked fierce opposition from the Royal College of Surgeons and some antagonism also from the Royal College of Physicians who had some Physician Accoucheurs amongst their members. The Royal College of Surgeons, having treated the speciality with something approaching disdain for so long, was now faced with the exodus of a body of abdominal surgeons that they felt belonged in the surgical college. Victor Bonney was the only gynaecological surgeon who had reached the Council of the Royal College of Surgeons and he was not in favour of a separate college. But William Fletcher Shaw (Manchester), Blair Bell (Liverpool),

George Comyns Berkeley (the Middlesex Hospital, London) and Ewen Maclean (Cardiff), set about the formation of their new college.

They marshalled the support of the members of the Gynaecological Visiting Society who fortunately were representative of the specialised hospitals, medical schools, and Professorial units throughout the country. They soon discovered that a Royal Charter was never granted where there was opposition. Their way around that was to form a College like a company attached to the Board of Trade, ask permission to drop the word Limited from the end and bide their time before becoming a Royal College. Their aim in forming the College was fourfold: to form a portal that all who wished to become consultants in their branch of medicine must pass; to prevent the separation of obstetrics from gynaecology; to bind together the teachers of their speciality for teaching and examining; and to be a spokesmen for the body of obstetricians and gynaecologists. They laid their plans for an excellent College, well thought out, with the rank of members for those who were more junior and Fellows who were senior, but both groups represented on the Council – which kept the interest of the younger members- , and they made sure that the Provinces and Scotland and Ireland could not be dominated by London. They published a notification of their planned formation in *The Times*, objections to be lodged before 11th July 1929. Both Royal Colleges, the Physicians and the Surgeons at the eleventh hour lodged objections and an Enquiry had to be held under the Chairmanship of the Parliamentary Secretary of the Board of Trade. The Royal Colleges both briefed the best of King's Counsels, money being no object for them, and the lawyers for the gynaecologists advised that they must do likewise though they could ill afford it – but found it money well spent as they had an excellent barrister and moreover were helped by the topicality of the problem of maternal mortality. Final agreement seemed to need resolution of the arrangements for holding present or future examinations – and the fees thereof – in obstetrics and gynaecology. Some ground was given by the gynaecologists, acceptable to the physicians, but still not enough for the surgeons. Blair Bell was urged to meet with the Presidents of the Royal Colleges and they convened in Moynihan's flat and negotiated for hours without the surgeons giving any sign of movement toward an agreement. After sufficient time was deemed to have elapsed, Blair Bell got to his feet to leave. This was enough to stimulate Moynihan who after further discussion agreed to the proposed wording of the compromise. Even then the Royal College of Surgeons delayed and did not communicate their agreement and made a further later attempt to negotiate a change of the wording. Eventually the solicitor of the Board of Trade simply communicated to the solicitor of the new College to go ahead.

They were a new College with nine male signatories, September 1929. It had taken three years only. Lord Riddell, newspaper proprietor, came to the rescue with funding. Elections were held. Amongst the Foundation Fellows, careful to represent all the University centres, the provinces, Scotland and Ireland, they proposed one woman, Dame Louise McIlroy, the first Professor of Obstetrics and Gynaecology at the London (Royal Free Hospital) School of Medicine for Women who had worked as a general surgeon during World War I operating on the wounded. Like all those who were surgeons on the foreign field during the Great War, she was not an FRCS.

The officials stepped down every three years. Subsequently, every three years, a woman gynaecologist was appointed to the Council. Following Dame Professor Louise McIlroy was Miss Louisa Martindale, three years later Miss Frances Huxley, and then Miss Alice Bloomfield, who was an FRCS, then in 1939 Professor Hilda Lloyd FRCS. In 1939, Professor Hilda Lloyd, FRCS and FRCOG, who held the Chair in Birmingham, was elected President of the Royal College of Obstetricians and Gynaecologists, the first woman to be the President of any Royal College. Fletcher Shaw comments that she commanded great respect in the city of Birmingham as a leader and in the Council of the Royal College. There were some who originally voiced doubts as to whether she would hold her own outside the College but the fears were groundless and her Presidency a great success.

With the foundation of their own Royal College, in the fullness of time, those who planned a career in obstetrics and gynaecology would mostly no longer need to seek to be Fellows of the Royal College of Surgeons.

Muriel Elsie Landau 1895-1972 FRCS 1920 MD 1921

Gladys Maud Sandes 1897-1968 FRCS 1930

Dame Hilda Lloyd (Dame Hilda Rose, Hilda Nora Shufflebotham) 1891-1982 FRCS 1920 FRCOG 1936 PRCOG 1949 DBE 1951

Margaret Mary Basden 1886-1974 FRCS 1919 MD 1924 FRCOG 1931

Alice Bloomfield 1895-1977 FRCS 1922 MB ChB 1919 ChM 1925 FRCOG 1935

Sybil Grace Mocatta 1898-1988 FRCS 1923 MD 1923 with medal MRCOG 1945
Gladys Marchant 1894-1969 MB BS Calcutta 1916 MRCS & DOMS 1922 FRCS 1928 MD Lausanne 1927 MRCOG 1937 FRCOG 1943
Dame Josephine Barnes (Alice Josephine Mary Taylor Barnes) 1912-1999 FRCS 1939 Honorary Fellow 1994
Elaine Margaret Katharine Salmond 1897-1982 FRCS 1936 FRCOG 1939
Edith Mary Hall 1896-1957 FRCS 1931 FRCOG 1940
Flora Bridges née Hargreaves 1906-1997 FRCS 1931
Margaret Moore White 1902-1983 FRCS 1931 FRCOG 1950
Jocelyn Adelaide Medway Moore 1904-1979 FRCS 1933 FRCOG 1948
Ruby Grace Sharp 1906-1989 FRCS 1935 FRCOG 1954
Gladys Hill 1894-1998 FRCS 1936 FRCOG 1943
Gladys Helen Dodds 1898-1982 FRCS 1937 FRCOG 1940
Mary Helen Mayeur 1910-1988 FRCS 1938 FRCOG 1953
Dorothy Anderton Sharpe 1903-1978 FRCS 1939 MRCOG 1938
Eleanor Mary Mills FRCS 1940 FRCOG 1958
Katharine Marian Robinson 1911-1998 FRCS 1940 FRCOG 1953
Janet Elizabeth Bottomley (Mrs Ritchie) 1915-1995 FRCS 1940 MD 1943 FRCOG 1958
Katharine Isabel Liebert 1912-1965 FRCS 1941 MB ChB Manchester FRCOG 1943
Eileen Mary Whapham 1907-2002 FRCS 1941 FRCOG 1954
Wendy Ellen Lewington FRCS 1950
Marjorie Olive Dunster 1915-2000 FRCS 1947 DMRT MD FRCOG
Jean Burton Brown FRCS 1948 FRCOG
Daphne Mary Scott FRCS 1953
Dorothy Mary Ridout FRCS 1952
Elaine Rankin née Joan Francis Elaine Lister 1920-2000 FRCS 1953
Pamela Mary Bacon (Pamela Spencer) died 2011 FRCS 1957 FRCOG 1973
Valerie Mary Thompson (Mrs S C B Yorke) FRCS 1958 FRCOG 1969
Margaret Witt FRCS 1961 MRCOG 1966 FRCOG 1979
Jill Margaret Evans (1929-1995) FRCS 1961 MRCOG 1959
Constance Ethel Fozzard FRCS 1967 FRCOG 1979
Dorothy June Whitney (Mrs Raeburn) FRCS 1962 FRCOG 1974
Eunice Ruth Burton FRCS 1964 FRCOG 1977
Anne Mary Jequier FRCS 1967 FRCOG 1982

CHAPTER 18

The Women's Hospitals

IT is not the purpose of this book to give a detailed account of all the many and varied dispensaries and hospitals formed and run by women doctors for women and children. However, the vision statement, to use a modern term, of many of them sheds light on the purpose that underlay their foundation and the benefit they provided to women doctors for their own advancement in the profession.

They all stated first the needs of the patient, often with a commitment to treating the poorest among the community. Then they affirm the desirability that women patients should be able to be treated by members of their own sex. Finally they do acknowledge the importance to women doctors that they have access to the full spectrum of clinical work only obtainable in the hospital setting. Because women doctors were seldom able to obtain training posts in the general hospitals of the land, they established their own hospitals. Occasionally a recognition of the need for gentlewomen of small means to have access to medical care suitable to their social class, but not otherwise affordable, was tacked on to the statement.

Of course poverty was a great barrier in itself against accessing medical care. One did not lightly call the doctor when ill. Not that the women doctors charged less than the men; from Elizabeth Garrett Anderson onwards, they were at great pains to maintain parity with their male colleagues in the fees that they charged and the salaries they were paid in public appointments. Nor were the men, however indisposed they might be to welcome women doctors as colleagues, keen to have the women undercut their level of fees or salary. The dispensaries and hospitals that the women founded nevertheless often expressed firm social and charitable aims and maintained a special commitment to treating the poor and disadvantaged. The institutions were usually, though not always, exclusive to women and children as patients, children under age seven. Like women in purdah in Victorian India, there were, undoubtedly, women in Britain who preferred to die of their disease or in childbirth rather than be subjected to examination by a male doctor, nor did some of the husbands agree to let their wives be examined by men.

Having put first their proper professional commitment to their patients, the mission statement of the women's hospitals then went on to acknowledge the importance of providing access for women doctors to clinical work in a hospital setting and to provide for the newly qualified women doctors the experience of the camaraderie and training within junior posts as house doctors, residents, registrars and assistants in these institutions, headed by women doctors of experience and special skills, and also of course provided staff appointments as specialists and consultants for some, positions that were not generally available for women in other hospitals in the land.

If they were not to be let in to work in the other hospitals in the country, then they would found their own. One unforeseen result in the formation of women-for-women's hospitals was the isolation of women in a parallel hospital world. They have now all closed and the inclusion of women doctors as colleagues to men in all general hospitals can only be salutary. In the field of surgery, the climate of work has changed, in part due to the presence of women colleagues, and both the Royal College of Surgeons and the GMC, the General Medical Council, are constantly exhorting what they call good behaviour toward patients and colleagues. Sometimes similar advice is given by surgical colleagues themselves, advice that can only be received with a wry smile when one recalls the former antics of those now setting themselves up as arbiters of good practice. The emphasis on teamwork, the more equal recognition of nurses as colleagues, and patient pressure have all served to further a more collegiate working environment. Nevertheless, in their time, the women's hospitals fulfilled an important function.

The New Hospital for Women, 144 Euston Road, was opened in 1890. It grew out of two previous institutions, first of all the Crawford Street Dispensary formed in 1866 when Elizabeth Garrett had first qualified LSA and which after some time opened ten beds over the Clinic and then moved on to become the first New Hospital in the Marylebone Road which opened in 1874 with Dr Elizabeth Garrett Anderson and Dr Frances Hoggan looking after the patients and having twenty-six beds. The New Hospital in the Euston Road when it opened in 1890 was a proper little hospital and had two circular wards, operating theatres, pathology and X-ray departments, outpatient clinics, a nurses' home, chapel, garden, and, over the years, specialists in many departments. The listed building still stands on the north side of the Euston Road, almost adjacent to the station, on the corner of Churchway. Unison have built their grand offices next door on the site of the nurses' home and have made a charming small museum in the entrance hall of the old hospital.

There was an outpost small hospital in Barnet, the Rosa Morrison House, a cottage home for convalescents at Aldebury, and a maternity nursing home in Belsize Park, Hampstead. Nevertheless the number of beds was insufficient to provide adequate clinical instruction for all the women medical students of the London School of Medicine for Women. The much larger number of beds of the Royal Free Hospital was essential to their training. Even so, house appointments and staff appointments at the Royal Free were slow at coming to the women, the men consultants at the Free displaying a characteristic reluctance to appoint their former women students to their junior training posts.

The Women's Hospital for Children was opened at 688 Harrow Road in 1912. It met two great needs: first to treat the poor of North Kensington and the surrounding districts and second to fill the need of women doctors to have the opportunity to study children's diseases. There was no other children's hospital in London that habitually welcomed women into their staff appointments or gave them full facilities. The hospital committee of the Harrow Road Hospital entered into agreements with the LCC to treat schoolchildren particularly with eye and ear, nose and throat problems and there was rich clinical experience and training. Louisa Garrett Anderson was associated with the hospital.

The building was rented from the Artisans, Labourers and General Dwelling Company. The nurses were said to have particularly good conditions of service in having each their own bedroom and only working for nine hours in each twenty-four hour day, and with one whole day free of work once every three weeks! A maid-of-all-work in a household that was only able to afford one servant, probably had similar hours of work.

Patients who could afford a fee paid sixpence for a weekly hospital letter but the purpose was to provide treatment for the children of the extremely poor. The hospital eventually closed in 1921 from lack of funds.

The South London Hospital for Women and Children in Clapham was established by Maud Mary Chadburn to replicate south of the Thames a women's hospital where women could be treated by women, to mirror that of Elizabeth Garrett Anderson's New Hospital north of the river. A suitable site was found on the south side of Clapham Common, two large houses one occupied by Bishop Hook and which could be bought for the £5000 that had been raised. A public appeal for funds in a letter to *The Times* provoked a scathing reply in a letter from a medical man stating that there was no need for a women's hospital and accusing the women doctors of forcing their way into the medical profession and creating an artificial demand. The flurry of exchange of letters had an astonishing response and an anonymous donor came forward with substantial sums, £53,000 for building and a further £40,000 endowment. The building was completed by 1913 and two surgeons, Miss Chadburn and Eleanor Davies-Colley, and two physicians and a pathologist set to work. Queen Mary opened the 80-bedded hospital in 1916. Frances Huxley, the gynaecological surgeon who had trained in Manchester and had worked at the Samaritan and Queen Charlotte's, joined the staff in 1916 and served on the staff for 21 years; she was married to Lieutenant-Commander Harold de Carteret Falle and they had two daughters. She served on the Council of the Royal College of Obstetricians and Gynaecologists, as one of three women who were co-opted to serve in turn for three years service, to provide a woman's representative. She was also in 1928 President of the Medical Women's Federation and gave a learned address on hospitals past and present.

The architect Sir Edwin Cooper designed extensions in 1922, 1926, a new x-ray department in 1932 and new theatres in 1936, in all 263 beds eventually. During the Second World War the hospital was designated part of the EMS, the Emergency Medical Service treating all casualties, men as well as women, and a team of boy scouts and rover scouts acted as volunteer porters and stretcher bearers. The hospital had its own coat-of-arms in 1947, featuring the cross of Chad, a seventh century merciful saint, the sun, and the motto *et dato gaudetis*, and in giving you rejoice.

Back in 1911 there was a separate Outpatient Department in Newington Causeway, numbers 88 and 90, near the Elephant and Castle, a short omnibus ride from Victoria. The clinics were extremely busy; thronged with women patients who for a penny could get a large cup of tea and biscuits. Nearby was an invalid kitchen where a penny dinner could be obtained. A twopenny tram-fare connected with the main hospital in Clapham. Later a new Outpatients was built at Clapham, and a nurses' home.

The South London Hospital for Women and Children in Clapham had three stated aims: first to meet the growing demands for women to be treated medically by members of their own sex; secondly to provide in addition to the general wards, private wards at very moderate fees for gentlewomen of small means; and thirdly to afford further scope for postgraduate training for medical women. This last was as important as the first, there being nothing to equal hospital training.

The management of change is fraught with problems and in the nature of things, the women for women's hospitals were not destined to have a future once women were allowed into the other hospitals of the land. And the advent of the National Health Service taking all hospitals under its umbrella predicated rationalisation. The existence of the women's hospitals owed as much to the needs of women surgeons to have a hospital base to practice in, as to the desires of women patients to be treated by women. Nevertheless there should have been no need for 'dirty tricks' to help closure of any of the women's hospitals and the spectacle of forty women police officers deployed to evacuate a sit-in is a sad reflection on the negotiating skills of management. For fifty years the South London, the Elizabeth Garrett Anderson and the New Sussex were beacons of considerate and compassionate practice.

There was in fact another older establishment in Clapham run by and for women. In 1866 the Dispensary for the General Diseases of Women and Children was established under the management of the Medical Mission. Being a dispensary, for years it was an outpatient clinic only, but two women doctors attended to the patients there. In 1899 the Maternity Hospital was opened on the site with twelve beds with Dr Annie McCall as resident physician. Its stated purpose was twofold: first to afford means by which poor women could be carefully attended in their homes in their confinements by gentlewomen, medical students, and trained nurses, under the supervision of fully-qualified medical women. Second, to give opportunity for a training in midwifery, taught by doctors of their own sex, to nurses, to gentlewomen who were aspiring to be midwives, to students from the London School of Medicine for Women, and to lay-missionaries. The Dispensary clearly did not share Elizabeth Garrett Anderson's objection to sponsoring half-trained women to go out to work on the mission field.

The admission policy for patients reflected the attitudes of the times: married women were admitted, and the unmarried for their first birth, a nodding acknowledgement that one could remain relatively respectable after falling from grace once, but multiple offenders had to resort to the Workhouse Infirmary.

The Hospital, although it was housed in converted houses in Jeffrey's Road, was run on strictly aseptic lines to avoid the puerperal sepsis of the larger Lying-In Hospitals. The Institution was recognised for medical students for a certificate qualifying them for the examination in midwifery by all the medical licensing bodies that admitted women to their examinations. When the Midwives Act came in 1902, Dr Annie McCall was appointed an Examiner on the Central Midwives Board and was Vice-Chairman of the LCC Board that supervised the training locally, a tribute to her and the work of her hospital.

The New Sussex Hospital for Women and Children in Brighton grew out of the Dispensary and a small number of hospital beds in the Ditchling Road branch of the Lady Chichester Hospital. Two of our early women surgical Fellows were appointed and worked there, Constance Ottley and Enid Rockstro. The New Sussex Hospital, the inspiration of Dr Louisa Martindale, had powerful sponsors: among them Mrs Yates Thompson, daughter of George Smith, the publisher of the Brontes and Thackeray, and Elizabeth Robins, American actress and author who made her home in England. Mrs Yates Thompson and Elizabeth Robins moved in literary circles with George Bernard Shaw, Oscar Wilde, Henry James, Leonard and Virginia Woolf, Margaret Haig, Viscountess Rhondda, editor of the radical journal *Time and Tide* that campaigned vigorously for women's suffrage and who fought for the right to take her late father's seat in the House of Lords, Lady Florence Bell, wife of Sir Hugh Bell a wealthy Yorkshire Ironmaster, Lady Astor, the first women to take her seat in Parliament, Dr Octavia Wilberforce who was the great-granddaughter of William Wilberforce, powerful in the abolition of slavery, and granddaughter of the Bishop of Winchester Samuel Wilberforce (Soapy Sam), and she became Physician to the Hospital. An early surgeon there was Elsie Maud Visick, a member of the Visick family studded with medical men and women, elder sister of Visick from York who classified duodenal ulcer; she was born in 1894, was educated at the North London Collegiate School and was a student during the World War I years at the London (Royal Free Hospital) School of Medicine, qualifying with the Conjoint Diploma LRCP MRCS in 1918. She married John Richard

Griffith FRCS and while he was a surgeon at Hove Hospital and the Royal Alexandra Children's Hospital, she was at the New Hospital. They had two sons, both doctors, one a very brilliant ENT surgeon who died young age thirty-three, and a daughter. Known as Mrs Griffith, she was renowned as a fine surgeon. She died age seventy-three in 1987.

Constance Ottley was an Oxford graduate and went on a scholarship to do her clinical training at The London Hospital in Whitechapel. She qualified in 1922 and was appointed to a house surgeon post in the receiving room at the London and honed her surgical skills there under Sherren and A J Watson. She had also worked in York and at the South London Hospital for Women. She remained single. She was a cellist. She took the FRCS in 1928. With only four years between them in age and in the year in which they passed the FRCS, Constance Ottley and Enid Rockstro formed a formidable team in the Women's Hospital in Brighton.

Enid Rockstro qualified in 1927 and attained the FRCS in 1932; after further training and posts, she was appointed consultant to the New Sussex Hospital for Women in 1937 and also at the Cuckfield Hospital at the age of thirty-five. She made an enormous success of her life and work there, settling down and adopting two baby boys, one during the first year and another two years later. She had a resident nanny for them and sent them to preparatory school and public school and one later became a doctor like his adopted mother.

Again in Edinburgh, when Dr Elsie Inglis focussed on the need for women doctors to have access to good experience in midwifery and appreciating that resident appointments in the Royal Infirmary and the chief maternity hospital were unlikely to be open to them, she responded at once by founding a small maternity hospital for women run by women. If women doctors were not welcomed to work in the main hospitals, the solution was obvious to her. Women doctors must found a maternity hospital of their own. Eschewing the offer of a house in George Square as too elitist, she chose instead a tenement in the High Street closer to where those women lived who would be likely to have need of the service offered and opened The Hospice with Dispensary and Outpatients on the ground floors and maternity beds above. She was recognised as a lecturer for the Central Midwifery Board and as an extra-mural lecturer in gynaecology in the University of Edinburgh and in this way the instruction for resident students, medical and nursing, were approved, for maternity at The Hospice, and for the care of children in the Bruntsfield Street Hospital which Dr Inglis had taken over when Dr Sophia Jex-Blake had departed.

There were more than twenty-five hospitals and dispensaries founded by women for women and children between 1866 and 1921, listed as follows:

The Dispensary and New Hospital for Women and Children, Crawford Street
The New Hospital for Women and Children, Marylebone Road
The New Hospital for Women and Children, Euston Road – later the Elizabeth Garrett Anderson Hospital after she died in 1917
The Rosa Morrison House of Recovery, Barnet
The Cottage Home for Convalescents, Aldebury
The Maternity Hospital, Elizabeth Garrett Anderson Hospital, Belsize Park
The Women's Hospital for Children, 688 Harrow Road, the Roll of Honour Hospital
The Dispensary for General Diseases of Women & Children 1866 Medical Mission
Clapham Maternity Hospital Dr Annie McCall 1899
The South London Hospital for Women & Children, Clapham
The Newington Causeway Dispensary at Elephant & Castle
Battersea District Maternity Hospital and Dispensary
The Marie Curie Hospital 1928
Canning Town Women's Settlement for Women and Children
Lady Chichester Hospital for Nervous Diseases, Brunswick Place, Hove
The Lewes Road Dispensary & Hospital for Women & Children (nervous diseases) Brighton
Lady Chichester Hospital, Ditchling Road, Brighton
The New Sussex Hospital for Women and Children, Windlesham Road, Brighton
Bristol Hospital for Women and Children
Edinburgh Hospital for Women and Children – Bruntsfield Hospital
Children's Hospital at Hull – convalescent home in Hornsea
The Manchester Babies' Hospital
The Duchess of York's Hospital for Children at Manchester
Redlands Hospital in Glasgow

The Tuberculosis Sanatorium in Rudgewick, nr Horsham
The Nayland Sanatorium (for tuberculosis) run by Dr Jane Walker in Norfolk and which accepted men and women.

Interestingly, the same development took place in Australia over the same time-frame. In 1893 Dr Constance Stone opened a small hospital in the hall behind the Welsh St David's Church in Melbourne which became by public subscription of the Shilling Fund, first the Victoria – named after the State, then the Queen Victoria Hospital for Women and Children giving a service by women for women with the motto, *Pro Feminis A Feminis*. Over the years, it expanded and changed with for example the Rachel Forster Wing, a midwifery wing, named after the wife of the Governor General, and many subsequent developments until today it is over 1000 beds and part of the Monash University campus. In 1950, Dr Janet Greig, one of the first women who graduated in the 1890s, wrote:

> One of the great benefits the QVH has been to medical women in Melbourne is that each woman who qualified, quite apart from the Honours Lists, was able to get a position as a Clinical Assistant to one of the Honoraries; even those who married could hold such positions and so carry on and gain practical experience. This has made the Hospital a vast training ground for all young graduates. If any showed any special capacity for Surgery, Obstetrics, Gynaecology or Paediatrics, they were given this opportunity. Through all the years the QVH has been a happy and congenial body of women working together with the same object and the same fervour – a high standard of medical work has always been the aim, and the high ideals of the Pioneer Medical women have been maintained.

In Sydney, which had its own appalling record from 1885 to 1905 on the treatment of the early women medical students and of the inequitable appointment to resident posts in the main hospitals, there was a small Medical Mission which started in 1900 and petered out toward the end of World War I. It was largely run by women and charitable in its aim.

In 1922, after attending the 25th anniversary of the Melbourne QVH, a group of Sydney women doctors started up the Rachel Forster as a women-for-women's service. It had two stated functions: first a hospital where women and children could be treated by women, and second a hospital where women graduates could put into practice what they had learned through their arduous medical course. Innovative services were added during the early years, a unit for the treatment of venereal disease in women and children, social services (Almoners), and child psychiatry clinics, as well as the more usual midwifery and general surgery and medicine and outpatient dispensary clinics.

CHAPTER 19

The Final Chapter

THE gathering together in this narrative of the lives of the first two hundred women surgeons who achieved the Fellowship of the Royal College of Surgeons of England as a historical record is as far as possible comprehensive and inclusive. The story is also told of the struggle of women to be admitted to medical education and practice as a whole.

We see how the Royal College of Surgeons resisted the inclusion of women doctors for fifty years. After the pioneer women had first sought to join the College in 1861 it was not until 1911 that the first woman doctor became an FRCS. Looking backwards over those fifty years from 1911 to the 1860s, the dogged faith of those early women doctors in pursuing the right of entry to a medical career at all against formidable obstacles showed their capacity for endurance.

We have seen how amongst these pioneers there were those whose medical bent and special talents of hand and temperament directed their ambition toward a surgical career and led them to press to be accepted as Fellows of the Royal College of Surgeons.

What are the landmarks in the history and achievements of the pioneers?

Women were denied entry to any or all of the medical schools in the land. So they founded their own medical school, The London School of Medicine for Women. This was an act of faith by Sophia Jex-Blake. There was then an inadequate number of hospital beds for their student clinical training. So they formed a liaison with the academically unattached Royal Free Hospital, a hospital that had no medical school partner. No college or university would allow them to sit for their qualifying examinations. The King and Queen's College of Physicians in Dublin and the University of Ireland were importuned and opened their doors to the women – and then others followed. Once qualified, the women were not being appointed to clinical posts in the general hospitals of the land. So they founded their own hospitals, a myriad of women-for-women's hospitals all over the country and passed the jobs round amongst themselves. It proved difficult to make headway as consultants in mainstream general surgery. So they diversified and opted to specialise in parallel surgical fields as described in earlier chapters, many choosing eyes, ENT, orthopaedics and particularly gynaecology. A huge debt is owed to these early pioneer women doctors, the trail-blazers, by those who came after.

It is fitting that the earliest of these landmarks for women was made in the New World, America being relatively free from the oppression of women that prevailed in Victorian England. Elizabeth Blackwell, English-born, was able to travel independently, determinedly seeking out practical experience and finding the rural medical school in upstate New York that would enable her to qualify MD in 1849.

As has been told, now as Dr Elizabeth Blackwell, she travelled to the home country, back to England, and gathered together a small committee to encourage English women to enter the profession of medicine. At one such meeting, Elizabeth Garrett heard her speak and was fired with the desire to become a doctor.

Elizabeth Garrett sought her medical training with stamina and determination, moving on to different venues to obtain the experience she needed and once qualified, 1865, applying again in vain to the Royal College of Surgeons with the moving words: 'I ask whether a Licentiate of the Society of the Apothecaries, being a lady, could apply to be a member of the Royal College of Surgeons.'

While the stance of the Royal College of Surgeons of England in taking fifty years, from 1861 to 1911, to resist the admission of women to the College has to be understood in the context of the time, there was already a ground-swell of movement amongst women from well-to-do families seeking freedom from the stifling oppression of the Victorian era. The frustration of Florence Nightingale for example in being confined to a meaningless social whirligig well illustrates the lack of choice for any educated young women with an active brain. Elizabeth Garrett in the 1860s and 1870s did have a concern that she should behave within the limits of propriety when taking tutorials with the Apothecary in the hospital. However, she then travelled alone and unaccompanied to St

Andrews and to Edinburgh and lived there in lodgings. When Karl Marx's daughter, Eleanor, went to meet Elizabeth Garrett Anderson, she was astonished to see her walking down the street toward her, striding along, unaccompanied. Until World War I, girls and women from middle-class homes were habitually escorted when going outside the house.

The first application by a woman for access to the diplomas of the College was made by Elizabeth Garrett in 1861 and again in 1865 after she had qualified with the LSA, the Apothecaries Diploma. We have seen how on receiving her letter the Council's lawyer admitted that there was nothing in their charter that stated that the examinations would be open only to men. His argument rested on that of precedence – candidates up to now had always been men – so let it continue so.

Ten years later, society was becoming accustomed to the idea of the possibilities of women in medicine, softened by cartoons and articles lampooning the lady doctoresses, the handful of women who had studied for the MD in Europe, and who were practising unregistered in England, and when three of the Edinburgh Seven who had been studying as extramural students in Scotland without being allowed to graduate and qualify, applied to take the College's diploma in midwifery, the Council declared themselves in favour but backed down at once when the examiners refused to conduct the test for any women.

The following year, when the 1876 Russell Gurney Act went through Parliament enabling universities and colleges to grant degrees to women, the Royal College of Surgeons again announced themselves to be in favour of admitting women in principle, but were against compulsion.

In 1895 at the first of two memorials to the Council Elizabeth Garrett Anderson as dean of her medical school, asked for admission to the Royal College pointing out that two hundred women doctors had now qualified and were practising.

Once again the Council expressed themselves in favour but, citing a vote against the admission of women in a meeting of the members and Fellows of the College, and in view of the hostile position taken by the Royal College of Physicians, they again resisted.

Seven years later, in 1902, mustering the names of all the great and good to support her plea, Elizabeth Garrett Anderson as dean tried again. Jenner of the Royal College of Physicians had died and with his death some of the hostility had gone. There were now over seven hundred women doctors qualified, four hundred of whom had trained at the London School of Medicine for Woman, and practising with competence and distinction. Still the Council hesitated.

The College then employed the delaying tactic of conducting the poll. There had to be a wait for the postcards to be returned from all corners of the Empire. Mail by boat from the Empire took months to be sent out, received and returned. And in fact the vote from the rank and file predictably enough was not in favour of the women. But the Council had had enough. Public opinion would probably be against them if they delayed further. They wrote to the London (Royal Free Hospital) School of Medicine stating that they were admitting women to their examinations.

And so Eleanor Davies-Colley calmly took the Final Fellowship examination in 1911 and became FRCS: a quiet enigma, silently supported by her antecedents, father, grandfather, two younger brother surgeons, taking her success in joining them without undue jubilation. And then there were no more women taking the Fellowship for eight years from Eleanor Davies-Colley in 1911 until the next in 1919. It is a mystery why it was 1919 before others came to join her.

Of the women who manned the hospitals for the wounded so splendidly in France and Belgium and Serbia in the Great War, wearing the practical khaki uniform they had designed themselves, with jackets with plenty of pockets, none on return took the FRCS though their surgical experience was as testing and demanding as the men's. It was instead to be a new generation of young women doctors coming fresh out of medical school who seized the opportunity to be surgical Fellows.

The organisation of a middle-class household in 1910 involved domestic arrangements that included support by servants. Eleanor Davies-Colley and Miss Chadburn had, in addition to their housekeeper, Miss Merrylees, five female servants, cook and scullery-maid, housemaid, parlour-maid, nursemaid, probably also a charlady to come in to scrub and do the household wash and a chauffeuse. Florence Nightingale, said to be a recluse in later years 'living alone' and sometimes entertaining formally from the couch that was her bed, was in fact supported by a cook and three maids. Dr Christine Murrell and Dr Honor Bone who set up in general practice together in Porchester Terrace, Bayswater in 1905 had a friendship that lasted over thirty years cemented by their professional partnership as doctors. It was practical and made good sense to share the organisation of a household. Dame Louisa Aldrich-Blake, the surgeon who became dean of the London (Royal Free Hospital) School of Medicine, lived at 17 Nottingham Place, W1 at first alone with cook, devoted maid Florence Small, with her for twenty-five years, and devoted chauffeur Everett – though she loved to drive her car herself and was an accomplished mechanic, but later congenially a friend Miss Rosamund Wigram, a Colonel's daughter, joined her. She never wished to be troubled by housekeeping. Work was her greatest pleasure. It was surgery that she regarded as her main work. As dean, she doubled the size of the medical school, greatly increased the number of beds at the Royal Free Hospital, founded the midwifery unit and put the finances of the medical school on a sound basis. And there are countless examples of women joining forces in a practical way to manage and share their households. The necessity of the support that servants gave persisted until World War II by which time there were more attractive options for employment than domestic work and the technology of home refrigerators, vacuum cleaners, washing machines, the electric iron, even to breakfast cereals and the dishwasher, had taken the place of servants. Even then, numbers of women surgeons found it congenial and practical to form a household with other women. The surgeon Muriel Crouch, her sister, and two retired nursing colleagues lived and later retired together. The Royal Free surgeon Geraldine Barry and her GP sister Dr Frances Barry shared their retirement home and garden.

The adoption of the children is an added aspect of the Davies-Colley/Chadburn household. The desire to include children to complete the family circle was not unique. The first woman doctor, Elizabeth Blackwell, MD 1849, did the same, visiting the pauper nursery on Randall's Island in 1854 where unwanted immigrant orphaned children were housed and picked out a little red-headed Irish girl, Kitty, to be her daughter, companion, secretary, housekeeper, and carer. Eileen Whapham, the renowned gynaecologist in the Southend-on-Sea unit with Flora Bridge (herself a mother), adopted a daughter when the little girl was twelve years old, and Doreen later became a midwife herself. Enid Rockstro, the surgeon at the New Sussex Hospital, Brighton adopted first one, then a second baby boy, bringing them up conventionally with a nanny, and one later following in her footsteps and becoming a doctor. Anne Bayley in her first foray to Africa took an interest in the education of a small girl in Ghana and later brought her to school in England. Her 'unadopted daughter' as she calls her is now married and settled here with children, her 'unadopted grandchildren'. Kate Fussell, the surgeon at Wigan and one of the exceptional few who made it to become a consultant general surgeon in England offered to sponsor a child, expecting a small girl from Africa; instead has supported a boy, now a young man, a graduate, from the Tibet/Nepal/Bhutan region. The parallels with others are apt.

Marriage and children did not need to be a barrier to their life's work as surgeons. Elizabeth Garrett Anderson herself, married with three children; employed a wet-nurse in addition to the usual nursemaids. Her colleague, the surgeon Dame Mary Scharlieb, had an ayah in India for her two little boys when she studying medicine in Madras. Married with two sons and a daughter, she wrote in her Reminiscences 'I also wished to supply an answer to those who ask whether professional life is compatible with wifely and motherly duties. I know that it is.' The acceptance in the early half of the twentieth century that children would be brought up by nannies and nursemaids in middle-class and professional households eased the responsibilities on working women surgeons. The pressure on mothers later by Dr Benjamin Spock with his book *Baby and Child Care*, 1946 and by J Bowlby (*Childcare and the Growth of Love* 1951), made life difficult for later women surgeons. Dorothy Adams Campbell, the eye surgeon, had a woman friend, Froebel-trained, who provided the care to her children when they were young, to her satisfaction. Edith Whapham, the Southend gynaecologist, is frank in her conviction: 'It is not possible to be an effective consultant without being totally free from domestic duties', she says. The concept of servants sat uneasily in some middle-class homes after World War II with the suggestion that the freedom of the emancipated privileged woman to work might have been bought by the unfreedom of the working-class women who supported her. Domestic work was increasingly done by daily women and home-helps. For the care of small babies and childcare though, nannies in England were still generally necessary. England has never (or not yet) developed the crèche and childcare that is universally available in France. Dame Josephine

Barnes has urged the necessity of spending the salary earned by the woman on generous comprehensive child-care.

The women were active in the clubs and societies of their specialties that gave opportunity for further education and fostered a collegiate spirit. In the Royal Society of Medicine the women doctors presented their cases and were made welcome and took part in discussion. The Women's Gynaecology Travelling Club, the very active regional ophthalmic societies, the British Association of Orthopaedics, were all inclusive of women and at least three joined the Soroptomists. Of course male bastions remained. Clubs for their male colleagues included a Freemasons' Lodge in all of the Greater London teaching hospitals, even including the Royal Free, associations that of course excluded women by the very nature of Freemasonry. The Rahere at Barts, 2546, the Sancta Maria at St Mary's, 63, the Chere Reine at Charing Cross, the London Hospital Whitechapel, 2845, Moorfields Eye Hospital, 4949, St Thomas' 142, indeed all had a Lodge. It might be thought extraordinary that the Royal Free would have a lodge as it was associated so strongly in the mind of the public as part of the original women's medical school, but of course the Royal Free existed as a hospital before its association with the women's medical school and the consultant staff continued to be predominantly male.

While the exodus of men in the war gave to the male doctors the camaraderie of Forces' life, and a rich experience of trauma surgery, it provided the women with an opportunity to fill the emptied hospital posts and gather clinical experience and it was noted that the resident jobs in Queen Charlotte's Hospital, elite obstetric training posts, were occupied for the first time by women during World War I and for a few years after, and then were not readily available to women again until the 1940s.

It is said that behind the successful married woman surgeon there is a supportive husband. Be that as it may, there does need to be an implacable woman with a steely determination to pursue her surgical career that brooks no impedance. It may be more true that lurking behind many a married woman surgeon who gives up surgery is a husband who has not given the necessary support to a working wife as he pursues his own career.

The women who followed Eleanor Davies-Colley were an entirely different generation – they had been medical students during World War I and so entered as young doctors into a society totally changed. The Great War changed everything. Liberated from Victorian oppression, from parental pressure, even in the clothes they wore, the layers of long heavy clothing down to the ground and petticoats and restricting corsets had given way to the garb that was practical for striding out as working women. Ida Mann going for her interview to the London School of Medicine for Women wore what she considered suitable – a brown gabardine suit with plenty of pockets – the hat enlivened by a small spray of pheasant's feathers – she loved colour. They travelled unaccompanied. And journeyed abroad.

An analysis of the difficulties encountered by a few amongst some of the later women surgeons, post World War II, in the second half of the twentieth century, in combining the surgical life with home life, is a discourse of seminal importance. Social class, the support of family money, the disappearance of domestic help, attitudes of society, disapproval from colleagues, feminism, the husband as a new man, these are subjects that should be able to be confronted and discussed. At a Women-in-Surgery, WinS, Conference at the College in 2008 attended by many young women medical students as well as trainee junior doctors, a set of over-sized photographic portraits taken by Jane Brettle had been commissioned of the six women who had achieved a seat on the College Council and were displayed, hung in the corridor outside the lecture theatre; none had children. It was not an encouraging stimulus to choose surgery as a career to the young women of today, who expect to be able to work and have a family life, to be confronted with the portrayal of six childless women. In the 1981 questionnaire that was sent out to the two hundred women surgeons on the college lists, opinion was particularly sought on whether the provision of part-time posts would be helpful to allow women more easily to combine work and family life. While the consensus was perhaps in favour, most at that time disapproved of the idea of part-time work during the training years. Twenty years later, however, it gradually has come about.

However, Margaret Louden's words (in response to the 1981 questionnaire) strike an important chord: 'Experience is everything in medicine and every reduction of working hours reduces the chances of gaining it.'

These women were born into a time when women could achieve greater economic and social independence. Into a time when there had been an explosive expansion of higher education for girls. The dilemma of being born female into a man's world was met by the opening up of opportunities for work and for service. The work they did no longer had to be purely philanthropic but could be remunerated. Women were allowed to retain their earnings, to earn to support themselves – whether married or single – which empowered them. They did not need to make one man the centre of their life. They did not need to make marriage and its progeny life's absolute and only aim. They were liberated from the assumption of repeated motherhood. In their 'time of hope', C P Snow's descriptive phase of young manhood that could equally apply to young womanhood, they were free to study and to work. There was not the need for envy of the male gender; what they sought were the privileges that men had. They looked at the ease of male lives and desired to emulate it. To have their existence supported by gainful employ. Some who were single enjoyed the activities and pastimes of their male colleagues: golf and dogs and cars and travel are mentioned. Some who were single adopted children creating a family life. And some who were single joined forces with other women in a household, enjoying the practical benefits of a shared life, love and companionship and friendship, reducing the expenses of servants and daily life, some of these adopting children and some not. And some had husband and children as well as a surgical life and vocation, and – as in the rest of life – not all the marriages survived – and some made compromises in their ambitions, and yet others felt in the end that they had managed to have it all.

'Women of the Fellowship', fellow-achievers, fellow-fighters, two hundred women who became Fellows of the Royal College of Surgeons of England. I hope that I have represented them as they are – successful professional women rejoicing in a life-time of the practice of their surgical skills... keenly aware what a privilege it is to be in a position to provide medical and surgical help to patients... and in no way as fellow-sufferers. I have tried to give a true idea of their lives, achievements, hopes and thwarted ambitions; adaptation and adjustments made, reconciliations, and the work they were able to do.

The support that women draw from each other is of vital importance to the advance of the women's cause. There need to be other women – they need the presence of other women – otherwise they stand alone as one exceptional person, and when that meteor has streaked across the sky it is gone, it has left no pathway for others to follow. Nor is the solitary woman achiever always supportive of other women – Eleanor Roosevelt said that there was a special place in hell for women who do not support other women. There is a saving grace in women's friendship. The love and friendship springs from a sense of identification with other women – not experienced as fellow-sufferers, but as fellow fighters, fellow-achievers in the public domain. On this the feminist movement depends, that women regard other women as 'we'.

Bibliography – The Fellowship of Women

Allen, Isobel. *Any Room at the Top – A study of doctors and their careers.* London: Policy Studies Institute, 1988

Allen, Maggie & Elder, Michael. *The Walls of Jericho.* London: BBC Books, 1981.

Beddoe, Deidre. *Discovering Women's History: A practical guide to researching the lives of women since 1800.* London: Longman, 1998.

Blandy, John & Ross, Sir Keith Bt. *The History of the College Council Club. 1869-2000.* London, 2001.

Blackwell, Elizabeth. *Opening the Medical Profession to Women – Autobiographical Sketches.* New York: Schocken Books, 1977

Bonner, Thomas Neville. *To The Ends of the Earth: Women's Search for Education in Medicine.* Harvard University Press, 1995.

Booth, Charles. *Charles Booth's London; a Portrait of the Poor at the Turn of the Century, Drawn From His Life and Labour of the People in London.* London, 1884-1889.

Bostock, Hugh. *Bostock's Memoirs.*

Bostock, Hugh. *Pack Horse Tracks.*

Brittain, Vera. *Testament of Experience – An Autobiographical Story of the Years 1925-1950.* London: Virago Press, 1984.

Brittain, Vera. *Testament of Friendship – Vera Brittain's Diary of the Thirties, 1932-1939.* London: Victor Gollancz Ltd., 1986.

Brittain, Vera. *Testament of Youth – An Autobiographical Study of the Years 1900-1925.* London: Virago, 2001.

Brittain, Vera & Holtby, Winifred. *Testament of a Generation – The Journalism of Vera Brittain and Winifred Holtby.* London: Virago, 1985.

Brooks, Ron. *King Alfred School and the Progressive Movement, 1898-1998.* Cardiff University Press, 1998.

Brown, Val. *Women's Hospitals in Brighton and Hove.* Hastings: Hastings Press, 2006.

Cassell, Joan. *The Woman in a Surgeon's Body.* Harvard University Press, 1998.

Cassell, Joan. *A Group Called Women: Sisterhood and Symbolism in the Feminist Movement.* New York. Waveland Press. 1977.

Clarke Wilson, Dorothy. *Lone Woman – The Story of Elizabeth Blackwell, The First Woman Doctor.* London: Hodder and Stoughton, 1970.

Cohen, Lysbeth. *Rachel Forster Hospital – The First Fifty Years.* New South Wales: Rachel Forster Hospital, 1972.

Cope, Zachary. *The History of the Royal College of Surgeons of England.* London: Anthony Blond, 1959.

Crawford, Elizabeth. *Enterprising Women – The Garretts and their Circle.* London: Francis Boutle Publishers, 2002.

Crofton. Eileen. *The Women of Royaumont: A Scottish Women's Hospital on the Western Front.* Tuckwell Press. 1997.

Dodds, Gladys. *Gynaecology: A Handbook for Nurses.* London: Faber and Faber Ltd, 1949.

Duncker, Patricia. *James Miranda Barry.* London: Picador, 2000.

Fawcett, Millicent Garrett. *Women's Suffrage: A Short History of a Great Movement.* Cheshire: Portrayer Publishers, 2002. First published in 1912.

Forster, Margaret. *Significant Sisters: The Grassroots of Active Feminism 1839-1939.* London: Secker & Warburg, 1984

Garrett Anderson, Louisa. *Elizabeth Garrett Anderson, 1836-1917.* London: Faber and Faber Ltd, 1939.

Gye, Caroline. *China 13.* London: Faber and Faber Ltd, 1964.

Gye, Caroline. *The Cockney and the Crocodile.* London: Faber and Faber Ltd, 1962.

Hallam, Andrew & Nicola, eds. *Lady Under Fire on the Western Front – The Great War Letters of Lady Dorothie Fielding MM, 1914-1917.* Barnsley: Pen & Sword Military, 2010.

Holmes, Rachel. *Scanty Particulars – The Life of Dr James Barry.* London: Viking, 2002.

Horlock Bennett, Alice. *English Medical Women.* Danvers, MA: General Books LCC, 2009.

Hutton Neve, M. *This Mad Folly! – The History of Australia's Pioneer Women Doctors.* Sydney: Library of Australian History, 1980

Hume, Ruth Fox. *Great Women of Medicine.* New York: Random House, 1964.

Jalland, Pat, ed. *Octavia Wilberforce – The Autobiography of a Pioneer Woman Doctor.* London: Cassell, 1989.

Jefferson Smith, Peter & Wilson, Alyson, eds. *Clapham in the Twentieth Century.* London: The Clapham Society, 2002.

Lady Hardinge Medical School, The. *The Golden Jubilee of the Lady Hardinge Medical School.* Delhi, India: 1961.

Landau, Muriel Elsie. *Women of Forty: The menopausal syndrome.* London: Faber and Faber, 1956.

Leneman, Leah. *Elsie Inglis – Scot's Lives.* Edinburgh: NMS Publishing, 1998.

Lewis, E Catherine. *Urology in Women, A textbook of Urinary Diseases in the Female.* London: Baillière Tindall/Cassell, 1932.

Lives of the Fellows of the Royal College of Surgeons of England, Volumes I & II. Plarr, Victor Gustave & Power, Sir Darcy. London: Royal College of Surgeons, 1930.

Lives of the Fellows of the Royal College of Surgeons of England, 1930-1951. Power, Sir Darcy & Le Fanu, W.R. London: Royal College of Surgeons, 1953.

Lives of the Fellows of the Royal College of Surgeons of England, 1952-1964. Robinson, R.H.O.B. & Le Fanu, W.R. London: E. & S. Livingstone, 1970.

Lives of the Fellows of the Royal College of Surgeons of England, 1965-1973. Paterson, Sir James & Le Fanu, W.R. London: Pitman Medical, 1981.

Lives of the Fellows of the Royal College of Surgeons of England, 1974-1982. Cornelius, E.H. & Taylor, Selwyn F. London: Royal College of Surgeons, 1988.

Lives of the Fellows of the Royal College of Surgeons of England, 1983-1990. Lyle, Ian & Taylor, Selwyn. London: Royal College of Surgeons, 1995.

Lives of the Fellows of the Royal College of Surgeons of England, 1991-1996. Blandy, John & Craig, Christina. London: Royal College of Surgeons, 2000.

Lives of the Fellows of the Royal College of Surgeons of England, 1997-2002. Blandy, John & Craig, Christina. London: Royal College of Surgeons, 2005.

Lopate, Carol. *Women in Medicine.* Baltimore, Maryland: The Johns Hopkins Press, 1968.

Louden, Margaret. *The South London Hospital for Women and Children.* London: The South London Hospital, 1958.

Mann, Ida. *The Chase.* Freemantle, Western Australia: Freemantle Arts Centre Press, 1986.

Mann, Ida. *Ida and The Eye.* Tunbridge Wells: Parapress Ltd, 1996.

Mann, Ida and Pirie, Antoinette. *The Science of Seeing*. London: Penguin Books, 1946.

Manton, Jo. *Elizabeth Garrett Anderson*. London, Methuen & Co Ltd, 1966.

Maxwell, Margaret D. *Women Doctors in New Zealand – A Historical Perspective, 1921-1986*. Auckland: IMS (N.Z.) Ltd, 1990.

Mayhew, Henry. *London Labour and the London Poor. 1861-1862*. Oxford University Press.

Moberly Bell, E. *The Storming of the Citadel – The Rise of the Woman Doctor*. London: Constable & Co. Ltd, 1953.

Murray, Flora. *Women as Army Surgeons – Being the History of the Women's Hospital Corps in Paris, Wimereux and Endell Street*. London: Hodder and Stoughton, 1920.

Partridge, Eleanor. *Baby's Point of View, the psychology of early babyhood.*

Peel, Sir John. *The Lives of the Fellows of the Royal College of Obstetricians and Gynaecologists 1929-1969*. London: William Heinemann Medical Books, 1976.

Phillips, Melanie. *The Ascent of Women – A History of the Suffragette Movement and the Ideas Behind It*. London: Little, Brown, 2003.

Price, Len. Hill, Bridget and Ghilchik, Margaret. *Safer Cancer Chemotherapy*. London: Baillière Tindall/Cassell, 1981.

Raikes, Elizabeth. *Dorothea Beale of Cheltenham*. London: Archibald Constable & Co. Ltd, 1908.

Riddell, Lord. *Dame Louisa Aldrich-Blake*. London: Hodder and Stoughton, 1928.

Robinson, Jane. *Bluestockings – The Remarkable Story of the First Women to Fight for an Education*. London: Viking Press, 2009.

Rowbotham, Sheila. *Dreamers of a New Day: Women Who Invented the Twentieth Century*. London: Verso, 2010.

Rowbotham, Sheila. *Hidden from History – 300 years of Women's Oppression and the Fight Against It*. London: Pluto Press, 1973.

Rowbotham, Sheila. *Promise of a Dream – Remembering the Sixties*. London: Penguin Books, 2001.

St. J. Fancourt, Mary. *They Dared to be Doctors*. London: Longmans, 1965.

St. John, Christopher. *Dr Christine Murrell M.D.: Her Life and Work*. London: Williams & Norgate Ltd, 1935.

Scharlieb, Mary. *Reminiscences.* London: Williams and Northgate, 1924.

Shaw, Sir William Fletcher. *Twenty-five years. The story of the Royal College of Obstetricians and Gynaecologists 1929-1954.* London: J & A Churchill, 1954

Shaw McLaren, Eva. *Elsie Inglis: The Woman with the Torch.* Dodo Press, 1920.

Smith, Barbara Furnell. *The Neuropathology of the Alimentary Tract.* London: Edward Arnold (Publishers) Ltd, 1972.

Smith, Joan. *Misogynies.* London: Vintage, 1996.

Swinburne, Gwendolen H. *A History – The First Fifty Years, The Queen Victoria Memorial Hospital.* Melbourne: 1951.

Whetnall, Edith & Fry, D.B. *The Deaf Child.* London: William Heinemann Medical Books Limited, 1964.

Williams, Shirley. *Climbing the Bookshelves.* London: Virago, 2009.

Willmott Dobbie, B.M. *An English Rural Community: Batheaston with S. Catherine.* Bath University Press, 1969.

Willmott Dobbie, Beatrice. *A History of the King Edward VIth School for Girls.* London: Ernest Benn Ltd. 1928.

Willmott Dobbie, Beatrice. *Obstetrics and Gynaecology: A Synoptic Guide to Treatment.* London: H.K. Lewis, 1948.

Willmott Dobbie, Beatrice. *An Attempt to estimate the true rate of Maternal Mortality, Sixteenth to Eighteenth centuries.*

Sources

Sir David Innes Williams telephone conversation and use of introduction to: Plarr, Victor Gustave & Power, Sir Darcy. *Lives of the Fellows of the Royal College of Surgeons of England, Volume I.* London: Royal College of Surgeons, 1930.

Memorial from the Dean of the London (Royal Free Hospital) School of Medicine for Women to the Royal College of Surgeons – papers from the RCS Library and Archives

Minutes of the Royal College of Surgeons 1910-1971

Annals of the Royal College of Surgeons 1947-

Letter from Oliver Sacks on his mother

Written Account and conversations with Michael Forbes and his wife Anne on life in Harley Street as the adopted son in the household of Eleanor Davies-Colley

Examination papers for the Primary and the Final FRCS 1911 Archives RCS

Discussions with the Archivist of King Alfred School

List of the Hunterian Lectures RCS of E given by women surgeons

Life of Robert Ludlow written by his son

Memorial Service Joyce Ludlow who died age 100. In Bournemouth

Margaret Spittle letter and conversation on the pioneer radiotherapists

Memorial service for Muriel Crouch and conversation with Rev nephew

A Basis for Medical Ethics; Suffering, does God Care?; Lying to Patients – to Lie or not to Lie – a perennial problem; Christian Doctor in the making; Imparting Ethics to Medical Students; Coming to terms with Suffering And Death: Muriel Crouch SPCK publications

Letter to Headmistress Dr (Dame) Kitty Anderson from Betty Underhill from the Archives of the North London Collegiate School

The Problem of Birth Control. Elaine Rankin

The Medical Foundation for the Care of Victims of Torture

Forty Folk Songs of Jamaica 1973; Rock It Come Over: the Folk Music of Jamaica 2000

Obituaries British Medical Journal

Appendix 1

Memorial from the Dean Dr Elizabeth Garrett Anderson MD
to the Royal College of Surgeons of England

The petition was signed by a bevy of names of the great and good, Elizabeth Garrett Anderson MD as Dean, Julia Cock MD, LRCP I, LRCS E as Sub-Dean, A J Norton FRCS as Treasurer and Lecturer in Surgery, Isabel Thorne as Honorary Secretary. Sir Gainsford Brine signed as Chairman of the Committee of the Royal Free Hospital, Charles Bell as Chairman of the weekly Board of the Royal Free Hospital. Dr John Cockle MD FRCP FRCS as Consulting Physician, William Rose MB BS, FRCS and Frederick J Gant FRCS as Consulting Surgeons.

There followed a list of the Royal Free Hospital Staff, fourteen in all, only one of them a woman – Louisa Aldrich-Blake MD BS.

The men were Samuel West MD FRCP, Harrington Sainsby MD FRCP, Thomas C Hayes MD FRCP, James Calvert MD FRCP, J W Andrewes MB FRCP, J W Carr MD BS FRCS, A Boyce Barrow, MD FRCS, James Berry MB BS FRCS, J Grosvenor Mackinlay FRCS, William H Battle FRCS, H Work Dodd FRCS, E W Roughton MD BS FRCS, Willmott Evans MD BS FRCS.

Then followed a list of the Lecturers of the Medical School, eight in all, two of them women. The women were Mary E Dowson LRCP I, LRCS I, Lecturer in Forensic Pathology, and Mary A D Scharlieb MD BS Lecturer in Midwifery and Gynaecology. The men were (with the subjects in which they lectured following their names) Stanley Boyd MB BS FRCS, Anatomy, H B Donkin MD FRCP Medicine, A Dupré FRS FCS Toxicology, W D Halliburton MD FRCP FRS Physiology, Charles Mercier FRCS Mental Pathology, A Quarry Silcock MD BS FRS Pathology. The six men numbered three Fellows of the Royal Society, FRS, amongst them.

After that there were thirty-one supportive names, and some with names still familiar to us today, including eleven further Fellows of the Royal Society, and several Knights and famous names, Sir William Broadbent, Sir James Paget, Sir Spencer Wells, Sir Henry Acland, Sir Thomas Crawford, Sir Alf Garrod, Sir Henry Thompson, Sir William Roberts, J Hughlings Jackson, W R Gowers, Victor Horsley, Frederick Treves, Jonathon Hutchinson – and no woman amongst them considered influential enough to be included.

Appendix 2

Examination Papers – 1911 Primary and Final Fellowship

1911, 5th May. Primary Examination of the FRCS, a three hour paper in each of Anatomy and Physiology. Answer 3 questions out of the four on each paper.

Anatomy

1. Describe the styloid process of the skull and give its relations to surrounding structures. Write an account of its development and ossification and mention its commoner abnormalities.

2. Describe the contents of the right iliac fossa.

3. Describe the contents of the spinal canal below the level of the twelfth thoracic spine.

4. Write an account of the astralgalus. Give its relations to surrounding structures and its mode of ossification.

Physiology

1. Describe the fundamental experiments on which our knowledge of the mechanism of absorption of soluble and diffusible substances from the alimentary tract is based.

2. Give an account of the physiology of spinal reflexes and how they are co-ordinated.

3. Describe the structure and composition of mammalian red blood corpuscles.

4. Describe and explain the haemolytic effects of foreign sera upon them.

5. How has it been shown that a respiratory centre exists in medulla oblongata? What are the chief conditions that modify its activity? Describe the experiments on which your answer is based.

1911 November. Final Fellowship paper, a 4 hour examination. Answer all four questions Pathology, Therapeutics and Surgery.

1. Give an account of the causes, symptoms and treatment of extra-dural abscess.

2. Discuss the diagnosis, course and treatment of aneurysm of the right subclavian artery.

3. What causes may give rise to chronic obstruction of the common bile duct? Give the differential diagnosis and appropriate treatment in each case.

4. Discuss the differential diagnosis and treatment of the swellings which may occur under the gluteus maximum muscle.

Appendix 3

List of Schools attended by Women Surgical Fellows

St Paul's School for Girls, London	5: Margaret Louden, Margaret Salmond, Mary Mayeur, Ruth Bowden, Jennifer Haley
Cheltenham Ladies' College	4: Enid Rockstro, Gladys Hill, Dorothy Ridout (Mrs Shortridge), Jennifer Haley
The North London Collegiate School	4: Dorothy Adams Campbell, Betty Underhill, Margaret Ghilchik née Childe, Elsie Maud Visick (Griffiths)
King Edward VIth School for Girls, Birmingham	3: Dame Hilda Lloyd, Beatrice Willmott Dobbie, Margaret Ghilchik
St Felix Southwold	3: Philippa Martin, Dorothy Knott-Barclay, Kathleen Branson
Wimbledon High School for Girls GPDST	3: Janet Bottomley, Gladys Sandes, Margaret Snelling
Dame Alice Owen School, Islington	2: Muriel Elsie Landau, Eileen Whapham
King Alfred School, Hampstead	2: Margaret Basden, Hetty Ethelberta Claremont
Roedean	2: Dorothy Sharpe, Gwen Hill (Gwen Hilton)
Harrogate Girls' School	2: Flora Hargreaves, Doris Barbara Brown
Queen's College, Harley Street	2: Eleanor Davies-Colley, Irene Cade
Aigburth Vale High School, Liverpool	Dorothy Hall
Aylesbury College	Irene Cade
Babbington High School, Eltham	Elaine Rankin
Bedgebury Girls' Public School, Lillesden, Surrey	Delia Cothay
Belmont School, Derby	Margaret White

Benendon	Iris Kane
Birkbeck College	Esther Rickard
Blackheath High School, GPDST	Eugenie Willis
Blackpool Collegiate School for Girls	Averil Mansfield
Brentwood High School for Girls, Essex	Jill Evans
Broughton Hall (Convent School)	Irene Irving
Church of England School for Girls, Baker Street	Eleanor Davies-Colley
City of London Girls' School	Phyllis George
Clifton High School for Girls, Bristol	Esme Hadfield
Colchester Girls' Grammar School	Anne Bayley
Convent of Notre Dame, Southport	Dorothy Collier
Dudley High School for Girls	Kate Fussell
Dunfermline High School	Gladys Dodds
Edgbaston High School for Girls, Birmingham	Anthea Connell
Edinburgh Ladies' College	Gertrude Beatrice Mary Morgan (Mrs Toland)
Eversfield School for Girls	Ruth Wynne-Davies
Eversley School, Folkestone	Mary Keene
Girls' High School, New Plymouth, NZ	Jean Sandel
Godolphin School, Salisbury	Mary Richardson
Hall School for Girls, Weybridge	Kathleen Branson
Hamilton House, Tunbridge Wells	Mildred Warde
Hampton School, Jamaica	Monica Lewin
Hamptons. Woolmer's, Jamaica	Pamela Ball nee Moody
Headington School, Oxford	Kate Fussell
Hereford High School for Girls	Mary Richardson
High Wycombe Girls Grammar School	Muriel Crouch
Huddersfield Grammar School	Valerie Thompson (Mrs Yorke)
La Rotraite, (Convent), Clapham	Elizabeth Gordon
Lewisham Prendergast Grammar School	Hilary Long
Malvern Girls' College	Irene Cade
Manchester High School for Girls	Katherine Liebert

Mary Thatcher Girls' School, Camberwell	Doris O'Doherty
Monte Sant' Angelo College, Sydney	Margery Scott-Young
Newport High School	Marjorie Dunster
Nonsuch County School	Ruth Wynne-Davies
Northern Polytechnic	Constance Fozzard
Norwood Technical College	Elizabeth Gordon
Notting Hill and Ealing High School	Wendy Lewington
Oswestry High School	Ruth Wynne-Davies
Oxford High School	Josephine Barnes
Penhros College	Kathleen Robinson
Perse School, Cambridge	Katharine Burkill
Polytechnic Regent Street	Esther Rickard, Ida Mann
Putney High School for Girls GPDST	Janet Bottomley
Queen Anne School, Caversham	Geraldine Barry
Queens' School, Chester	Diana Beck
Rochester Grammar School for Girls	Mary Keene
Roedean, Johannesburg	Iris Kane
Sherborne	Margaret Dix
Skipton Grammar School	Dorothy Sharpe
St George's, Harpenden	Muriel Waterfall
St Margaret's Bushey	Marjorie Powys
Streatham High School for Girls' GPDST	Keren Parkes
Sunderland High School	Delia Cothay
The Mount, Leamington Spa	Marjorie Powys
Torquay Grammar School for Girls	Ruth Hickson née Robinson
Tremarth School, Hampstead	Margaret White
Welsh Girls School, Ashford, Middlesex	Muriel Hulke
Wycombe Abbey	Jocelyn Moore
Wycombe House,	Ida Mann
Wyggeston Grammar School, Leicester	Hilda Linford
Wynberg Girls' High School, Cape Town	Ruby Sharp

Appendix 4

Questionnaire to Fellows on the RCS List 1981

KENSINGTON AND CHELSEA AND WESTMINSTER AREA HEALTH AUTHORITY (T)
NORTH WEST DISTRICT

Sector Administrator:
Mr. P. F. Rand

Telephone: 01 959 2488 Ext.

ST. CHARLES HOSPITAL
Exmoor Street.
London, W10 6DZ

Dear Doctor,

I am writing to all the women with the FRCS (ENG) to try to get some information which would help the young women doctors of the future.

Would you, be so very kind as to fill in the enclosed Questionnaire and return in the enclosed S.A.E.

Yours sincerely,

Mrs. M. W. Ghilchik, M.S., F.R.C.S.

QUESTIONAIRE

1. Are you presently working in Medicine YES [ ] NO [ ]

1a. If yes, whole-time
part-time
No. of sessions worked
Are you married YES [ ] NO [ ]
Is your husband in the Medical Profession YES [ ] NO [ ]

1b. If no to 1, which is the last year you worked
Is this due to
(1) Husband
(2) Household duties
(3) Care of elderly relatives
(4) Difficulty in getting right job
(5) Personal choice
(6) Children
State years of their birth:
(7) Other

1c. If part-time work had been available, would you now be working YES [ ] NO [ ]

2. Do you feel that part-time positions would help keep women doctors at work YES [ ] NO [ ]

3. Do you feel you have been prejudiced against, as a woman in Medicine YES [ ] NO [ ]

4. Did your own mother work YES [ ] NO [ ]

5. Do you feel that the Royal College should allow Specialist training part-time YES [ ] NO [ ]

6. Regarding Domestic help:-

	Now	Past
Have you a Resident domestic help	[ ]	[ ]
Have you a non resident domestic help	[ ]	[ ]

How many people
Number of hours

Appendix 5

Data of the Women Surgical Fellows on the 1981 College List responding to the Questionnaire

Name	First name	Date FRCS	Date MB	Medschool	Specialty	Marital Status	Cons Hosp	Prejudice (1)	PT work would help (4)	PT during training (5)	Mother Worked (2)	R Resident D Daily DomHelp (3)
Faulkner	Mildred (Warde)	1922	1921	Royal Free Hospital	Cons ENT Sur	M 4ch	RFH	N	Y		N	-
Baker	Alfreda Helen	1927	1921	Qu U Belfast	Cons Gen	S	EGA	N	Y	Y	N	R DD
Ottley	Constance May	1928	1922	London	Cons Gen	S	New Sx	N	N	N		D
Smith	Gwendoline	1929	1926	UCH	Cons Sur	S	SthL Hom	N		N	N	D
Martin	Philippa	1930	1922	UCH	Cons Eyes	M Dr 3ch	LondEye	Y	Y	Y	N	R
Ludlow	Joyce	1931	1929	Royal Free Hospital	Gen missionary	M 3ch	Nigeria	N	Y	Y	N	D
Bridge	Flora	1931	1930	UCH	Cons O & G	M Dr 2ch	Southend	N	Y	N	N	R D
Dobbie	Beatrice Willmott	1931	1929	Cam & Bham	Cons Gen/OG	M	Birmingham	N	Y	Y	N	R
Moore-White	Margaret	1931	1930	Royal Free Hospital	Cons O & G		Hitchin & RFH					-
Parks	Keren	1932	1929	KCH	GP	S	GP	Y	Y	Y	N	-
Rockstro	Enid	1932	1927	UCH	Cons Sur	S 2ch	New Sx	Y	Y	Y	N	R D
Boney	Muriel Long	1934	1931	KCH	Cons Sur	M Dr 1ch	Llandudno		N	N	N	DDD
Linford	Hilda Margaret	1934	1924	Manchester	Public Health		Public Health	Y	Y	Y	N	-
Salmond	E Margaret K	1936	1921	Royal Free Hospital	FRCOG	M Dr 1ch	N	Y		Y	Y	D
Hill	Gladys	1936	1923	UCH	RT	M Dr 1ch	UCH	Y	Y	N	N	-
Sharp	Ruby	1936	1930	S Africa	O&G	S	S Africa	N	Y		N	R DDD
Dodds	Gladys Helen	1937	1922	Edinburgh	Cons O&G	S	Hackney	N	N			-
Loudon	Margaret	1938	1934	Royal Free Hospital	Cons Sur	M 2ch	SouthLondon	N		N	N	R D
Mayeur	Mary	1938	1933	Royal Free Hospital	Cons O&G	M	Ormskirk	N	Y		Y	-
Shepherd	Margaret Mary	1938	1930	Manchester	Cons Gen Orth	MDr	India	Y	Y	Y	Y	R D
Barnes	Dame Josephine	1939	1937	Oxford & UCH	Cons O & G	M Dr 3ch	Ch+ & EGA	N	Y	Y	Y	R DDD
Wadge	Winifred	1939	1936	UCH	Cons ENT Sur		UCH	N	Y	N	N	R D
Mills	Eleanor	1940	1936	Manchester	Cons O&G	M ch	Manchester	N	Y	Y	N	R DD
Mullaferoze	Perin K	1940	1937	Bombay	Con paed orth	S	Bombay	N	Y		N	RR
Robinson	Kathleen Alice Mau	1940	1936	RFH	Cons O&G	MDr 3ch	QuCh RFH	N	Y	N	N	R DD
Ritchie	Janet Bottomley	1941	1938	Royal Free Hospital	Cons O&G	M	Cambridge	N	Y	Y	Y	R
Branson	Katherine	1941	1938	Royal Free Hospital	Cons Gen	S	Edinburgh	Y	Y	Y	N	R D
Whapham	Eileen	1941	1932	Royal Free Hospital	Cons O&G	S 1ch	Southend	N		N	Y	R D
Dix	Margaret Ruth	1943	1937	Royal Free Hospital	ENT	S	H Neurology	Y	Y	Y	N	D
Snelling	Margaret	1944	1938	Royal Free Hospital	Cons RT	S	Middlesex	N	Y	N	N	R D
Nightingale	Doreen Ann	1945	1940	UCH	Cons thoracic	M	UCH	N	Y	N	N	D

Slesser	Betty	1945	1941	Edinburgh	Cons thoracic	M	Leicester	Y	Y	N	N	d
Crouch	Muriel	1946	1940	Royal Free Hospital	Cons Sur	S	Slondon EGA	Y	Y	Y	N	D
Lessington-Smith	CarolineSimVanDo	1946	1941	Royal Free Hospital	Cons ENT Sur	M	KCH	N	Y	Y	N	R D
Waterfall	Muriel	1946	1944	Royal Free Hospital	Cons Sur	S	Kingston-on-Th	N	Y	N	N	-
Bennet	Marjorie	1947	1939	Bristol	Cons O&G	MDr ch	Bristol	N	Y	Y	N	R D
Bartlett	Marian Josephine	1948			Cons Gen	M	Zambia	N	Y	N	N	D
Burton-Brown	Jean Rosemary Carr	1948	1940	Royal Free Hospital	Cons O&G	S	Canterbury	N	Y	Y	N	R DD
Mason	Margaret	1948	1945	KCH	Cons ENT	S	King Geo Ilford	Y	Y	N	N	d
Powys	Marjorie	1949	1935	RFH	Surgeon	S	(StCh) GP	N	Y	Y	N	-
Savory	Mary	1949	1939	Camb & UCH	Cons Eyes		St J & Royal Eye	N	Y		N	R
Smith	Barbara	1949	1944	Res	HistopathRes		Barts Research	Y	Y	Y	N	-
Lewington	Wendy Anne	1950	1946	Royal Free Hospital	Cons O&G	S	South London	N	Y	N	Y	-
Hadfield	Esme	1951	1945	Oxford	Cons ENT Sur	S	HighWycombe	N	Y	Y	N	DD
Panchalingam	Sehar	1951					Sri Lanka	Y	Y	Y	N	R D
Cade	Irene Marion	1952	1947	Westminster	Cons RT	M	Portsmouth	N	Y	N	N	R
Daws	Joyce Margaretta	1952		Australia	Cons paed& Gen		Melbourne	N	Y	N	N	D
Frith	Kathleen Alice Mau	1952	1946	Royal Free Hospital	Cons O&G	M	Ranford	N	Y	N	N	D
Mellor	Helen	1952			Cons Gen	M	Cyprus	N	Y	N	N	D
Ridout	Dorothy	1952	1943	Royal Free Hospital	GP & Gyn	M 1ch	GP	Y	Y	N	N	DD
Simpson	Elizabeth	1952	1941	Dublin	Cons Eyes		StJStGeoSouthLo	N	Y	N	Y	D
George	Phyllis	1953	1948	Royal Free Hospital	Cons Gen	S	Royal Free	N		N	N	-
Rankin	Elaine	1953	1946	Royal Free Hospital	GP	M Dr 2ch	GP	N	Y	Y	N	D
Scott	Daphne	1953	1943	St. Andrew's	Gyn FPA	MDr ch	FPA	N	Y	Y	N	D
Underhill	Betty	1953	1948	Oxford RFH	Cons Gen	S	Bahrein	N	Y	Y	Y	-
Ball	Pamela Margaret	1954	1950	Birmingham	plastic surgery	M Dr 3ch	Bham	N		N	N	D
Campbell	Dorothy Rose	1954	1926	Cambridge & UCH	EyeSur	M Dr 2ch	Coventry	N		N	N	R D
Mehita	DR	1954				M	India	N	Y	N	N	R D
Adams	Rosemary HM	1955	1948	Edinburgh	A&E Cons	M ch	Norwich	N	Y	Y	N	D
Brown	Betsy	1955	1945	Glasgow	Cons ENT	M	Bradford	N	Y	N	N	-
Orton	Peggy	1955	1943	Royal Free Hospital	Cons ENT Sur	S	EGA	N	Y	N	Y	D
Hickson	Ruth Margaret	1956	1951	Royal Free Hospital	MedAss Orth	M Dr 2ch	Stoke	N	Y	N	Y	R D
Richardson	M	1956	1942	Oxford		M	Hereford	N	Y	N	N	D
Selsnik	Frances	1956		USA			USA	N	Y	Y	N	-
Shelswell	Mary	1956	1948	St Andrews	Cons Orth	M	Portsmouth	N	Y	Y	N	D
Fussell	Katherine	1957	1951	Birmingham	Cons Sur	S	Wigan	Y	Y	Y	Y	DD
Green	Jean Anne	1957	1953	UCH	Med Ass Sur	M	Wales	N	Y	Y	N	D
Irving	Irene Marion	1957	1952	Liverpool	Paed Sur	M 3ch	Alder Hey	N	Y	Y	N	-
Spencer	Pamela	1957	1950	UCH	Cons O&G	M Dr 1ch	WhittingtonEGA	N	Y	N	N	D
Alimchandani	Kamal Rupchand	1958		Bombay	Cons O&G		Bombay	N	Y	Y	N	R

Name	First name	Date FRCS	Date MB	Medschool	Specialty	Marital Status	Cons Hosp	Prejudice (1)	PT work would help (4)	PT during training (5)	Mother Worked (2)	R Resident D Daily DomHelp (3)
Fowler-Wright	Joan Yolande	1958	1947	Royal Free Hospital	clin ass gen		Tunbridge Wells	Y	Y	Y	N	-
Ransome	Joselen	1958	1949	RFH	Cons ENT	M	Ch Cross	Y	Y	Y	Y	R D
Taylor	Katherine	1958	1956	UCH	Cons A & E	MDr5ch	Stoke	Y	Y	Y	N	-
Thompson	Valerie	1958	1948	Royal Free Hospital	Cons O&G	M Dr 2ch	RFH	N	Y	Y	N	D
Busby	Eileen Rosemary	1959	1955	Charing Cross	Cons RT		Kingston	Y	Y	Y	N	-
Goddard	Una Kathleen	1959	1955	Sheffield	Cons Eyes	M ch	Hull Royal Inf	N	Y	N	N	R D
Jones	Mary Allan Craig	1959	1948	Birmingham	Cons Eyes		Sheffield	N	Y	Y	N	DD
Mehta	Mini Hoshung	1959	1951	Calcutta	Lect in Orth		RoyNatOrth	Y	Y	Y	Y	-
Starbuck	Mary	1959	1952	King's	Cons EyeSur	S	Canterbury	Y	Y		N	D
Cothay	Delia MHH	1960	1951	Westminster	ConsOrth & A8	S	Guildford Roy	Y	Y	Y	Y	DD
Forshall	Isabella	1960	1927	Royal Free Hospital	paed surg	S	Alder Hey					-
Irani	Dhun Jal	1960				M	-	N	Y	Y	N	D
Johnson	Anne Elizabeth	1960	1956	UCH	Radiotherapist	M	Mt Vernon	N	Y	N	N	R
Wynne-Davies	Ruth	1960	1953	Royal Free Hospital	ConsOrth Read	M	Edinburgh	Y	Y		N	-
Gammon	Veronica May	1961	1948	Royal Free Hospital	Cons ENT Sur		MidGlamorgan	?			N	DD
Whitney	DJ	1961	1953	Guy's	Cons O&G	M	Cuckfield Sx	Y	Y	Y	N	D
Witt	Margaret	1961	1955	Barts	Cons O&G	S	N Miidx	Y	Y	N	N	D
Birks	Doreen Ann	1962	1949	Royal Free Hospital	Cons Eyes		St Thomas's	N	Y	Y	N	D
Dunsmore	Ramola Diana	1962	1949	Royal Free Hospital	Cons ENT		Doncaster	Y	Y	Y	N	DD
Evans	Jill Margaret	1962	1954	Cambridge & Barts	Cons O & G	S	Oldham	Y	Y	Y		D
Goodman	Helene Valerie	1962	1951	Rheumatology	Rheum.N	M	Marsden/StStepl	N	Y	Y	N	R D
Handscombe	Marion Christine	1962	1954	London	Cons Eyes	M	Coventry	N	Y	Y	N	R D
Lewin	Monica Cynthia	1962	1952	Royal Free Hospital	Cons Gen	M Dr 2ch	Jamaica	N	Y	Y	Y	R D
Baker	Clarice Ann	1963	1958	Oxford	Cons O & G		Winnipeg, Canad	Y	Y	Y	N	-
Figgins	Loris Freda	1963				M	Australia	Y	Y	Y	Y	-
Phelan	Mary Patricia	1963				S		N	Y	Y	Y	D
Price nee Davies	Doris Mar Clewitt	1963	1953	Birmingham	Cons Eyes	M	Harlow	N	Y	Y	N	R DD
Ahluwalia	Jennifer nee Haley	1964	1955	Middlesex	neurosurgery	M Dr 2ch	Delhi	Y	Y	Y		R
Burton	Eunice Ruth	1964	1957	Middlesex	Cons O&G	S	Harold Wood	Y	Y	N	N	-
Chowdhury	Joya	1964					India	N	Y	Y	Y	R5 D5
Connell	Anthea Mary Stewa	1964	1952	Birmingham	EyeSur	M 1ch	Bahamas	N	Y	N	N	R DD
Ege	Gunes Nurettin	1964		Westminster	Radiology	S	Canada	N		N	Y	-
Johnston	Shirley Jean	1964	1959	London	paed surg	M	Scotland	Y	Y	Y	Y	R D
Shepherd	Mary	1964	1957	RFH	thoracic	S	Hatfield	N	Y	Y	N	D
Bajwa	Raj	1965	1956	India	Cons ENT		Basingstoke	N	Y	N	Y	D

Name	First name	Date FRCS	Date MB	Medschool	Specialty	Marital Status	Cons Hosp	Prejudice (1)	PT work would help (4)	PT during training (5)	Mother Worked (2)	R Resident D Daily DomHelp (3)
Morrell	Tessa	1965	1962	Cambridge/Oxford	Cons Gen	S	‹shton under lyme					-
Taylor	Enid	1965	1957	London	Cons Eyes	M	N Middx					-
Zilahi	Clara Clotilde	1965	1956	Cambridge	asst gen surg		Cambridge	Y	Y	Y	N	-
Bayley	Anne Christine	1966	1959	Cambridge/UCH	Prof Surgery	S	Zambia	Y	Y	Y	N	D
Kapila	Leela	1966	1962	Christian Vellore	Cons Paed Sur	M	Nottingham	N	Y	N	N	D
Lewis	Elizabeth Ann	1966	1962	Cambridge			Australia	N	Y	N	N	d
Challis	Margaret Thornton	1967	1957	London	Cons Eyes		WhippsCross	Y	Y	N	Y	D
Fozzard	Constance Ethel	1967	1958	Charing Cross	Cons O&G	M	Truro	Y	Y	Y	Y	D
Ghilchik	Margaret Winifred	1967	1961	Barts	Cons Sur	M 4ch	StCh/StMarys	Y	Y	Y	Y	R D
Gordon	Elizabeth Mary	1967	1962	Charing Cross	Cons Sur	S	Ch+ St J StGeo	Y	Y	Y	N	-
Jequier	Anne Mary	1967	1961	Royal Free Hospital	Cons O&G		Perth Aus	N	Y	Y	Y	D
Mansfield	Averil	1967	1960	Liverpool	Cons Sur	M	Lpool/StMarys	N	Y	N	N	D
McKenzie	J	1967					Australia	Y	Y	N	Y	-
Wengraf	Carol	1967	1962	Guy's	Cons ENT Sur		Greenwich	Y	Y	Y	N	R D
Cook	Noelin nee Fehily	1969	1963	Uni Coll Dublin	Cons ENT	M	Worcester	N	Y	Y	Y	-
Lobb	Dorothy Meryl	1969	1971	Wales	Cons Eyes	M	Salisbury	Y	Y	N	Y	D
Sandland	Ruth	1969	1964	Melbourne	Radiotherapist	S	GOS/Barts					-
Doig	Caroline May	1970	1962	St. Andrew's	Cons Paed Sur	S	Manchester	N	Y	Y	Y	-
Khanna	Urmilla	1970					India	N	Y	Y	N	-
Wells	M	1970				M	Y	N	N	N	N	-
Arnold	Sheila May	1971	1954	RCSI	Cons ENT Sur	M	Frimley	N	Y	Y	N	R D
Dukes	Heather Margaret	1971	1965	Birmingham	Gen vasc renal t	M	Rhodesia B'ham	Y	Y	Y	Y	-
Gardener	Zoe Nora Conquest	1971	1960	Barts				Y	Y	N	Y	-
Magauran	Denise Mary	1971	1963	Charing Cross	Cons Eyes		Glos	N	Y	Y	Y	d
Steach	BE	1971				M	N	Y	Y	Y	Y	D
Zhotnik	J	1971	1966	Edinburgh				Y	Y	N	N	-
Barnes	Dagmar	1972			EyeSur	M	Australia	N	Y	N	N	-
Radford	Rita C	1972	1967	Guy's	Cons A&E		Bromley	N	Y	N	N	-
Robson	Winifred Joan	1972	1967	Liverpool	paed surg	M	Alder Hey	N	Y	Y	N	DD
Turner	Jean Gillean Camero	1972	1966	Aberdeen	Cons Gen & O	M	XianMissGorveh	N	Y	Y	Y	R
Wright	Vanessa	1972	1966	UCH	Cons Paed Sur		UCH	N	Y	N	N	D
Bowden	Ruth	1973	1940	Royal Free Hospital	Prof of Anatom	S	Prof RFH	N	Y	Y	N	R DD
Abadir	Wedad Faltas	1973	1958	Cairo	Cons ENT Sur	M	West Mid	Y	Y	Y	N	D
Costa	PP	1973				M	Sri Lanka	N	Y	Y	N	R
Eagling	Elizabeth Mary	1973	1967	London	Cons Eyes		Birmingham	N	Y	Y	Y	D

Name	First name	Date FRCS	Date MB	Medschool	Specialty	Marital Status	Cons Hosp	Prejudice (1)	PT work would help (4)	PT during training (5)	Mother Worked (2)	R Resident D Daily DomHelp (3)
James	Helen Anne	1973				M	MiamiBeach Fa	Y	Y	Y	N	-
South	L Marie	1973	1968	Barts	Sen Reg (Sur)	M Dr ch	Cons Maidstone	N	Y	N	Y	R D
Taylor	Rosemary Helen	1973	1966	Royal Free Hospital	Lecturer in Sur	S	BartsBotswana	N	Y	N	Y	-
Brocks	Ashley Margaret	1974	1968	Aberdeen		M		Y	Y	Y	N	D
Robinson	Hillary Ina	1974	1965	King's	Cons Orth		Shotley Bridge	Y	Y	Y	N	-
Seymour	Anne	1974	1959	London	Cons A & E		Tyneside	Y		N	Y	D
Swifts	R	1974					Australia	Y	Y	Y	Y	-
Agrawal	Meena Ram	1975						Y	Y	Y	Y	-
Agugua	Nene Elsie Nwada	1975					Nigeria	Y	N	N	N	RR
Frank	Helena Janet	1975	1969	Royal Free Hospital	EyeSur		Portsmouth	N	Y	?	N	D
Hanief	Humaira Jamal	1975						Y	Y	Y	N	-
McDermott	Maeve A	1975	1968	Nat U Ireland			Ireland					-
Van Der Berg	Teresa Maria	1975	1969	Westminster				N			N	-
Watson	Deirdre Clare Torbi	1975	1971	Guy's	cardiothoracic	M	Birmingham	N	Y	N	N	D
Carruthers	Joan Diana Areul	1976			EyeSur	M	Canada	N	Y	Y	Y	R D
Enoch	Bridget Elizabeth	1976	1971	Newcastle	EyeSur		Oxford	Y	Y	Y	N	-
Hocking	Margaret Ann	1976	1971	Leeds	Gen Surg		Brunei		Y	Y	N	R
Laskiewicz	Bozena Maria	1976	1968	NatU Ireland	Sen Reg ENT		KCH	N	Y	Y	N	-
Mody	P	1976			EyeSur							-
Mohan	Veena	1976	1963	Delhi	SenReg Eyes		Birmingham	Y	Y	N	N	d
Durning	Patricia	1977	1973	Manchester	Gen Surg		Middlesborough	N	Y	Y	N	-
Evans nee Belfer	Kay Frances	1977	1973	Cambridge & St. Mar	EyeSur	M						-
Fagg	Sarah Louise	1977	1973	Wales	Urology		Independent Urolc	N	Y	Y	Y	d
Frangoulis	Medea Angelica	1977	1972	Charing Cross	EyeSur	M	Merton&Sutton	N	Y	Y	N	d
Gaston nee Shepl	Hannah	1977	1972	Royal Free Hospital	EyeSur	M	Southampton	N	Y	Y	N	D
Higgs	Janet Margaret	1977	1968	Guy's	Cons Gen	S	mid Wales	Y	Y	N	N	-
Jones de Cossart	Linda Mary	1977		Liverpool	Cons Gen	M	Chester	N	Y	Y	N	D
Mannell	A	1977					South Africa	Y	Y	N	Y	D
McKay	Roxane	1977						Y	Y	Y	N	-
Ng	Clarice Ann	1977				M	Singapore	N	N	Y	N	R
Pieris	Seedevi Jayaranjani	1977			Cons Eyes	M	Ceylon	Y	Y	Y	Y	R
Porter	Janet E	1977	1972	Cambridge		M	N	Y	Y	Y	Y	D
Beck	Marilyn	1978	1966	St. Mary's	Sen Reg Eyes	M	Cardiff	N	Y	Y	Y	DD
Duggan	Elizabeth Joan	1978	1973	Edinburgh				Y	Y	N	N	-
Matlock	E	1978	1973					Y	Y	Y	N	-

Name	First name	Date FRCS	Date MB	Medschool	Specialty	Marital Status	Cons Hosp	Prejudice (1)	PT work would help (4)	PT during training (5)	Mother Worked (2)	R Resident D Daily DomHelp (3)
Niuzi	Zabinnh	1978				M	Zahore	Y	Y	Y	N	RRR
Prince	Heather Gail	1978	1972	Liverpool				N		N	N	-
Ackroyd	Jenny Susan	1979	1975	Cambridge	Cons Gen	M Dr ch	QuE Welwyn	N	Y	N	Y	D
Athow	Anna Christine	1979	1971	St Marys	Cons Sur	M	North Midx	N	Y		N	-
Bateman	Patricia Jane	1979	1966	Barts	EyeSur	M	Kampala, Ugand:	N	Y	Y	Y	D
Brain	Anne Nicole	1979	1973	Royal Free Hospital		M		N	Y	Y	N	-
Buswell	Wendy Anne	1979	1973	Liverpool				Y	Y	Y	Y	-
Davies	Anne Caroline	1979	1975	Oxford & KCH								-
Hoff	Diana Fenwick	1979				M		N	Y	Y	N	D
Kaushik	Suman	1979				M		Y	Y	Y	N	-
Kritzinger	Erna Estella	1979	1974	Birmingham	EyeSur		Birmingham	N	Y	Y	Y	-
Moore	Fionna Patrick	1979	1974	UCH		M			Y	Y	N	d
Nevlikar	SV	1979	1972									-
Senapali	A	1979						N	Y	N	Y	d
Sims	Pamela Frances	1979	1969	Cardiff				Y	Y	N	N	-
Sullivan	Shona Clare	1979	1974	Cardiff		M		N	Y	Y	Y	-
Chauhuri	Maitreyee						New Delhi	Y	Y	Y	Y	R DD
Mukerjee	Prem					M	New Delhi	N	Y	N	N	RRRR
Mutch	Elizabeth Margaret	1975	1968	Manchester	vasc/cardiothoracic							-
Rayment	Ruth					M		N	Y	Y	Y	-
Walker	Andrea N		1972	Charing Cross	EyeSur	M		N	Y	Y	N	-

Note:
1 On prejudice: 69 women felt they had experienced prejudice against them as women but 155 felt they had not. About one third.
2 55 of the mothers of the women surgeons worked - again about one third
3 R- resident help; D - daily help and d if daily help is very pa art-time. Multiple letters indicate the number of helps
4 A majority felt that the availability of part-time would help women surgeons to stay in work, 168 in favour and only 5 against.
5 However there was a substantial number who felt that part-time during the training years was less acceptable, though a majority were still in favour. 109 in favour, 64

INDEX

Appendix 5 is an alphabetical listing of women Fellows with professional and personal details that may be useful along with the Index.